by Ivan T. Sanderson

THE DYNASTY OF ABU (*1962*)

THE CONTINENT WE LIVE ON (*1961*)

THE MONKEY KINGDOM (*1957*)

LIVING MAMMALS OF THE WORLD (*1956*)

FOLLOW THE WHALE (*1956*)

HOW TO KNOW THE NORTH AMERICAN MAMMALS (*1951*)

ANIMAL TALES (*1946*)

LIVING TREASURE (*1941*)

CARIBBEAN TREASURE (*1939*)

ANIMAL TREASURE (*1936*)

THE Dynasty OF ABU

THE Dynasty OF ABU

A HISTORY AND NATURAL HISTORY
OF THE
Elephants and Their Relatives
PAST AND PRESENT

BY

IVAN·T·SANDERSON

F.L.S., F.Z.S., F.R.G.S.

Alfred·A·Knopf New York 1962

FRONTISPIECE: Bull Bush Loxodont. (From a photograph taken in the Kruger National Park, Union of South Africa.)

L. C. catalog card number: 61–8530

THIS IS A BORZOI BOOK,

PUBLISHED BY ALFRED A. KNOPF, INC.

 Manufactured in the United States of America, and distributed by Random House, Inc. Published simultaneously in Toronto, Canada, by Random House of Canada, Limited.

PUBLISHED NOVEMBER 5, 1962
SECOND PRINTING, NOVEMBER 1962

The chapter entitled "Of the Collapse of Their Empire" was published originally in different form as "Riddle of the Frozen Giants" in *The Saturday Evening Post*, and the chapter entitled "Of Slaves and Ivory" was published originally in different form as "A Passion for Ivory" in *Horizon*.

This book

is dedicated with profound respects

TO

DR. W. C. OSMAN HILL

presently Prosector

of the Zoological Society

of London

ACKNOWLEDGMENTS

The idea that this book should be written was originally made by somebody, whom I have never met, and whose name I do not know, to somebody else, who then referred the suggestion to another person, who put it up to an old friend of mine named Stuart Cloete—the famous South African author, born "bush-whacker," and sincere student of both animal and human psychology. (Stuart's ancestors appear in this tale somewhat before half of it has been told, for although the Cloetes were British of, originally, Hungarian extraction, they landed in South Africa concurrent with the Portuguese and prior to the Hollanders.) Stuart Cloete then apparently told somebody else to have another party suggest it to me. That party finally came to me, through a string of still other people, representing my publisher, Mr. Alfred A. Knopf.

Why none of these parties had thought of writing such a book before, I do not understand. What is more, I haven't the slightest idea why I didn't think of it myself or, rather, why I didn't do something about it, because actually I had often considered it. In this I was not unique, for some 2,000 other people have had the same idea over the past two centuries, and a substantial number of them have done something about it (see the bibliography). Strangely, moreover, somebody else also decided to do something about it at just the same time that I did—namely, Richard Carrington, of England—and he worked faster. His book came out three years ago, just when I had submitted my first draft to Mr. Knopf. I wish, therefore, to avail myself of this opportunity to execute a profound obeisance in his direction, not only in recognition of his fine work, but also because his source material (naturally), his whole approach (reasonably), and even his chapter heads (parenthetically) ran more or less neck and neck with those that I had devised from profound and protracted labors for that first draft. But then, there is a long history of "great" discoveries and novel ideas being initiated at the same time by at least two people who never met, had no idea what the other was doing, and who were usually separated by mighty oceans.

In the meantime, also, there have been others who have labored in the same vineyard more swiftly than I, and produced some excellent squeezings. Some may now almost be said to be of old vintage, for information on this subject pours off the presses all over the world without cease. Yet, I make so bold as to say that there is still more to be said on this subject. So I look forward to this book also, in its turn, being adjudged of a fine old vintage.

I don't think I have ever in my life enjoyed preparing any work so much as I have this one; but I am quite sure that I have never disliked writing one so much. I love writing almost as much as I do eating, and it was not this that at first irked and then nearly killed me: it was the overwhelming plethora of the material that I wanted to cover, the terrifyingly contradictory nature of so much of it, and the endless necessity for that most horrendous bugbear of all writers—the blue pencil. It has already gone on and on, and it could continue to go on more or less forever, as far as I can see, but my publishers have finally and wisely called a halt. For this I want to thank them, as well as for their really extraordinary patience with what is now some years of overenthusiasm and overwriting on my part. And, as this is the place where I am allowed to cast any other bouquets I may happen to have in hand, I shall now avail myself of this prerogative.

My deepest thoughts are actually for that long string of Abu whom I have known, played and worked with, and come to love and respect. But I must not get off on that tack yet. Apart from them, my heart really bleeds for my normally not very patient wife, who typed the manuscript at least ten times to my personal knowledge, and my good friend Professor W. C. Osman Hill, Prosector of the Zoological Society of London, one of the greatest living zoologists and author of the indispensable *Atlas of the Elephant,* who has waded through the manuscript, using, I can only imagine, immense blue pencils as crutches. Mere thanks are, in his case, an insult.

In addition to these I want the many "bullhands" I have known over the years—Otto Schmidt, Damoo Doohtré, Bill Green, and others—who taught me so much about the Abu, to know that I have had both them and their words of wisdom in mind at all times. I then want particularly to add some expression of praise, and my real gratitude, to Stanley Ivan Rowe, who has an inexplicable genius for ferreting out the esoteric and the neglected on almost any subject in any library of old literature. This book is bespattered with little gems that he brought to light.

Now, perhaps, I may proceed to try and explain what I am talking about.

IVAN T. SANDERSON

New York, 1962

CONTENTS

DRAWINGS

by Sidonie Coryn, after sketches by the author

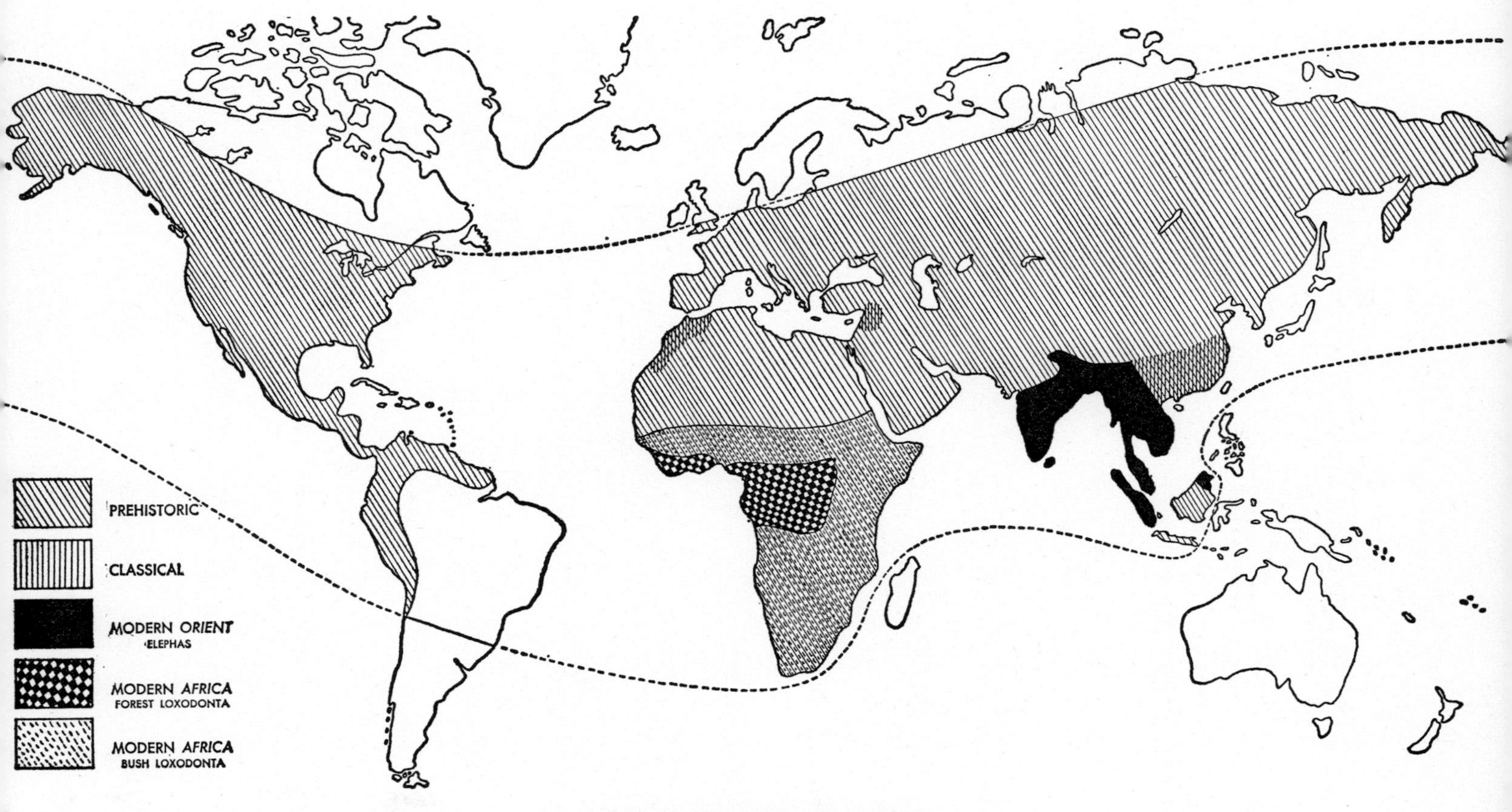

WORLD DISTRIBUTION OF THE ABU

THE Dynasty OF ABU

[I]

OF THE NATURE OF THE BEASTS

Why and what are the Abu?

The living species; their taxonomy, external form, and anatomy.

This book is about olifonts and loxodonts, and their extinct relatives. Ordinary citizens might say that it is about elephants, but they would be wrong. Elephants are very particular creatures, and although we shall have occasion to discuss them at some length later on, they constitute only a small part of this story—and that a latter-day and a rather specialized one. Hundreds of better persons than I have written about elephants and with much more background and aplomb. So, for the moment, to Hyderabad with elephants, and on with the subject at issue.

There are living today on the surface of this planet more than a million different forms of animal life which have been examined and given names. Most of these live in the sea, and they vary in size from minutiae that you require an electron microscope to see (if you include things called bacteriophages) to the mighty Blue Whale, the largest of which ever examined was a female measuring 113½ feet and weighing, by the modern formula, 170 tons. Of those animals that live on land, the largest is a mighty creature called the Bush Loxodont, which inhabits the orchard bush and savannas of Africa outside the closed-canopy equatorial forests and which may, as we shall see later, stand over 13 feet at the shoulder and weigh over 12 tons. This is a colossal mass of anything, let alone flesh, to be held above the ground on bones, and still to able to move about, and stand on its hind legs as it has to do when it copulates to procreate. This creature is known commonly (and we use this designation advisedly) simply as the "African Elephant."

However, if the proboscidean pachyderm of the Oriental Region of Asia is to be called an "elephant," this African animal is altogether misnamed, for it is quite different in many respects. And here comes our first problem and the reason why I was constrained to say that ordinary citizens would be wrong if they thought this book was about things called "elephants." Further, while the Bush Loxodont is the biggest living thing today on land on this earth, it is neither the biggest thing that ever lived on land nor even the biggest of its own kind that has existed. Some of the dinosaurs may have been more bulky, and there once lived in North America a distant relative of living loxodonts which was two feet taller and much more weighty, having a chassis shaped rather like a vast shoe box.

If, then, this creature is not an "elephant," what is it; and why should I make such a to-do about it? This is an exceedingly difficult question to answer, so I will resort to a kind of analogy. Military tanks and Cadillacs are both driven by internal-combustion engines, and even specifically by such engines as burn gasoline. They may both therefore be called "automobiles." However, while both are indeed of the same general class of mobile machines, very few people would insist that they are of the same specific class. When it comes to differentiating between a Volkswagen and a Cadillac, however, most of us begin to get into difficulties; and if we are asked to define the differences between an army jeep and a Land Rover, we may well give up unless we are mechanics or engineers. So it is with loxodonts and elephants; if the former may be said to represent Cadillacs, the "elephants" are the Volkswagens.

But as these two kinds of animals once long ago had a common origin, we cannot even attempt to define them until we learn something about that common ancestor. In the meantime we are stuck with the word "elephant," as we are with "motorcar," and there is naturally nothing we can do about it. Would that the old spelling for one could be revived—namely, "olifont" for those pachydermatous creatures that today inhabit the Oriental Region of Asia; and that the scientists' term, "loxodonts," could be adopted for the somewhat similar-appearing creatures of Africa. But this cannot be, either. As, however, we are determined to talk about both herein, plus a large number of other related creatures all of which are notably, and sometimes surprisingly, different, we need a word to include them all. Unfortunately there is no such word in our or any other modern language.

"Pachyderms" has been tried, but we don't know if many of them had *pachos* (thick) *dermos* (skins), and even if they had, these were probably not nearly as thick as the skins of many other quite different creatures. "Proboscideans" is no better, for while admittedly both olifonts and loxodonts have trunks, so also do Tapirs, some seals, certain small insectivores, and other creatures, whereas many extinct animals having nothing to do with olifonts or loxodonts seem also to have sported such idiosyncrasies. Also, there seem to have been relatives of the olifonts and loxodonts which did *not* have trunks. Then, we have to bear in mind that the living olifonts and loxodonts, together with their extinct relatives, which are exceedingly numerous and varied in size and shape, are unique in the scheme of life on this earth. They deserve a title.

The coining of names is both an abomination and an unacceptable procedure. Also, one can almost always find some appropriate, recognized, and acceptable term in some dictionary which covers one's needs; but in this case there does not appear to be any such. I therefore looked long and closely in all manner of other places, both obvious and obscure, for what was needed. And eventually a name floated into view in, of all unlikely but most propitious quarters, Dr. Wallace Budge's *Dictionary of Ancient Egyptian Hieroglyphics.* This word has everything—simplicity, validity, and comprehensibility. It is "Abu."

Strangely, this word has enormous significance to our story. First, it was used by the Dynastic Egyptians to cover both loxodonts and elephants; second, it is from an ancient stem, A, that originally seems to have meant "hard" or "a hard substance," which the early Egyptians wrote "*Aab*" and which they used for ivory. In this the "Ȧ" was merely a hesitation in speech and might be transliterated as a very short "e," while the "ab" was more nearly "abr" or merely "br." This gives, in speech, "é-br," which seems to be the origin of the Coptic *ebur,* for ivory. It is further stated by philologists that the Hebrew *elaph,* meaning "ox," may have been derived from this word, and that the Greek *elephas* is, in turn, a derivative of this. The more cautious etymologies class the origin of the Greek *elephas* as "obscure"; but the

---

Bull Forest Loxodont. (From a photograph taken by Quentin Keynes at the former Belgian training center at Aru, the Congo.)

more bold come right out and derive it from *elaph.* As the hard substance *Ȧab,* or ivory, was obtained from either loxodonts or olifonts, both were called *Ȧ-bu,* or "Abu" to us.

The Dynastic Egyptians were one of the first peoples known to catch, tame, and train Abu, and they even have a little hieroglyph, found in very early carvings, to denote such a domesticated creature. This is quite clearly a picture of a loxodont with a tiny man riding on its neck. But, even more important, these people came in time to know also the Asiatic Olifont or Elephant, and they spoke of it, again in their beautiful picture writing, by means of a similar little hieroglyph, but this time just as obviously a drawing of one of those animals, with small ears, humped back, bulbous forehead, and other typical characteristics. However, they still called them Abu. Finally, it just so happens that some of the earliest discoveries of the ancestors of the living Abu were made in Egypt—in a strange desert basin known as the Fayûm, about which we will read more later. The Ancients had no knowledge of these ancestors; but they sat on them for four millennia, and if they had ever seen them reconstructed, they would undoubtedly have called them Abu.

So, we have a name for our tribe: what of its status? Elephants, olifonts, loxodonts, or just plain all-round elephants, wherever they be and in whatever circumstances, somehow manage to remain glorious, dignified, and royal. Personally, I cannot quite bring myself to regard them as animals; while they are manifestly not human beings, they have all sorts of attributes that one has been taught the Good Lord bestowed only upon us. It is not just their power and their size: they have something else besides. And the more you come to know them and about them, the more you find yourself standing in awe of them, and the less able you are to class them with the common herd—either of beasts or of men. Thus they are imperial, in a manner of speaking. Ergo, the Abu are not just a tribe: they are a Dynasty.

For these reasons I am presuming to call them just this,

and shall try to follow and elucidate their progress as such through the ages. We should not (and I cannot) inquire into the affairs of these wondrous creatures in any common way. So, as we go along, I hope that you will see what I mean, and come to agree with me. In face of the Abu we stand before one of, if not the, greatest of God's creations—ourselves not excepted.

Before we go any further, therefore, we should ascertain what Abu there are and where they live in the wild state.

The map preceding this chapter shows the over-all distribution of the Dynasty today and at two earlier stages in its history, and thus at once illustrates its decline since the beginning of what geologists call the Pleistocene Age. These stages represent roughly certain major changes in climate during the latter part of that age, which it is now believed spanned about one million years. Formerly of almost world-wide range (excluding Australasia and some islands), Abu are now found only in three areas in Africa and five in Southeast Asia. These comprise a total area of about seven million square miles, or less than an eighth of the land surface of the earth and only about a seventh of the range of the Abu at the time of their greatest glory. The solid black on this map must not be taken too literally, however, because it represents their present *over-all* range. This does not mean that Abu are found everywhere within these blocks. On the contrary, the actual distribution of the animals today is spotty. There are great stretches in all of these areas where no Abu have been seen for generations, and there are large tracts where there is no food for them. Huge swaths of human habitations now surround most of the towns and sprawl along all the new roads therein, and between these, cultivation and plantations have almost everywhere gnawed into the bush.[1]

Abu are great wanderers and indulge in seasonal migra-

[1] This map is after Deraniyagala and is, in my opinion, somewhat misleading about the southern border of China and too detailed in India, where he shows a large number of small "islands," rather than a general over-all distribution.

tions of some magnitude, and these may sometimes be cumulative, the herd moving onward for several years instead of ranging back and forth between two points. There is evidence that some herds in Africa may follow a more or less oblong course for ten years before returning to any one place. Despite India's enormous population and the very thorough clearing of the primal forests from most of her central provinces, elephants that have lived in one of the "islands" in Deraniyagala's map one year may turn up in another the next; clearly, they must range over intermediate areas that are not specifically elephant country. However, before I may discuss the distribution and population of the Abu any further, it is necessary to define the existing members of the Dynasty.

There are three known living Abu: two loxodont and a single Elephant species. As we explained at the outset, these genera are quite distinct. The three species are *Loxodonta africana* and *Loxodonta cyclotis*, of Africa, and the Asiatic *Elephas indicus*. Innumerable subspecies of each have at one time or another been created, but it has now been decided that almost all of these are nothing more than herd or family likenesses. They were based chiefly on the shape of the ear, which is now found to be variable. The Bush Loxodont (*L. africana*) displays the same range of variation and the same variations all the way from Senegambia to Abyssinia and south to the Union of South Africa. The little Forest Loxodont (*L. cyclotis*), on the other hand, seems truly—though anybody would have a hard time proving it—to be divided into a few distinct geographical races. There appear to be such races (1) in the Guinea Coast forest block; (2) from the Niger to the Ubangi-Congo north-south divide; and (3) in the inner Congo Basin. In addition, there is the oft-debated and troublesome matter of the "Water-Elephant," which, if it exists at all, could be a really distinct subspecies of this animal, another full species of loxodont, or even quite another kind of Abu.

This animal has been reported by the river natives of certain rather limited areas about the central Congo, especially around Lake Leopold II, and more particularly where the rivers run through large swamps. The animals are alleged to have been seen by half a dozen Europeans, shot at by two, and killed by one. The skin and skull of this last animal is preserved in Belgium. The skin is covered by a light red fluff, and the trunk is said to have only one "finger," like the Asiatic Elephant's. The animal stood only 5 feet 5 inches at the shoulder, but had a pair of tusks weighing 43 pounds, which is heavier than the tusks carried by a young male Forest Loxodont of comparable size. This creature was named *Loxodonta fransseni,* after its captor, by Dr. Henri Schoutenden, Director of the Congo Museum at Tervueren in Belgium.

So far this specimen has not been accepted as a valid example of a new species of loxodont. There is even debate as to whether it has one or two "fingers" on the tip of its trunk, and nobody seems to have bothered to go and look. Even if it has only one, however, we have to contend with another point of controversy about Abu. Lewis, who not only has lived with elephants all his life but is a very acute observer, states categorically that he never could see the difference between the two forms of trunk. Piqued by this remark, I went to look at a baby *Loxodonta africana* and a young *Elephas indicus* that happened to be housed side by side in a private zoo, and I have to report that Lewis can be right—at least in the case of some young animals. There was so little difference between the trunk tips of the two that when the animals were placed together and a coat was hung across the bars of their stall, leaving a hole so that only their trunks came out, I could not in several tries tell one trunk from the other. Much disturbed, I went to the National Zoo in Washington, where I had quite an argument with one of the keepers, who was thoroughly irked that I should question this precious belief. I was about to go off and appeal to Dr.

William Mann, who was then still Director and was one of the greatest living experts on the Abu, especially circus animals (having probably been introduced to every one that has entered this country in the past fifty years), when both the keeper and I saw something that brought us and the argument to a dead stop. The African animal, in reaching for an orange, first tried to take it in its two fingers but failed, then *withdrew* the bottom digitlike process, and took the fruit as an Indian Elephant does, by curling its upper finger over the orange. The skin of the Water-Elephant in Belgium may have dried, so that the lower "finger" of its trunk tip is now retracted.

But, returning to the subject of the Water-Elephant in general, we encounter a much greater mystery. One of the accounts of these animals given by a European to a trained naturalist states that he once watched a herd of them for five minutes through binoculars and insists that they had slick, shiny skins like those of hippopotamuses and the following other extraordinary features. The largest, he said, was between 6 and 8 feet tall; the neck was double the length of that of any loxodont, while the head was low, oblong, and protracted, and bore a trunk only 2 feet long. The ears were very small, so that the whole head looked like that of a big Tapir. None of the animals had any tusks at all. He further stated that he had examined the spoor on level ground, and the animals were found to have widely separated toes like those of hippos, and only four on each foot. The plantar surfaces of the feet did not appear to carry the weight of the animals. They dived into a deep river, he said, and the local natives asserted that they were nocturnal, spending the day in the water as hippos do. The trouble is that this description does not resemble that of the preserved Water-Elephant at all, and it sounds more like that of some gomphothere (see below) than of any loxodont. Are we to suppose, then, that there are still other Abu to be discovered in Africa?

Then there is a still more ticklish business. I refer to the so-called Pygmy Elephant. There has probably been more rumpus about this alleged beast than any other animal that might be called big game. Pygmy Loxodonts have been reported from all over the Congo and the Guinea forests. Numerous native tribes, notably the Uele pygmy men of the eastern Congo, have a distinctive name for them which clearly distinguishes them from the Forest Loxodonts. The biggest bulls are said to be not more than 6 feet 6 inches tall when full-grown, but sometimes to have tusks that reach the ground. By contrast, the Forest species grows to about 8 feet 6 inches maximum, and the Bush to 12 feet 6 inches.[2]

Quite a number of alleged Pygmy Elephants have been brought out of Africa, both dead and alive, but not one of these has shown any features that differed from those of the Forest Loxodonts of the area in which they were found. Yet the official guidebook of the Congo, under the heading FAUNA, stated: "*Elephant,* 'Tembo' in Kiswahili, 'Nzovu' in Kivu, and 'Njoko' in Lingala, are very common throughout the Congo. *Dwarf Elephant,* 'Abele' in the Uele District, reach only half the weight of the African Elephant [*sic*]. The species is fairly rare and is found only in the center of the Congo." And this, be it noted, was the basis of the official game law of that country. People actually paid handsomely for licenses to shoot Pygmy Elephants. This is a ridiculous situation for the following reasons.

Either there *is* a Pygmy Loxodont, or, as museum specialists insist, there is *not.* If there *is* such an animal, it can obviously be found, and it is no good relying solely on the local native peoples for information or for specimens, because they can miss an animal on their own hunting grounds just as easily as a scientist can in a museum. (The African Water-Civet, *Osbornictis,* was captured by the

[2] A mounted specimen of a Bush Loxodont was unveiled on March 7, 1959, in the Smithsonian Institution's Natural History Building in Washington, D.C.; it measures 13 feet 2 inches at the shoulder. This was shot by one J. J. Fenykovi in 1955 in the Cuando River region of Southwest Africa. It originally weighed 12 tons. These figures, moreover, are officially accepted.

Lang-Chapin Expedition in 1916 in country where it has never been seen since and whose natives do not even know of its existence.) If a Pygmy Elephant does *not* exist, no charge can legitimately be demanded for shooting it.[3]

It is claimed that the *L. fransseni* type-specimen is only a young *L. cyclotis*, and the author who makes this claim goes on to point out that the famous Pygmy Elephant obtained by the Bronx Zoo in 1906 and widely publicized grew from 3 feet 7 inches (weighing 601 pounds) to 6 feet 8 inches between 1906 and 1915 and was still not full-grown at death. This, he states, puts it in the *L. cyclotis* class. Further, the famous Jumbo, who was a Bush Loxodont, grew 6½ feet during seventeen years at an annual rate of 5 inches, which is the same rate as that of the alleged Pygmy. Guinea-forest *L. cyclotis* bulls measure from 6 feet 8 inches to 9 feet 7 inches and cows from 6 feet 7 inches to 6 feet 11 inches, both at twelve years of age. Tusks of alleged Pygmies, weighing 7 pounds each for bulls and 2 pounds each for females, have also supposedly been collected, but as they were without skulls, there was no way of telling how old their bearers had been. (Incidentally, the Forest Loxodont [*cyclotis*] carries the largest tusks in proportion to its size of all living Abu.) A British Governor of Sierra Leone, Sir Arnold W. Hodson, once sent six skulls of alleged Pygmies to London, and Major Powell-Cotton sent two more from the Cameroons. All proved to be young animals, and they differed in no way from young of *L. cyclotis*. To date we have *no* evidence of a Pygmy Loxodont unless the type-specimen of *L. fransseni* is one; but this is definitely immature and yet was already 5 feet 11 inches when it was killed.

The Asiatic Elephants have also been split up by enthusiasts into all manner of subspecies and then combined again into one, with what are called regional races. Both

[3] It is possible that the Belgians meant the Forest Loxodont when they listed *Dwarf Elephant.*

terms are most misleading and seem to have little validity in this case. All these populations of elephants show the same variations and "varieties" in each of their separate areas of distribution, although there are differences both in the percentages of these variations and in their average size and some other features. Thus, in Ceylon only one male in about 300 has tusks and all others are *muknas,* or tuskless, but in India only one in fifty is a *mukna.* On the other hand, the elephants of Sumatra are recognizably different both in some points of external form and even in their bone structure. The elephants of Borneo are passing strange in both appearance and habits. In fact, there appear to be four distinguishable races of elephants—the Ceylonese, the Indo-Burmese-Chinese or Bengali, the Malayan or Hairy, and the Sumatran. The Sumatran may indeed be a subspecies; the status of the Bornean has not been determined, but it is listed as of the Malayan race.

One would have thought that the easiest thing in the world would be to obtain a list of standard and record weights and measurements of loxodonts and elephants and of their tusks, but this is very far from the case. Not only has no such list ever been compiled, but we simply have no records of many of the facts we would like to know.

Of several hundreds of domesticated and wild elephants measured in Burma none reached 10 feet at the shoulder. The two largest females were 8 feet 5 inches and 8 feet 3 inches. However, the famous Tusko, a male show animal in America, stood 10 feet 2 inches. The method of measuring these animals is often open to grave suspicion. One method is to throw a tape measure over the animal's shoulder at the highest point, bring it to the ground on each side, and then divide the result by two. This is, however, inaccurate to the extent of 9 inches in 9 feet. The only reliable method is to have the animal stand on firm ground in a doorway, lower a bar with a spirit-level on it till it just rests on the elephant's back, mark where the beam touches the door uprights on either side, and then measure the distance from these marks to the floor. Consequently, no exact measurement of the height of a live wild elephant or of a dead animal can be obtained. In the case of dead elephants, the weight of the body pushes the supple shoulder blades upward.

It is true, nonetheless, that twice around an elephant's forefoot—and twice around plus ten per cent for a loxodont —almost always equals the standing height at the shoulder. (The average person, if asked how many times the circumference of the forefoot would equal the height, usually says from ten to fifteen times!) Adult elephants and loxodonts vary considerably in size, shape, proportions, and weight. The record height for Indian Elephants is variously given as 10 feet 7½ inches to 11 feet, and for those from Ceylon 12 feet, but these measurements cannot be accepted as final.

Fully mature Bush Loxodonts standing less than 8 feet are known, but there is much debate about the record. A specimen shot by Major Powell-Cotton, very carefully measured in various ways by him and mounted in his private museum in England, measured a full 12 feet 6 inches at the shoulder. This is 6 inches taller than the "official" records give, but is still short of the 13 feet 2 inches of the Smithsonian specimen mentioned above. The Imperial Mammoth grew to 15 feet by bone measurement, so there is no reason why 13 feet should be excessive; yet this is a tremendous height, and the top of a loxodont's head is well above its shoulders. Official weights run from 3,000 to 7,000 pounds, but there are even several records of elephants weighing 7½ tons, or 15,000 pounds, and the new Smithsonian specimen is said to have weighed 24,000 pounds! The Forest Loxodont is only 2 feet 6 inches tall at birth and 4 feet 11 inches at ten years.

Published information on tusks and records of their measurements are even more widely controversial. Here the ivory dealers are more to be relied upon than sportsmen or even museum records. The "official" records for a bull Bush

Loxodont are tusks measuring 11 feet 5½ inches (left) and 11 feet (right) and with a combined weight of 293 pounds; and another pair, of which each measures 10 feet 4 inches, with a combined weight of 336 pounds. One loxodont in the British Museum, however, has a pair of tusks weighing together 440 pounds. In the past, enormous tusks were recorded, though how much faith one should place in the measurements and weights given is hard to say. Hartenfels tells of a 14-foot tusk seen in a merchant's store in Venice and gives individual tusk weights of 137, 208, 325, and 350 pounds. It may be suggested that the real all-time record is the famous "Kilimanjaro Elephant," a Bush Loxodont killed on the Kenya side of that mountain; it was not a particularly big animal, but its tusks together weighed 460 pounds and measured, when placed end to end, 24 feet. The animal could not raise its head, owing to their weight.

Forest Loxodonts often have tusks over 11 feet long, but they are comparatively slender. Pairs of tusks do not usually differ more than 6 inches in length, one or the other being used for digging, according to whether the animal is left- or right-handed. Bull-Elephant tusks average between 90 and 100 pounds, and 157 pounds seems to be the record. Incidentally, Elephants born with only one tusk—usually the right—are called *gunesh* and are frightfully holy.

The tusks of males of both loxodonts and Elephants show at birth and are not replaced; the tusks of females of both are present at birth, but are usually inside the gums, point downward, and are really tushes. They usually break off or drop out and are not replaced in the Elephant, but they persist and grow in the loxodonts.

The *teeth* of the Abu, as opposed to their *tusks,* present us with another most muddling and muddled situation. Living Abu all have only four cheek teeth at any one time, one on each side, top and bottom. However, they have several sets during their lifetime. Exactly how many has not been decided and possibly never will be because only the shells of the old teeth are shed, the crowns being ground away by use and the roots reabsorbed from below; and often the shells are eaten by their owners. Some authorities say that Elephants have endless sets; others declare that they have only six sets, the last of which has to serve them all their adult life. Still others give the following chronology:

First set (milk teeth)	1st year
Second set (permanent)	2nd year (some solid feed)
Third set	2nd to 6th year (fully weaned)
Fourth set	6th to 10th year
Fifth set	10th to 14th year (start to breed)
Sixth set	14th to 19th year
Seventh set	19th to 25th year (maturity)

However, this expert, G. P. Sanderson, did suggest that they might have further sets at ever-increasingly long intervals.

Apart from a few exotic species of mammals (such as the toothed whales and the Giant Armadillo) which have great numbers of simple teeth, there is a basic number of teeth for all mammals: i.e., forty-four, made up of four molars, three premolars, one canine, and three incisors on either side of each jaw. Canines and incisors, or *front* teeth, have simple roots and never double up either through having more than one root or by dividing into several teeth. Molars and premolars have multiple roots and may so subdivide. Now, there is a total of twenty-eight (or seven sets of four) of these back or compound teeth available, and if they are used only in sets of four at a time, an Abu should thus have seven sets. At the same time, mammals also have a set of

Bull Elephant. (From a photograph of a sacred Elephant of Madura, in the Italian magazine *Natura Viva.*)

milk teeth and these may vary in number from a second complete dentition of forty-four teeth, all of which are shed in youth to make way for the permanent set, to none at all. Thus, there could be fifty-six (or fourteen sets) of grinding teeth available to the elephant; the first seven sets used up in reaching maturity would really be the milk teeth, and the second seven the permanent adult teeth. This would give the animal its last new set when it was about 120 years old. This is of great significance, as we shall see when discussing the age to which Abu are alleged to live. It is thus manifest that if Abu had only seven sets and used up five or six before they reached maturity, the construction of the last set would have to be much different from the others; otherwise, it would be worn away in a maximum of eight years. As the last set does *not* appear to be any more rugged or dense than the earlier sets (whereas Abu definitely live longer than twenty-five years), we can only assume that they *do* have more than seven sets.

The teeth themselves are unique, being oval in outline when looked at from above. They have flat crowns crossed by a series of alternating cross-ridges—narrow ridges that are white, hard, and raised, and duller-colored wider bands that are depressed. The Elephant has twenty-seven of these cross-plates, the loxodonts ten or eleven. These ridges are really decapitated up-and-down folds, like a series of very steep mountains with alternating thin-and-hard and thick-and-soft strata pressed together. In chewing, which these animals normally do for about eighteen out of every twenty-four hours, the lower jaw is moved backward and forward, so that the ridges are like two files working against each other. With this mechanism the Abu can pulverize very hard woods.

Loxodonts may be immediately distinguished from the Elephant by many features other than the lesser number of tooth ridges. In general shape, they are quite different. The Elephant has a straight or arched back, its highest point being about amidships; the loxodonts are sway-backed, the highest point of their bodies being either at the shoulders or over the rump. Elephants carry their heads at right angles to the long axis of their bodies; loxodonts at an angle of 45 degrees upward, though heavily tusked individuals have to tip their heads down to a right angle. The shape of the head is another distinguishing characteristic. The Elephant has a short "face" and a bulging forehead forming two domes on the front of the temples; the loxodonts have more protracted heads and sloping foreheads with a single slight dome above the trunk. The ears of the Elephant are comparatively small triangles with a point at the bottom-front, and their upper edges turn over progressively with age, starting at the front where they join the head. The ears of the loxodonts are rounded and "ear-shaped," very much larger, and have rounded "lobes." The ears of the Bush species, however, are larger in proportion and more rounded than the Forest species, which has no lobe. It is believed that the ears of loxodonts are primarily fans; they are rather delicate, and excellent leather is obtained from them.

The trunk, originally *trompe* (trumpet) in French, is really an extension of the nose and upper lip, and the corrugations on its underside correspond to the ridges across the roof of our mouth. With their trunks the Abu can pick up a small shirt button from a polished floor or, in the case of a big Bush Loxodont, reach twenty feet up a tree and pull down branches. A mother can carry her baby in her trunk until it is a month old.

The trunk of the Elephant is comparatively smooth in outline, although covered with little wrinkles, and it appears to end, as we have noted, in a single fingerlike projection on the upper tip. The trunk of the loxodonts is cross-corrugated and ends in two fingerlike projections that are somewhat splayed, making the loxodont trunk more trumpet-like. Forest Loxodonts have trunks that are intermediate between those of Elephants and their Bush cousins. This species is also intermediate in another matter, i.e., the number of nails. Like the Elephant, they have five in front and four behind, while Bush Loxodonts have four in front and three behind. However, the Elephant may have a total of either sixteen or eighteen. The Forest Loxodonts' skin, too, is more like that of the Elephant, being dark and fairly smooth, while that of the Bush Loxodont is pale gray and very rough. But then both the former are forest animals and quasi-aquatic, while the Bush Loxodonts live on savannas, graze in full sunlight, and bathe less often than the others, sometimes not at all for long periods, so that their skin becomes dry and roughened. Tusks of the Bush Loxodont curve outward and upward; those of the Forest type are long and straight and often point slightly downward and toward each other at their tips.

Internally also there are differences in shape, size, proportion, and, in some small ways, distribution of the organs. The bones, too, are distinguishable, but all these differences are apparent only to an anatomist and cannot be specified without intricate diagrams, so that in these respects we may speak of the Abu as a whole. Their bones have no marrow. Their skulls are a mass of various-sized holes or cells walled with comparatively thin bone, constructed rather like the hard part of a sponge. The largest of these cells have about a two-wineglass capacity, and the walls between are paper thin. They have larger brains than any other land animal—about 5,000 to 6,000 grams, or from 10 to 13 pounds, in weight. This is more than three times the weight of man's. The brain is of "high quality," but it constitutes only 1/800 of the total animal, while ours comprises 1/40 of our body. Their brains, like ours, are highly convoluted.

Abu have no collarbones and no gall bladder, and they have four sets of salivary glands, as rodents do. Their legs are unique in that they are straight and their "knees" flex forward like ours. The knees are on their front legs and are really their wrists. It is with their front feet, or "hands," that they deliver deadly kicks and play football. They walk on the very tips of their toes, the rest of the clublike, cut-off-at-the-bottom foot being a great wedge-shaped pad like a certain style of woman's shoe known as a wedgie. Their nasal, or nose-ridge, bones are very small and are pushed back on to the top of the head, so that the nasal passages enter through the forehead. The mammary glands, or breasts, of the Abu are on their chests, as ours are, and otherwise among mammals only among the sirenians and hyraxes. The testicles are internal, and the penis can be so completely withdrawn that it is often hard to tell a tuskless male from a female.

Altogether, the Abu are today unique in many respects and highly original in others from the anatomical point of view. If we knew nothing of their past and their ancestry, they might be regarded as absolutely unique. As we shall now see, however, despite their exaggerated size and form today, they can be linked to the rest of the mammalian kind, and specifically to certain other unique living forms which, as relatives, are most unexpected. Let us therefore unravel the somewhat tangled skein of their past and see how they came about.

OF THE ORIGIN OF THE BEASTS

The origin of mammals.

The first Abu. The crazy ones.

Mastodons, men, and mammoths.

If you go to a zoo at a time when the house where the Abu reside is empty of humans, and stand quietly before one of these great creatures, strange thoughts may come into your mind. In the silence, but for the gentle shushing of wisps of hay being moved about by the trunks of the Abu, a sense of both awe and incomprehension may very likely descend upon you. The animals there, rocking gently from side to side and watching you covertly from under their long eyelashes, do not seem somehow to be either real or even possible. How, you may find yourself asking, did they ever come about?

Geologists have divided the history of our earth into a number of ages (see chart on page 348), the last four of which are of progressively shorter duration. These together represent the over-all span of time during which life has unquestionably existed on the surface of this planet, leaving evidence of its existence in the form of fossils. These four ages may be called those of the backboneless animals, of the fishes, of the reptiles, and of the mammals. Between two of these—that of the reptiles and that of the mammals —there appears to be a world-wide "break," so that the last (or uppermost) strata of the *Age of Reptiles,* known as the Cretaceous, contain numerous reptiles great and small, but only a few very primitive mammals, while the oldest (or lowest) strata of the *Age of Mammals* lack almost all of the reptiles, but contain numerous mammals of many widely distinct kinds and some already very large. Our story begins somewhere in that "break."

The first strata laid down after this break are called those of the Palaeocene Period. They are found, among other places, in North and Central America and in the extreme south of South America. These rocks were discovered by geologists only comparatively recently. Up to that time, strata known as the Eocene had been thought to be the oldest of the *Age of Mammals,* so there was considerable excitement when the Palaeocene came to light. In view of the complete discontinuity between the life of the Cretaceous and Eocene periods, everybody hoped that on discovery of these intermediate strata we might at last find out what had gone on in the interval. At first, some extravagant claims were made for these Palaeocene rocks, notably by the famous Argentinian palaeontologist Florentino Ameghino, including a statement that dinosaurs and primitive mammals had been found together in some of the strata. Unfortunately, more thorough investigation disproved this, and, instead, an even greater puzzle came to light, for these Palaeocene strata, like those of the Eocene, contained all kinds of already highly evolved mammals, but no dinosaurs' bones. Among these were representatives of three groups of four-footed beasts to which the names *Dinocerata, Pantodonta,* and *Pyrotheria* were given.

The first two appeared in North America, the third in South America. They were strange creatures, some as large as rhinoceroses and of grotesque form. These monstrous creatures just appear, ready-made, as it were, and last for eight, thirty-four, and twenty-nine millions of years, respectively; then, just as suddenly, they vanish from the record of the rocks. The earliest were the *Pantodonta* of North America and the *Pyrotheria* of South America, both found in the Middle Palaeocene; the *Dinocerata* appear only in the Upper Palaeocene. Their interest for us lies in the particular branch of the family tree of mammalian life to which they had to be assigned after their anatomy had been studied. This turned out to be a large group with the delightful name of the *Paenungulata,* which means the "Almost Ungulates," or "Almost Hoofed Ones."

Now, this group also contains an assortment of strange-looking beasts that at first sight seem to have nothing to do with one another. All have a great deal in common, however, including a common ancestry. Some of these forms are still living, but the great majority are extinct. The six living genera include the curious little rabbit-shaped creatures known as rock-hyraxes and tree-hyraxes, the aquatic manatees and dugongs, and the loxodonts and the Elephant. These three pairs of animals have more in common than any or all of them, collectively, have with any other animals, and they had a common ancestor with the *Dinocerata,* the *Pantodonta,* and the *Pyrotheria.* This ancestor lived sometime during the "break" between the *Age of Reptiles* and the *Age of Mammals.* What it looked like we do not yet know.

In order to make this clear and to simplify what follows, I shall borrow a device employed by family historians to condense much detail into the sort of neat and comprehensive form that those specialists employ. This, then, goes as follows:

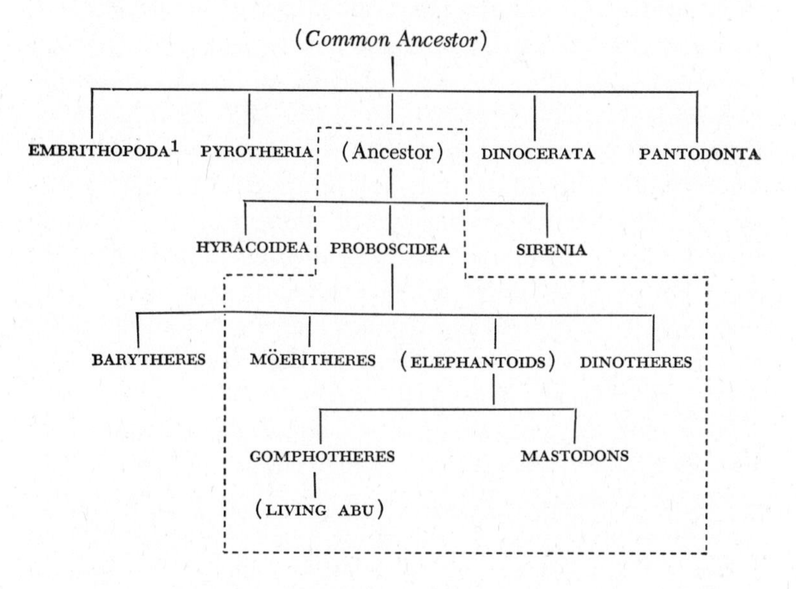

(*The dotted line encloses the Dynasty of Abu.*)

That a paenungulate ancestor of the Dynasty of Abu was contemporary with the *Pantodonta, Dinocerata,* and *Pyrotheria* is manifest from the discovery of primitive forms of proboscideans, or Abu, in the immediately succeeding period (the Eocene). But these could not, by their constitution, have been derived directly from any of those three types.

One might well at first sight think there would be some justification for associating loxodonts and Elephants with rhinoceroses, hippopotamuses, and perhaps even pigs; and just this was once done by zoologists. That their true rela-

[1] An incredible related beast, named *Arsinöitherium,* forming still another group, called the *Embrithopoda* or the "Heavy-footed Ones," found in the Oligocene strata of the Fayûm in Egypt along with the remains of the earliest Abu.

tives have turned out to be the little hyraxes and the bumbling, aquatic manatees and dugongs surprises everybody and seems hardly credible to any but students of mammalian anatomy. You could hardly pick two kinds of animals which look less like relatives of the Abu. Yet the hyraxes, sirenians, loxodonts, and the Elephant all have their mammary glands on their chests, lower-abdominal testicles, and hearts with a double apex. Further, the development of their teeth proceeds along exactly the same lines in all of them, and the male dugong and the hyraxes even have a pair of tusks that are *incisors,* or front teeth, like those of Abu, and not *canines,* or true tusks, like those of other mammals. The anatomy of their fore-limbs is also in all cases identical in construction.

The dugong and the manatees are placid munchers that drift about creeks on tropical coasts, up rivers, and along the bottoms of shallow seas, browsing on sea grasses and other vegetation. The dugong has a tail shaped like a whale's; the manatees' are like large, rounded paddles. In both animals the bony remnants of the hind limbs are hidden in the body. They are called sirenians because some person (who must never have seen one face to face) thought they might have inspired the mariners' stories of sirens and mermaids; for they have a habit of standing upright in the water, staring steadfastly at you, and exposing the upper third of their bodies, on which the prominent breasts of the nursing mothers are situated almost as they are on humans.

The hyraxes are small, exceedingly irascible, and—if grabbed by hand—dangerous little animals of rabbitlike

---

Möeritherium, the earliest known ancestor of the Abu. (From photographs of skeletal remains found in the Fayûm, Egypt.)

shape. They live in colonies among rocks in mountainous places throughout Africa and parts of the Near East, or solitarily in trees in African jungles. They are tail-less, with rather large bottoms, short legs, and very strange, short-toed feet, with four toes on the forefoot and three on the hind, all bearing small, rounded, and thickened nails. The soles of their feet are naked and centrally are shaped into cups or discs that act as adhesive suckers, so that the animals can scramble and even gallop about on sheer rock faces and along the branches of trees. Their heads are rodent-like in appearance, but their teeth are quite different from those of rodents. They have at the extremity of the upper jaw a pair of small tusks that, like those of the Abu, are incisors, and four chisel-shaped front teeth in the lower jaw, with which they can give most unpleasant bites. Their back teeth look like those of tiny rhinoceroses. Both rock- and tree-hyraxes make all manner of indescribably horrible loud noises, mostly at night.

These strange little animals—called "coneys" in our common translations of the Bible—gave early zoologists more trouble than almost any other living mammals. Nobody knew exactly how to classify them, because their anatomy was "all wrong." Finally, one bold and brilliant soul (none other than the great Cuvier) placed them in a group then called that of the pachyderms, along with the proboscideans, or Abu, and the rhinoceroses. When the pachyderms were broken up as an empirical class, the hyraxes were set off on their own as living paenungulates. And there they remain—enigmatic, isolated, and apparently rather angry about it all.

Of other relatives of the original ancestors of the Dynasty of Abu there are none alive today. The pyrotheres, the *Dinocerata,* and the pantodonts disappeared quite early, as we have already noted, and the sole embrithopod—the incredible *Arsinöitherium*—seems to have vanished almost as soon as it had appeared. This vast beast, the top of whose head consisted of a pair of sickle-shaped horns, was bigger than any living rhinoceros but otherwise not unlike one in outward form. It turned up in the Lower Oligocene beds of the Fayûm, in Egypt, along with three early groups of the Dynasty of Abu. It cannot have sprouted from nothing, and it is obviously the end-product of a long evolutionary line, but from what line is not known. It is the only paenungulate of early vintage so far found in Africa, and this clearly indicates that the original ancestors of the Dynasty of Abu were not confined to the New World, as was previously thought. All of these must have had some ancestral roots somewhere in that lost age between the end of the Cretaceous Period and what we call the Palaeocene.

The place in Egypt called the Fayûm is an odd, interesting, and extremely important landmark in the early history of mammalian life. It is a large depression in the desert about fifty miles south of Cairo, known today as the Birket Karun or the Madinat al Fayûm, containing a lake six miles wide and twenty miles long. In earlier days it was filled with a much larger lake known as Möeris, and in ancient Egyptian times was an overflow basin by which the level of the Nile was to some extent regulated during floods. This depression is gouged out of layers of rocks of various ages (Eocene, Oligocene, Miocene) which there lie in horizontal beds. Many of these strata contain fossils, as was discovered in 1879 by a German named Schweinfurth. During the years 1901 and 1904 Dr. Charles Andrews, of the British Museum, ran a series of exploratory digging expeditions in this area, and turned up the remains of a whole galaxy of hitherto unknown creatures.

The first was this *Arsinöitherium.* Next came something that was named *Eosiren,* or the "Dawn Siren," which pushed the Sirenians' ancestry back to the earliest times and to the paenungulate level. Another creature, called *Barytherium* (or the "Heavy Beast"—a fair title), looked like nothing else so far recorded on earth, but seemed to have most in common with the Abu and is therefore appended to the family tree of the Dynasty. Last came a 2-foot-tall creature of robust if not corpulent form, which appeared to be a wallower in marshy places and a browser; the conformation of its face indicated that it must have carried a small trunk like a tapir's. This animal was named *Möeritherium,* after the ancient lake Möeris. On closer study, it proved to be a very primitive Abu—which, of course, caused quite a hullaballoo.

Later, other expeditions went to dig thereabouts—notably that of Dr. Henry Osborn, of the American Museum of Natural History—and other creatures came to light, especially in the somewhat younger Lower Oligocene beds. The most notable were two other forms of primitive Abu, which were named *Phiomia* (which is the pseudo-Graeco-Latin form of the word "Fayûm") and *Palaeomastodon* (meaning simply the "Ancient Mastodon"). These were so different from *Möeritherium* that a new *family* had to be created for them, and for this the delightful name of *Gomphotheriidae* was eventually agreed upon.[2]

There are now known to have been several species of both, and some of them were as big as the present Forest Loxodonts of Africa. They had greatly elongated faces, with rather useless-looking lower jaws bearing a pair of tusks (which were spoon-shaped in *Phiomia*) and somewhat

2 *Palaeomastodon* has now been separated and made the foundation member of the family *Mastodontidae.* The correct name for this family is actually *Mammutidae,* but this is far too confusing, because the mammoths, which are elephants and not mastodons, are now named *Mammuthus.*

Trilophodon, of the Miocene Period. A very widely distributed type of early Abu, with elongated lower jaw bearing two small tusks. (From complete fossil skulls and reconstructed skeletons.)

elongated upper jaws also bearing two small tusks. There is reason to suppose that these creatures had short trunks, the purpose of which must have been to help transfer to their mouths the food rooted up by the shovel-like lower jaw. As animals grow in size and their bodies rise from the earth, their mouths are automatically carried farther away from the ground. Something has to be done about this, and various methods have been employed by different animals. Our ancestors stood on their hind legs and used their front paws to bring their food up to their mouths; the giraffes' elongated necks enabled them to reach down; these gomphotheres got at their food by elongating their jaws, but this necessitated a sort of "fork" as well as a spoon. Whether the small tusks in the upper jaw were developed for offense or defense or for assistance in grubbing out roots is a moot point, but the last idea is probably nearest the truth.

These subelephantine beasts had six cheek teeth on either side of their upper jaws and five on either side of the lower; long, bony extensions of both jaws; and two little down-curving tusks in the upper and two very short ones in the lower, right at the tip of the jaw. The little *Möeritherium* had twenty teeth in its upper jaws and sixteen in the lower. In the upper jaw, there were two small incisors in the mid-front; next, two very big tusklike ones; then, two more small ones; and, behind them, two tiny canines or eyeteeth; and behind these again three premolars, and three molars on either side. In the lower jaw there were two incisors in the middle and two small tusklike ones right at the tip, with again six grinding teeth on either side. This business of teeth is very important, as it tells us what was going on during the development of these animals, and also demonstrates that the tusks of loxodonts and elephants are not true tusks but greatly elongated front teeth.

As the only true ancestral Abu per se—as opposed to paenungulates generally—have so far been found in Africa, there is a tendency to believe that the Dynasty evolved on that continent. However, we do not at present know nearly enough about the past geography of our earth to be able to define just what was "Africa" at any previous time. Moreover, if the crust of the earth periodically moves about, either in parts reciprocally or as a whole, what is now North Africa could well have occupied, and not too long ago, almost any other position on the surface of the globe. Besides, though all the first proboscideans have appeared in what we call Africa today, there is at least an even chance that their ancestors lived somewhere else without leaving any fossil records that we have as yet found.

We know that in the first stages of the Oligocene Period there were pantodonts in North America, pyrotheres in South America, embrithopods and primitive hyracoids in Africa, sirenians in Madagascar, Africa, Europe, and western North America, and three distinct kinds of primitive Abu in Africa—the möeritheres, the first gomphotheres (*Phiomia*), and the first mastodons (*Palaeomastodon*). By the end of the Oligocene, all these had vanished except the hyraxes, the sirenians, the gomphotheres, and the mastodons. But at the same time a new branch of the Dynasty of Abu had appeared on the scene.

In 1613 the skeleton of a vast beast was found in the Dauphiné in France. Its excavator, a man named Mazurier, claimed it was that of a "giant" and said it had been contained in a 30-foot stone coffin. Then, in 1715, René-Antoine Ferchault de Réaumur (inventor of the Réaumur thermometer) found a remarkable tooth, which was later examined by a German named Johann Jacob Kaup, who called it that of a *Dinotherium,* or "Terrible Beast." Next, in 1836, a monstrous skull of a creature with similar teeth was dug up at Eppelsheim in Germany. Meanwhile, Baron Cuvier had shown that all these bones and teeth were those of the same type of extinct animal (not giant man);

but, it was not till 1908 that a complete skeleton of one such was assembled in Vienna. This was a comparatively small example, standing only 8 feet at the shoulder.

This animal proved to have bones not unlike those of elephants, and it was therefore set up in conformity with the stance of such animals. However, its massive head bore a very solid lower jaw that curved downward at an angle of almost 90 degrees and carried two large, recurved tusks that turned downward and backward toward the chest of their owner. Before the whole skeleton was known, several leading savants of the day had insisted that the beast had been a marine type and had used these tusks to haul itself out on to ice floes, just as the walrus does today. In time, many more skeletal remains proved that dinotheres existed in several forms, ranging to an enormous size; that they lasted almost twenty million years all over Africa and Eurasia; and that they were apparently still around in Pleistocene times in the former continent contemporaneously with early man.

At the beginning of the Miocene Period the Dynasty of Abu consisted of two main branches, apart from these dinotheres. These were the descendants of *Phiomia* and *Palaeomastodon,* which are called the gomphotheres and the mastodons. As the former were the more numerous, the more exaggerated, and the first to disappear, I shall start with them.

The gomphotheres were an incredible assemblage of beasts. They seem to have concentrated at first on size and a continued elongation of their faces, until they were more than one-third head, with tremendously extended jaws bearing two large tusks in the upper jaw and two not inconsiderable ones on the end of the much elongated lower jaw. The head was rather flat and bird-like, and was carried almost straight forward on a fairly long neck. The eyes seem to have been quite large. There must have been at least a short trunk. Fossil skeletons of these creatures first turned up in

France and later in Africa, Asia, and North America. They appear to have reached a zenith and then, as a family, to have begun to deviate in various, most extraordinary manners.

When these monstrous, beaklike front ends began to get in the beasts' way, evolution took two separate paths. On the one hand, the lower jaw began to get progressively shorter, starting with a species found in Europe and now called *Tetralophodon* and continuing thus until there were gomphotheres that had skulls almost like those of elephants. One such was called *Stegomastodon* and is really a very important actor in our drama. The rest of the gomphotheres appear to be one of evolution's wilder jokes.

These wild exaggerations have been given the names *Amebelodon, Platybelodon,* and *Torynobelodon*—or "Amy," "Platy," and "Tory," as an unexpectedly cheery palaeontologist recently observed. They may be called collectively the "Shovel-tuskers." Appearing first in the Miocene, they lasted into the Pliocene, both in Eurasia and North America. "Amy" and "Tory" were found in the Pliocene of Colorado and Nebraska, and "Platy"—the most ghastly of all—in the Upper Miocene of the Caucasus and Mongolia. For a lower jaw, "Platy" had a monstrous shovel ending in a sort of bulldozer blade formed of two enormous, scoop-shaped teeth. This must have been used for plowing up the roots of water plants or some other fairly loose material; otherwise, no imaginable neck muscles could have supported such a "machine" and made it work at the same time.

But there were other exaggerations almost as outrageous among the gomphotheres. The "Beak-snouts" of North and Central America, which also lived during the Miocene and Pliocene, had enormous down-curving lower jaws. The "Twisted tuskers" (named *Cuverionius* and *Cordillerion*) had fairly normal tuskless lower jaws, but possessed a pair of upper tusks each with a spiral twist like an exaggerated screw. *Cordillerion,* a little beast, inhabited Arizona, California, and South America, where it was hunted and eaten by primitive man.

Finally, there were the "Straight tuskers" (genus *Anancus*), which were really *quite* absurd. They looked for all the world like real Abu, but they carried their rather small heads almost straight forward and bore with them monstrous straight tusks that were actually more than two-thirds as long as their heads and bodies. The tusks of the ultimate mammoths were just as grotesque, but were better devised from a mechanical point of view: they were not nearly so massive, and they were better balanced, due to their wide spiral conformation. The tusks of *Anancus* just do not make any sense at all, to our way of thinking, and yet they were developed and carried for countless centuries by their very numerous owners.

By comparison with the fantastically wrought gomphotheres, the true mastodons are extremely dreary, though not much is really known about them. They are presumed to have been derived directly from the *Palaeomastodon* of the earliest days of the Fayûm, which displayed several features typical of these later numerous beasts, but the first true mastodon did not appear until the Lower Miocene, in Europe. However, between even those and the typical members of the genus *Mastodon* of the later Pleistocene and prehistoric periods, there is a considerable blank. The two creatures once known rather dully as *Miomastodon* and *Pliomastodon,* from the Miocene and Pliocene, are obviously related to the true mastodons but just as obviously not in their direct line of descent. We are thus left with the end-product of this line, members of which were finally spread all over Eurasia and North, Central, and South America.

Several species of mastodons were, in their last days, contemporaneous with several species of loxodonts, mammoths, and elephants, and many were known to have been hunted and eaten by men. There were moderate-sized mastodons and there were some very large species—one in North

America stood about 11 feet at the shoulder. Although not taller than the living Bush Loxodont, it must have had a much greater bulk, for this animal was elongated and very deep-bodied. One species of mastodon which lived in North America is known to have been clothed in long, coarse, reddish hair; to have had an extremely heavy trunk but moderate tusks; and to have been a browser.

There is a great deal of misunderstanding regarding these animals because comic strips, movies, and much printed matter often confuse them with mammoths or extinct elephants, and sometimes even with dinosaurs. It has been almost a century since we came to accept the idea that our ancestors knew the mammoths in Europe and Asia, but only much more recently have we learned that man knew and hunted the mastodons (as well as various species of mammoth) in North America.

The true mastodons, like the gomphotheres, finally became extinct, but other Abu survived. Why the former vanished is impossible to say, though the profile of the mastodons, with their low foreheads, may at first seem to offer a clue. But then what of the mammoths, which had foreheads like government psychologists yet nevertheless also became extinct, while the distinctly low-browed loxodonts have survived? At this point some reappraisal is called for.

You may note from the chart on page 27 that there are five major stages in the history of the Dynasty of Abu. These are (1) some as yet undiscovered ancestor, lost in the mists of time between the end of the Cretaceous Period and the laying down of the first Palaeocene strata; (2) the stage of the paenungulates of various kinds, which first appeared in the Palaeocene, the Eocene, and the early Oligocene; (3) the splitting apart of the hyraxes, the sirenians, and the primitive ancestors of the proboscideans; (4) the appearance of the little möeritheres, the monstrous barytheres, the dinotheres, and the first elephantoids (i.e., the gomphotheres and mastodons); and, finally, (5) a long period of proliferation of the elephantoids, giving rise to all sorts of odd creatures. It was during this last period that the loxodonts, mammoths, and elephants came into existence.

Somewhere about the Middle Miocene a creature that has been named *Stegolophodon* appeared. This was a kind of mastodon, but it showed anatomical characteristics, notably in its grinding teeth, that were unusual. It proved to be a rather successful type that lasted for some thirty million years and was still around when fairly advanced kinds of submen were cracking flints. However, about ten million years later, in the Lower Pliocene Period, a creature that we now call *Stegodon* cropped up alongside *Stegolophodon,* and was obviously evolved from the latter. This was even more "elephant-like"; and, sure enough, not so long thereafter, geologically speaking, there appeared three other distinct types, which may be called the loxodonts, the mammoths, and the true elephants. The stegodons are derived from the mastodons, but they are distinguished by having no less than fourteen cross-ridges of dentine and enamel on each of their back or grinding teeth. This is close to the unique arrangement found among elephants, and it is one of several reasons why the stegodons are considered to be the ancestors of the elephants. We thus have an extension of the family tree of the Dynasty which goes like this:

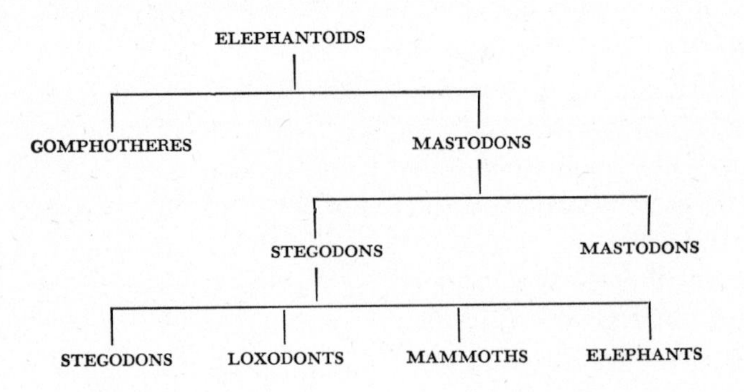

(This shows only the family connections, not the time sequence. For the latter, see the chart on page 348.)

The stegodons—the name means "Roof-toothed Ones," referring to the up-and-down or pentroof-like formation of their cheek teeth—were quite elephantine, and they are regarded as being members of the family *Elephantidae.* They lasted well into the Pleistocene Period and must have been encountered by early man, along with the true mastodons, the straight tuskers, the twisted tuskers, and the last of the dinotheres.

Of loxodonts, mammoths, and elephants, several distinct types are known, but all the species are now considered to be included in only three genera, known as *Loxodonta, Mammuthus,* and *Elephas.* All are comparatively new creatures, for no bones of any have been found in deposits prior to the last stages of the Pliocene. The first is known in fossil form from Eurasia and Africa and alive in Africa today; the second in fossil form from Eurasia, North Africa, North America, and possibly South America (if a single tooth fragment from French Guiana has been properly identified); the third both as fossils and alive only from Asia. The mammoths and the elephants are somewhat alike, and both are somewhat different from the loxodonts. In fact, the mammoths may be looked upon as northern representatives of or, more exactly, replacements for the true Elephant of southern Asia; the loxodonts are considerably different African animals that once inhabited also the Mediterranean Basin and parts of western Asia.

Early forms of loxodonts have turned up over a wide area, ranging from India to Spain and south to Rhodesia. Two of the most outstanding came to light on the island of Malta in the Mediterranean; one of these was fairly large, but the other was a true pygmy, standing only about 3 feet high at the shoulder when fully grown. Another form from India had most extraordinary and enormous bony structures, like false brow ridges, on its forehead, so that it must have looked more like an exaggerated Elephant than a loxodont, which usually has a sloping forehead.

The first known true Elephants, which used to bear the pleasant names of *Platelephas* and *Hypselephas,* or the "Flat" and the "High" Elephants, were Asiatic and of monumental size and very distinctive appearance. The living species of both loxodonts and Elephants appeared quite early, and over a much wider range than they occupy today.

The first mammoth (named *Mammuthus planifrons*) appeared in the last phases of the Pliocene of Eurasia, before the onset of the most recent ice advances and retreats. Four distinct species of mammoth are known—the Flat-browed (*M. planifrons*) and the Southern (*M. meridionalis*), both of Eurasia; the Imperial (*M. imperator*) of the early Pleistocene of the United States and Mexico; and the Woolly (*M. primigenius*) of the late Pleistocene of northern Asia, central Europe, and North America. There were also dwarf forms: little creatures such as those now being unearthed on the islands off the coast of California.[3]

The mammoths are a very difficult group of animals to sort out; many specimens are represented only by fragments of teeth and bones, and they were such common animals that all manner of variations have come to light. This sug-

[3] These diminutive elephantines were originally named *Parelephas exilus* by Stock and Fennel, but Osborn changed their identification to his genus *Archidiskodon,* which he applied to many but not all the mammoths. What scientific name should be applied to them is in doubt, but those who are excavating them are currently referring to them as *Parelephas.* Examination of these interesting fossils is not yet completed, but it is possible that there may be more than one species represented among the remains so far unearthed on the Californian islands.

Platybelodon, a Shovel-tusker of the Miocene of Asia, with spoon-shaped lower jaw tusks. (Composite from various sources.)

gests that their origin was not from only one kind of creature, and that they not only evolved differently in different areas but possibly that various races interbred and perhaps even "outbred" with other loxodont-like and elephant-like species in some peripheral areas.

Two mammoths apparently survived the coming of man, and one of these possibly existed until the dawn of history, though unfortunately in a land where history was not *written* until recent times. The first is the Imperial Mammoth of the early Pleistocene, which existed in enormous numbers all over the upland plateaus of what are now the West and the Southwest of the United States and in central Mexico. This may have been the bulkiest land mammal ever to have existed, for specimens measuring over 15 feet high at the shoulder have been unearthed. A fabulous animal distantly related to the rhinoceroses, named *Baluchitherium*, grew to a greater over-all height and could reach food above 18 feet, but, although its skeleton was grossly massive, its body sloped almost like that of a giraffe, whereas the Imperial Mammoth appears to have been an almost solid mass, with a rectangular or box-shaped chassis. A large male Bush Loxodont can weigh over 12 tons; an Imperial Mammoth bull, it has been calculated, could have weighed over 20, due to its shape and to its more massive skeleton. Recent discoveries indicate that this monster may have been known to very early men.

The other mammoth, the best known, is the so-called Woolly Mammoth, which at the apex of its glory ranged all over Asia north of the Elburz-Pamir-Himalaya-Tsingling-Shan (west-to-east) mountain spine of that continent; the whole of Europe south of the Scandinavian peninsula and Finland; and the greater part of North America. This too was an impressive beast, even "undressed," or relieved of its 2-foot-long shaggy coat, being sometimes as tall as the largest Bush Loxodont but having a steeply sloping back and a huge, bulbous, fatty dome of flesh on the top of its head. At the end of its reign, some old bulls carried enormous, sweepingly curved tusks, one of which has proved to measure 16 feet 5 inches around its outer curve. These tusks came out of the front of the skull quite close together and proceeded forward and downward, separating at first gradually and then rapidly, curving outward and around, in some cases far enough to form a complete circle, with tips crossed and parallel to the ground.

There has been endless discussion about the uses of these extraordinary adornments, the suggestions ranging from the notion that they were mere sexual decorations to the possibility that they may have been employed as weapons. None seems to be altogether satisfactory, even the idea that they were protection for the animals' trunks or that they were snow plows. Yet there is one theory that possibly makes some sense. Several whole Woolly Mammoth corpses have been found in the frozen ground or *muck* of northern Siberia, and many bits of them in Alaska and elsewhere have come to light. So well preserved were some of these that their flesh was eaten by wolves and dogs. The contents of their stomachs could be analyzed by botanists, who were able to identify grass blades, seeds, leaves, and even flowers contained therein. Some of these plant-remains were still on the animals' tongues and wedged between the ridges of their teeth. Those analyses confirm the common-sense conclusion that the Woolly Mammoths did *not* live on Arctic snowfields. Any animal so vast has to eat almost continuously, and enormous quantities of food must have been required to sustain a population so large as that of the Woolly Mammoths. A sufficient food supply would not have been available, even *under* the snow during half the year. Further, the plant-remains found inside them were fresh and often *in flower,* and they were of species that are today found all over the more southerly parts of Siberia where the climate is much milder than that of the Arctic Ocean rim.

The tusks, then, could have been useful as snow plows

only during the late fall, when (and if) the animals had occasion to build snow corrals or "pens," as does the Moose. At all *other* times, however, they may have been extremely useful as "sweeps" to push aside bushes, tough sedges, and small trees that the mammoths did *not* relish, so that the animals could get at the more succulent and comparatively small foods that they obviously *did* like. To this the obvious retort is: "What, then, of the females and young, which did not have any such sweeps?" The answer may be readily obtained by watching a herd of elephants feeding: the bulls push over trees and pull down branches, and very often the females and young partake of the results. Bull Woolly Mammoths may have cleared a path with their vast ivory hoops so that their females and young could get at the foods of their choice.

A great deal is known about the Woolly Mammoth, but several aspects of its final demise have completely baffled both our common sense and our logic. The whole question of extinction is obscure enough in itself, but here we must consider also how tens of thousands of these creatures (and of many other species of animals) met their *individual* ends (either simultaneously or at various times) so suddenly that they had time neither to lie down nor even to swallow their last mouthfuls of food. We will return to this puzzle later.

OF THE RISE OF THEIR RIVALS

The origin of Man. His early association with the Abu. Man and Abu in America, in Eurasia, and in Africa.

The sixty million years between the end of the Cretaceous and the onset of the Pleistocene appear to have constituted a period of comparative world-wide geologic quiet, though toward its end there are signs that earth movements were beginning on a major scale in several areas. The mammals had by the beginning of the Pleistocene proliferated in an amazing manner, transcending anything accomplished previously by the reptiles, and they appear also to have existed in almost countless numbers. Among them were various creatures belonging to the group called technically the Primates, which includes lemurs, monkeys, apes, and men. At the beginning of the Pleistocene these were very numerous, and they included quite a number of apes of rather advanced capacities. By then there may also have been some men-apes —though not as yet any ape-men, submen, or true men. The story of Man himself is not our concern here, but his appearance on the scene is, for he quite soon began to make a profound impact upon the rest of mammalian life, and on the destiny of the Dynasty of Abu in particular. Moreover, Man appears in some respects at least to be almost as much the cause of certain radical changes in recent terrestrial history as he was himself an outcome of those changes.

It has been manifest for some time now that while evolution undoubtedly proceeds all the time at a steady pace and upon what we may call broadly Darwinian lines vis-à-vis all individual species, there have also been a few brief periods in the history of life on this planet when it seems to have accelerated. These periods seem always to have been times of upheaval, with "breaks" in the record and with evidence of volcanicity, of mountain-building, and of major crustal shifts. Also, while the evolution of some types seems to have spurted forward at these times, the universal extermination of others seems often to have coincided with this. In other words, times of great change may stimulate the rapid evolution of some forms of life while they prove lethal to others. The comparatively recent Pleistocene was such a time, and during its brief one million years Man welled up from simioid obscurity to a position of world-wide pre-eminence, while innumerable other mammalian forms were totally swept away. Among the latter were almost all the proud members of the Dynasty of Abu.

At the beginning of that period that dynasty was represented by no less than eleven genera—mastodons, stegodons (both *Stegolophodon* and *Stegodon*), mammoths, loxodonts, and elephants; straight tuskers (*Anancus* and a near relative named *Stegomastodon*); twisted tuskers (*Cuverionius* and its near relative *Notiomastodon*), and, finally, some relict dinotheres. These were spread all over the earth, except for Australia and its associated islands, and Oceania. Asia had *Stegodon* and *Stegolophodon,* loxodonts, elephants, mammoths, and straight tuskers. Africa had the last dinotheres (and some mammoths in the north), while loxodonts appeared there latterly. North America had mammoths, *Stegomastodon,* and the twisted tusker (*Cuverionius*); South America also had *Stegomastodon* and *Cuverionius,* plus *Notiomastodon,* and possibly some mammoths.

It usually comes as a surprise to learn that this continent and more so South America were so replete with elephantines until very recently, and that these animals were for millennia intimately associated with men. This is not by any means due to a lack of discoveries of fossil, subfossil, or even fresh bones of such creatures here, for enormous quantities of skeletons of all of them have been unearthed all over North America since early days—none other than President Thomas Jefferson filled whole rooms in the White House with their bones—but rather due to an almost complete misunderstanding, until recently, of Man's past on this continent.

That there might have been men of other races in the Americas long before the arrival of the Amerindians, that some of these built in monumental stone, and that the earlier of them fed on horses, mastodons, camels, ground-sloths, and mammoths, was not seriously considered. Further, that this could have happened not only before the last ice advance but possibly before the last but one, or even earlier, was until recently quite unthinkable. Finally, that there might even have been submen here before that is still considered impossible. However, all these suggestions have not only now been made, but physical evidence of them has also been put forward for serious consideration.

It was E. H. Sellards and J. O. Figgins, of the Denver Museum of Natural History, who first broke the ice. These students were the first to bring to light and publish unmistakable evidence of a primitive age wherein beautifully chipped stone implements were found in association with the bones of all manner of now extinct animals. At the same time, sculptures of some of these animals, notably of elephantines, were reported from several widely separated points in tropical America. At first these discoveries were either ignored or attributed to historic times, but then Dr. Helmuth de Terra brought to light Tepexpan Man from the ancient bottom of what used to be Lake Texcoco near Mexico City, to which he then assigned the date 11,000 B.C. This date is now, however, believed to be about 2800 B.C. But this is not the only, or by any means the oldest, evidence of Man in association with Abu in that area. A small carving of a human foot, which may have been a part of a small statue or an amulet, was discovered in a nearby deposit and has been dated at 20,000 years. This was carved from the molar tooth of a mammoth, and is doubly startling, as the art of carving implies quite an advanced culture. Now, however, Dr. Juan Armanta has uncovered evidence of very much older man in association with Abu, including an engraving on a large portion of a large bone that shows what appears to be a Tetrabelodon-like type, with an enormously elongated lower jaw bearing two tusks, and two larger tusks in the normal position in the upper jaw. The date 43,000 B.C. or 45,000 B.P. (before the present) is now spoken of for this.

These discoveries, despite all the debate that has gone on regarding their age, has encouraged others to publish their findings, and to resuscitate many well-documented reports that had been accumulating over the years but that had been hitherto ignored. Some of the odd items which have come to light were immediately accepted; others were not. Numerous stone implements turned up, either in association with, or actually lying *under,* the skeletons of both mammoths and mastodons; and later, in South America, even with twisted tuskers. In fact, our ideas about early man in the New World suddenly changed drastically. The over-all results were summated by Dr. George F. Carter in a most pithy manner in 1951 in an article in *Science,* which shocked and still shocks many, but which has in no way been refuted and stands as a monument of simply stated facts. Dr. Carter's suggestions were actually based almost wholly on an analysis of reports that had already been published by others but that had not previously been integrated or synthesized. When he assembled them as he did in this article, they brought to light the inescapable fact that Man had been in the Americas not just for a few millennia but for an extremely long time indeed—and certainly since long before the last ice advance, which is called the Wisconsan and which has been shown by radioactive carbon analysis to have ended only about 12,000 years ago. Dr. Carter demonstrated that man has been here since before the last-but-one ice advance, the Illinoian, now dated between 80,000 and 40,000 B.C. More recently a camel-eating people have been dated in Texas as having lived in and before 44,000 (plus) years ago—a radiocarbon date obtained by the Humble Oil Company.

There is still much debate as to the dating of the various earlier ice advances and retreats in North America and of the length of the periods between them. The most conservative in point of actual time—but, thus, the most *radical,* as geology textbooks still call for much earlier dates—are 40,000 years ago for the start of the last advance; 80,000 for the start of the next to last; and 130,000 for the one before that. Thus, Man has been here for at least 40,000 years, very probably for more than 80,000, and possibly for more than 130,000. It can no longer be denied, moreover, that he ate mammoths or that he harried mastodons on this continent long before the ice-cap crept over Long Island Sound.

There are also stone implements of crude design, which may date back much farther in time than that; antedating, in fact, by eons the famous and beautifully made Folsom points, which were the work of efficient and quite advanced hunters and were at one time thought to be the earliest works of Man in the New World. Who these people were we do not know.

If we now reverse our journey and move forward in time toward the present, we encounter perhaps even more remarkable things about Abu in the New World. Man in association with mammoths and mastodons 20,000, 30,000, 50,000, or even 130,000 years ago on this continent does not seem so odd, should one be forced by proper evidence to accept the fact that they were both here at those times; but when it is suggested that such an association continued into what is called postglacial times—i.e., after the last ice retreat, which is now thought to have ended at the latest about 10,000 B.C.—the average person, as well as the specialist, is apt to recoil in dismay. However, there is now considerable evidence that the men who made the so-called Clovis points prior to Folsom man hunted both mammoths and mastodons at just about that date, for their artifacts have now been found intimately and undeniably associated with the bones of those animals in several places. Therefore, either the men who made these tools lived much earlier than we previously supposed, or the animals only became extinct much later than we thought. One of these finds has now been dated (see Agogino and Haynes) at 10,780± 375 years. We cannot have it both ways unless the whole lot of them—Abu and men—all lived here only for one brief period. Yet the anthropologists categorically state otherwise. Therefore, either Man is very much older in the New World, or Abu existed here till very much later than we previously supposed.

However, something very drastic manifestly occurred at the end of the Pleistocene—which is to say sometime during, and most probably at the beginning of, the last ice advance. This was a widespread if not a universal extinction of a great part of the larger mammalian fauna, and particularly of the Abu, throughout the Americas and Eurasia north of the great east-west mountain chain that extends from southern

China to the eastern Mediterranean. The date of at least one of these mass destructions has been recently pinned down by Soviet scientists as not later than about 12,000 years ago in Asia, but we do not yet know precisely when it took place in America. Hibben and others have pointed out that Alaska was not the only place where most, if not all, of the larger fauna were wiped out—apparently instantaneously—and their remains frozen into the *muck*, as it is called. There are vast bone beds in Florida, all down the western side of this continent, and in Central and South America, in which tens of thousands of animals—including whole herds of all ages together—are heaped in seemingly endless masses, in some cases in blown sand but in other cases in what are obviously flood deposits. There must be some explanation for these wholesale slaughters, many of which seem to have been contemporaneous and to have taken place at the end of the Pleistocene or at the beginning of the last ice advance.

Was there a single world-wide or hemispheric catastrophe, or was there a series of them of such monumental proportions as to have not merely decimated but totally eliminated the major part of the fauna, and particularly their larger members? There is increasing evidence that there were such events. But how, then, did bison, moose, the larger brown bears, and the puma, as instances, survive in America, while mammoths, mastodons, the giant bison, horses, the giant beaver, and other great cats, to name only a few, all vanish suddenly? The old idea that the cold of the ice-cap, once again advancing southward, was alone the cause is no longer tenable, for some large animals did survive, while millions of others were destroyed—and far south, to boot, in what was obviously a mild climate. Some factor other than mere cold must have been the cause.

All kinds of suggestions have been put forward. There may have been several processes occurring at once, such as sudden cold in the north, vast floods farther south in one place, and giant dust storms in others, while coincidental earthquakes or volcanic eruptions with accompanying landslides and tidal waves could account for what we find in still other places. The question that interests us is, did any Abu survive these cataclysms in the Americas?

Mastodons have been unearthed all over a very wide area of the northeastern part of the United States and mostly in the top layers of bogs that simply could not, in all but a very few cases, themselves have survived the bulldozer action of the Wisconsan ice sheet as it passed over them. Therefore, either these animals survived the catastrophes and the last ice advance, or their corpses were caught *in* that ice at the outset of its formation and were then "dropped," along with all manner of other material, *out* of that ice as it melted away, and were preserved in those places where bogs could be formed along the foot of the retreating ice front. The latter seems to be the sounder theory; though the immense volume of bits of flesh, skin, and bone (and even the stomach contents) of these animals that have been found, in proportion to the comparatively minute number of bogs investigated, is utterly perplexing. Further, there is now also a considerable volume of reports of other remains of both mammoths and mastodons found associated with human artifacts that are, as we have noted, definitely postglacial and that involve typical Amerindian weapons and tools, and even pottery. It has been stressed, however, that there is still a chance that these pots, tools, and animal remains may be of different ages, and have been assembled during more recent floods, as may occur in some caves. The only alternative is that the human artifacts are of a much earlier date than had previously been believed, as indicated by several extraordinary discoveries in which stone weapons of excellent workmanship have been found actually sticking in mammoth bones. Several aspects of this business are indeed hard to explain unless we accept the idea that elephantine creatures survived the last great ice advance on this continent. Dates as late as 6,000 to 5,000 B.P. are now being given for finds of their remains.

More than one Amerindian tribe had legends (often accepted traditions) that they had hunted large creatures with long, shaggy brown hair and trunks until not too long before the arrival of Europeans on this continent. What is more, these legends were recorded by the colonists long before the first modern Elephant or loxodont was brought, or even known, to America. Also, carvings of elephantines are alleged to have been found in the mounds of the Mississippi Valley, and one of these mounds itself is said to be in the form of a mastodon. Both facts have been questioned, but the form of the mound is hardly to be gainsaid, as no animals other than Abu have full trunks. Then, there are the extraordinary tales of the English sailor Ingram, and of the escaped slave Edwards.

This is admittedly an excursion into the realm of the historically dubious, but the stories should be considered. Both tales are reputedly reports made to officials of the British Crown concerning events that took place about 1580. The first was given before a Royal Commission in 1595, more than a dozen years after the events, by a common seaman who had been put ashore with thirty others on the Gulf Coast of North America, to the east of the Mississippi, by the British Admiral Hawkins, whose decimated fleet was overcrowded with rescued compatriots. Ingram and two companions set off to the northeast; the rest went west and, after many losses, reached Mexico. One of Ingram's companions died, but he finally reached Nova Scotia, where he stumbled upon a Basque summer fishing camp and was taken back to Europe. In his account he mentioned meeting herds of bison in what is now the area of Pennsylvania, and also seeing huge, shaggy animals with large, floppy ears which were being hunted by the Amerindians.

Edwards, who said he had been captured and enslaved

by the Spanish and taken to Mexico but had escaped, allegedly made his way back to England via a route that took him up the middle of the North American continent to the region of the Great Lakes and thence east to the coast near the mouth of the St. Lawrence, where he also happened to stumble upon a summer camp of Basque codfishers. The strange thing about his story is that, considering the time when it was recorded and the unbelievable distance the lone traveler is alleged to have covered, it is singularly free, with the exception of one statement, from the "marvelous," so rife in those days. This is to the effect that the narrator had encountered Amerindians hunting considerable herds of huge, shaggy creatures with long trunks in the valley bottoms of the great central plains. The most intriguing question about both these stories is the date when they were recorded.

Hawkins is alleged to have been along the coast of Africa, but you cannot see African loxodonts along the coast—they live inland; Abu were not domesticated in those countries; and in any case loxodonts are not *shaggy*. Both Ingram and Edwards may have visited India and other Oriental countries where elephants were commonly seen, but elephants are not shaggy, either. A sixteenth-century common seaman might almost be expected to embellish his story, however fantastic it might actually have been, by adding the colorful picture of "Indians" chasing "elephants" in America, because knowledge of the animal life of the continents other

---

Dinotherium, a very large and specialized form of Abu of the Old World that was probably known to earliest man in Africa. (From photographs of a mounted skeleton in Vienna.)

than Europe was both extremely limited and much muddled in those days. But to make "elephants" shaggy with long hair is a most peculiar and unlikely addition, since, of all animals, they are outstanding and almost unique in their nakedness.

I know where there are published statements of an even more exaggerated nature about the presence of living Abu in North America until an even later date. Personally, I cannot bring myself—at least as yet—to lay any store by these, historically, and therefore hesitate to interject them here in any detail; but it has been alleged that remnants of their herds existed in early colonial times in the forests west of the Appalachians and east of the great open prairies, all the way from Canada to the bayous, and that they were exterminated by the Amerindians and the first lone white trappers and traders who penetrated those regions, with *firearms.* While this sounds highly improbable, it is truly amazing how whole species of large animals have been overlooked until today in countries that have been heavily populated for centuries. The most extraordinary example is that of the second largest wild species of ox, known now as the Couprey, the males of which have extraordinary tasselated horns, which was found only in 1938 in Indochina. In early colonial days most accounts that both the Amerindians and the first unofficial "explorers" told about inland North America were discounted as mere "travelers' tales"; and, let us not forget, this whole land was one of continuous forest in those days.

The idea of extinct forms of Abu in association with prehistoric man has not yet become a popularly recognized combination in American prehistory. The concept of such an association in Europe, however, has been accepted for almost a century, and we no longer regard cave paintings of mammoths by palaeolithic man as either dubious or exceptional. Similar proofs in Asia and Africa are even less well known, but they have now been recorded for several decades and they are constantly being added to. In fact, it is slowly becoming clear that Man and Abu of all kinds were most intimately associated throughout the rise of the former and the decline of the latter. And this association very likely continued even after the last southward ice advance all over the northern hemisphere.

For some years now, scientists—and notably Dr. L. S. B. Leakey—have been excavating sites where men have lived for countless centuries along the shores of a now dried-up lake at a place called Olduvai in Tanganyika, East Africa. In 1957 one of these sites yielded an astonishing assemblage: the bones of a pig bigger than a rhinoceros, with tushes as big as loxodont tusks; baboons as large as gorillas; stone hand-axes so heavy that they cannot be efficiently used by an average modern-day man and, in fact, can hardly be lifted in one hand; parts of some enormous loxodonts, and the skull of a very primitive hominoid now named "Nutcracker" Man (*Zinjanthropus*) because of his enormous jaws. There were also the bones of all sorts of other animals—some still living, like the lion, and some extinct. The remains have been declared to be over 600,000 years old, and the skull and the hand-axes have been assigned to a race known as Chellean Man, whose primitive tools are found in great abundance over an enormous area of Africa and Eurasia. Here, men were obviously associated with Abu at the end of the first ice advance.

When the similar association started in Eurasia we do not yet know, although worked-ivory artifacts, made from elephantine ivory, go back to the earliest Aurignacian cultural levels—in other words, to the time of the first sudden appearance of Cro-Magnon Man in western Europe. We have no direct evidence as yet that the submen, called Neanderthalers, hunted mammoths, loxodonts, straight tuskers, or stegodons, although all these creatures were available to them. But there were other kinds of manlike creatures contemporary with the Neanderthalers, and it is possible that some of these may have done so. It is only with the Cro-Magnons, however, that we come across direct evidence of man doing so in these areas.

These people would seem to have lived at the end of the last ice advance, at least in Europe. There is still a complete mystery as to their origin, for they just appeared suddenly on the extreme western fringe of that continent and nothing like them or their considerably advanced *maritime culture*, with its fine stone and bone implements, is known to have existed previously anywhere. Nor has their superb cave-painting art ever been found in circumstances that might indicate its antecedents. Prior to the introduction of the radio-carbon dating method, the date of Cro-Magnon Man's appearance was put at 25,000 B.C., in southern Europe. However, the last of the ice-cap was, we now know, still withering away in Scandinavia as late as 8000 B.C.—a date that coincides with its final disappearance in North America. If this new dating be accepted as valid for both Europe and North America, we must change our conception of when Cro-Magnon Man lived. We must either move him forward in time some 10,000 to 15,000 years into the postglacial period; or we must move him back twice that distance, to a point prior to the beginning of the last ice advance, for he was obviously associated with and hunted animals that manifestly could not have existed on an ice-cap. There is, however, a third alternative: namely, that he may have lived *during* that advance but at some distance south of its periphery—i.e., in a great arc from Spain to the Danube Valley. All three possibilities pose equally real problems.

Anancus, the Straight Tusker. (From a bas-relief reconstruction in the Museo di Storia Naturale di Milano, Italy.)

Besides painting on the walls of his caves the most beautiful, realistic, and perhaps occasionally slightly humorous illustrations of obvious Woolly Mammoths, complete with curving tusks, great bulbous heads, sloping backs, and fur trailing to their ankles, Cro-Magnon Man also depicted hairless elephants with straight backs, or backs with a bump in the middle, and with lumpy, rounded heads like those of exaggerated true Elephants. These are found in the Spanish caves (e.g., those of Castillo, Santander; and Pindal, Asturias), and the climate of Spain may have remained mild while northern and central Europe were glaciated. This looks as if Cro-Magnon Man both antedated the last ice advance and knew Abu other than mammoths, and also survived the cold in the north by staying in southern peripheral areas, while the Abu were exterminated up there.

It is not nearly so easy as might be supposed to correlate the succession of deposits *in caves* with those laid down outside them; and, since almost all we know of Cro-Magnon Man comes from cave floors, we cannot as yet state definitely how long he existed. That he knew intimately both mammoths and some other Abu in southern Europe is manifest, and that he killed these with spears and caught them in some kind of pitfall or elaborate cage trap is certain, for drawings in these caves clearly show this. He may even have employed a primitive form of *keddah* (see Chapter 9), for some later cave drawings show deer being driven by groups of men into what resemble corrals. But there is very little likelihood that Cro-Magnon Man—or man in general—was solely responsible for exterminating the mammoths, since men were still rare creatures in those days, while mammoths appear to have been very numerous. Moreover, if living elephants, which are the nearest relatives of the mammoths, are any criterion, the mammoths probably had a powerful reproductive capacity.

What happened in northern, far-eastern, and southern Asia and in Africa during the Pleistocene Period, vis-à-vis the decline of the Abu and the rise of Man, we do not as yet know. We have a few inklings and we may make some educated guesses, but that is all. It is plain that at the beginning of this period there were very large numbers of many different Abu wandering about all over these vast continents, and it is equally clear that by the end of that period, and especially by the time human history was initiated, the Abu had retreated into Africa south of the Sahara, apart from a strip along the southern Mediterranean coast, and into Southeast Asia with a possible outlier in Syria and the upper Tigris-Euphrates Valley. By that time they were gone from Europe and, it would appear, also from northern Asia and probably from all the Americas, unless some of the abstruse records we have cited above and some purely historical ones (to be cited later) prove otherwise.

What caused this decline in numbers and in variety of forms, and, above all, their retreat from such vast areas? Was it wholly climatic change? Was it wholly the rise of man the hunter? Was it widespread epidemics? Or was it a combination of either two or all three of these? Or were there other major causes, which we do not yet suspect?

That it happened cannot be denied, and the current revolution in our knowledge of the actual dates of recently geologic past events makes it ever more apparent that it took place much more suddenly and abruptly than we previously supposed, and much more recently. It now transpires that at the end of the last southward ice advance, not more than 10,000 years ago, in both Europe and North America there were quite modern types of men, hunting, drawing pictures of Abu, and perhaps even making pottery. By 5,000 years ago, in Europe at least, all Abu seem to have vanished. What wrought that drastic change in so short a geologic period of time? But, more pertinent, what produced the same effects in the vast and, as far as we know, comparatively *uninhabited* (by man) expanses of North, Central, and, above all, South America?

[4]

OF THE COLLAPSE OF THEIR EMPIRE

The great extinctions.

What caused them. The disappearance

of Abu from the northern world.

We come now to a most remarkable and puzzling turn of events in the history of the Abu—and of Man, for that matter. The whole business forms a web of apparent contradictions, and in it, not a few matters seem to verge on the impossible. Yet the facts exist, and they cannot be gainsaid. There has to be an explanation of them. The whole thing is a sort of fossil detective story.

The main point at issue is that all but three species of Abu—the living Elephant and the two loxodonts—became extinct in a surprisingly short space of time; and not just geologically speaking, but in actual years. Moreover, their extinction caused the range of the Abu as a whole to shrink by about eighty per cent. At the outset we find Abu spread all over Eurasia and Africa, North America and substantial parts of South America; at the end, they are confined to Africa south of the Sahara, a narrow strip along the north of the Sahara to Syria, and to Orientalia, i.e., what we call Southeast Asia. The question is, why did this happen; and, second, how did it happen?

Before diving into this enigma, I am constrained to ask another question: why and how do *any* animals become extinct? Nobody really knows, and nobody has as yet come up with a theory that will stand up in all circumstances. Until recently, the best and seemingly most logical idea was that species (and genera, and families, and orders, and even larger groups of animals) have a life span, just as individuals do. This means that they are evolved and thus "born," just as a child is; then they have a period of youth, middle age, and finally old age, ending in extinction or death, just as we do. Supporting this theory was one that suggested that some animals got too specialized in bodily form and in various ways—such as by the development of vast tusks, like the straight tuskers and the mammoths—which made breeding difficult. Both theories have, however, gone out of the window of reason in face of two facts: on the one hand, the shellfish-like creature called Lingula, a member of the Brachiopod group of marine animals, has been around absolutely unchanged as far as we can ascertain since Cambrian times, now estimated to have been some 500,000,000 to 600,000,000 years ago; and, on the other hand, it has been observed that only the old animals develop the impossible excrescences, such as overweight tusks, and often only after their prime, whereas the fully active breeding males, with their youthful virility, are not so encumbered. Dr. George G. Simpson has pointed out still another mystery connected with this problem: to wit, the almost countless types of creatures that must have existed *between* one kind of animal (with primitive characteristics) and another (with very advanced ones) evolved from it, none of which has left for us so much as a single bone.

Concerning the Abu, there has long been a popular belief that they were just too big; and, in fact, there does seem to be some justification for this. There were a very large number of giant forms of animals before the events that we are about to consider took place; whereas after them, most of these had vanished. There were giant baboons, pigs as big as rhinoceroses, and beavers as large as giant hogs. Curiously also, the surviving giants today are all found in Africa or Orientalia, the largest animals remaining in South America being the tapirs, and in North America and Eurasia the bison. That any giants have remained sets at naught the bizarre suggestion once made: namely, that either the earth's mass or its gravity increased suddenly, so that animals above a certain size literally collapsed under their own weight and so became extinct. Another theory, and one that is more agreeable to orthodoxy, is that the majority of extinctions seem to have come in waves and were due to sudden changes in over-all world temperature—either excessive heat with widespread aridity initiating a "desert age," such as the Triassic is alleged to have been, or great cold in what used previously to be called "ice ages." And this brings us to the kernel of our present problem.

From geological (and now, it seems, possibly even from actual historical) evidence, we know that great parts of the land surface of the earth which today have what we choose to call a temperate climate (though actually it is just about the most *intemperate* type found on this planet) were recently glaciated to the extent of being covered by enormous ice-caps, such as now cover Greenland and the Antarctic continent. The principal areas involved were eastern North America and western Europe, over which, it has been demonstrated, the ice once extended south to St. Louis and Long Island Sound on one continent, and to southern England and Germany on the other. However, at that time neither northwest North America nor northern Asia were so glaciated; nor were they during any of the four times that the ice crept over other lands during the last million years.

This is very odd if the cause of those other parts' being glaciated was an "ice age," for if the whole earth suddenly got colder, so that the polar caps became greatly enlarged, the northern cap must have covered the *whole* Northern Hemisphere down to the latitude of St. Louis—or at least to southern England, allowing for the warming effect of ocean currents flowing north from the tropics. Then again, the tropics would have become temperate; yet there is no evidence that they did so, and most of their plant and animal inhabitants remained unchanged.

This calls into question the whole concept of "ice ages" and the belief that the entire earth suddenly got colder. The only alternative is to suppose that the "cold spots" (i.e., the polar caps) shifted. However this was accomplished, in order to produce the observed effects in the Northern Hemisphere, the North Pole would have to have been located somewhere about central Greenland—and not just once, but four times during the past million years—and then to have either gone back to where it is now or to somewhere else in-between times. There now arises another problem, namely: we do not know if the four glaciations of Europe were contemporaneous with those of North America. It has been suggested that they may have alternated, and this means that the polar cap could have wandered about even more, being at one time over Hudson Bay; then "gone back home," as it were; and then moved to the North Atlantic, centering about Jan Mayen Land, halfway between Greenland and Norway.

Astronomers tell us that the presence of polar caps (as well as of the tropics, and the general zoning of climates all over the earth) is due to this planet's axis of rotation being set on at an angle of 23° to the plane along which it travels around the sun. This tilting results in alternating periods of lack of sunlight at the North Pole at one time of the year (our northern winter) and at the South Pole at another (our summer). Thus, if the northern polar cap moved south to, say, Hudson Bay, the southern polar cap must have moved out into the southern Pacific Ocean. This would mean the deglaciation of Antarctica's ice-cap and, reciprocally, the unfreezing of the Arctic Ocean ice-raft. (An *ice-cap* can form only on land but can get as thick as two miles; an *ice-raft* forms only on water, and can reach only a few hundred feet in thickness.) Here, however, we meet another conundrum, for engineers point out that the earth is really a vast flywheel—and almost perfectly lubricated, to boot—and that if the direction (or angle) of its axis of spin were changed in the slightest degree—supposing there was any known force great enough to do this—the whole thing would fly to bits, just as any flywheel will do if so treated.

This presents a pretty picture. On the one hand we have definite proof that the poles several times recently were not where they are today; and, on the other, we apparently have just as cogent argument that they could *not* have moved! I may add, at this point, that they *must* at *some* times not have been where they are now, for all kinds of plants and animals have been found fossilized in rock strata within the polar circles and close to the poles themselves. Not only could these creatures *not* have lived under an ice-cap, or at temperatures sufficiently low to form such, but they certainly could not have survived the annual periods of sunlessness in those high latitudes. By the same token, if there were periods when the earth got so hot (over-all) that there were no polar caps, everything outside of them would have boiled, and all the water on the earth would have evaporated into steam. That this has never happened we know positively because there has been no break in evolution on this earth for 500,000,000 years, let alone during the past 500,000. So if the poles cannot move, and yet they did so, what are we to suppose? There is only one remaining alternative: the skin of the earth moved—either in parts or as a whole.

At this point you may well be asking what all this has to do with extinctions of living things, and the history of the Abu in particular. I beg you to be patient for a little while longer since it has the profoundest bearing upon both matters, and especially on the latter. The principal reason for my saying this may be clear by pointing out that the Abu, being land animals and large ones, needing a great deal of food daily, are like a ship's company adrift on a raft. The continents are, in fact, great rafts, connected to each other only by very slender and tenuous bridges, mostly of lowlands. Only a slight change in ocean level would separate South America from North America, and Africa from Eurasia; only slightly greater ones would send a sea up through mid-Russia to the Arctic and so lop off Europe (and there is evidence of this having happened once); today the narrow Bering Strait *does* separate North America from Eurasia. If, therefore, such a separation were to take place when a polar cap crept over a continent, the land animals on it would have nowhere to go, and so be exterminated: and if after the ice-cap went away, that continent remained separated from others where animals *had* survived, it would still not be repopulated, except very slowly by those that could devise ways of crossing the channel between the two.

The idea that it was the crust of the earth rather than the poles that from time to time shifted was suggested over half a century ago by a German geomorphologist named Wegener. His theory was that the continents are truly "rafts," but with roots (like ships' keels) that float in the next layer down. The upper, or outer, crust of the earth was in those days referred to by geologists as the *sial,* due to the fact that its predominant rocks were composed, for the most part, of various combinations of silicon and aluminum. The continents were also composed of this and they floated on the next layer, which was called the *sima* because its principal components were silicon and magnesium, which is denser, or heavier. Wegener further suggested that the continents have been drifting about; and to demonstrate this, he cut out tracings of them (in paper) from a global map and showed that, for instance, the eastern side of the Americas, if bent a bit about the Isthmus of Panama, fitted exactly along the Western face of Europe and Africa. He finally assembled all the continents, like bits of a jigsaw puzzle, and fitted them neatly together. From this arose the theory that they formed all that is left of a once complete outer skin of sial which originally enveloped the whole earth, so that all the water formed a complete aqueous envelope outside that. The obvious inference from this was that the missing and larger part of that skin of sial (which is only about twenty miles thick in any case) was wrenched off, sometime and somehow, and then sailed out into space. There were even those who computed its volume and suggested that it forms the substance of our moon.

This latter idea was not at all acceptable, even as a hypothesis; and Wegener's theory was not received with much enthusiasm, either. It was too radical for those days. However, it slowly gained recognition as the pertinent observations of astronomers, engineers, and geologists penetrated the minds of geomorphologists. But, during this time, some very serious objections to it were raised, several of which appear to be valid. The whole question then fell, rather indecently, into oblivion.

This impasse continued until 1957, when Charles H. Hapgood published a book entitled *The Earth's Shifting Crust,* in which he proposed another alternative, or rather a variation of Wegener's theory. This is very simple, and states that the *whole* skin of the earth—that is to say, the continental rafts plus the flooring of the oceans—shifts in one piece (though there would be wrinklings and fracturing around the edges of the continents to build mountains, and of the thin ocean floor to form those vast suboceanic ranges that have been brought to light by the International Geophysical Year).

To envision this hypothesis, imagine an orange spinning

(on an axis) and imagine that the skin comes unstuck from the fruit within, but is still semi-attached to it by a thick molasses-like goo. Should the skin have a large, heavy lump on its surface, eccentric to its axis, the whole skin would then start to shift over the inner core. What is more, if there were a *very* large bulge near one of its poles, this eccentricity would exert a pressure directly towards its equator. Hapgood's theory supposes that just such an off-center mass existed, and still exists, in the Antarctic ice-cap, which is enormously heavy and massive. His idea is that the constant pressure it exerts toward the equator is the very force that causes the next layer below, in the earth's crust, to heat up (pressure being equivalent to heat), so causing it to "melt," or become more plastic. When a certain point is reached in this process, the whole skin would then become "free" and, under the influence of the constant pressure from the Antarctic, begin to shift.

This theory has not by any means yet been accepted: in fact, it was at first most roundly rejected by almost everybody. However, it is now being critically examined by an ever-increasing number of specialists, not only because it may explain many of the most fundamental and least understood major aspects of geological history, such as mountain-building and the so-called ice ages, but also because the book in which it was originally propounded is almost wholly a reiteration of facts discovered and published by the greatest recognized geologists and geomorphologists of the past fifty years. In a manner of speaking, it is really *their* theory—though mostly by default—but it just had never been put together before; nor had the mechanics been worked out relative to the known properties and qualities of rocks before—as was done by Hapgood's collaborator, the engineer James H. Campbell.

Whatever the outcome of the critical analysis of this theory may be, there can no longer be any doubt that the crust of the earth has periodically shifted; and, what is more, if you will take a globe and follow the shifts suggested in this book, you will find that the land plants and animals of the world must have had a very rough time of it during the past four shifts. In fact, so drastic, and possibly sudden, were these shifts on North America, from which there was no avenue of escape, that they may truly have played a major part in the general extinctions that took place in this period (known to geologists as the Pleistocene). However, it is manifestly not the sole cause of these effects in other parts of the world.

This is rather annoying, for it would indeed be nice simply to be able to say that both the general and the particular extinctions of Pleistocene fauna were due to the movements of the earth's crust, which, in turn, caused the polar caps to move over the land. There is, however, another bugbear that is even more aggravating, and this needs most careful attention because both its existence and its importance are obscure.

As we noted in previous chapters, there is overwhelming evidence that early Stone Age man was intimately associated with Abu all over the world outside of Australia and some islands. Some of the most cogent evidence for this comes from researches in North and Central America, and in Europe. The types of men involved in both areas were very advanced, with highly developed implements and hunting techniques. In Europe they (the Aurignacians, and some later peoples) left magnificent cave paintings of mammoths and certain other Abu, which prove beyond a doubt that these animals existed where these people lived and when they lived. The real stickler, however, is that these people are said to have lived around 25,000 years ago, while the last ice-advance is now dated as having begun about 40,000 years ago but only come to an end some 10,000 years ago. This puts these artists and the Abu they depicted right in the middle of that "ice age" so that it could not have been the onset of that catastrophe that extinguished the Abu; at least in Europe. In America the story is even more surprising, for there is now not only concrete evidence of Abu-hunting men during the last ice-advance there—though again, as in Europe, south of the ice-cap itself—but also after it, and the remains of some mastodons found in peat bogs at middle latitudes may still be shown to be of comparatively very recent date. Then, of course, there are also all the myths and legends found among the Amerindians of the existence of such creatures in immediately precolonial times, and the strange stories of the British sailors of historic times. If the Abu continued to exist in the Americas and Eurasia during the last ice advance it was not that force which exterminated them in those lands. In that case, what did?

The whole problem of the extinction of the mammoths (particularly) has been bandied about for well over a century now but no worth-while explanation of it has yet come to light, though a lot of suggestions have been made. One of the earliest and commonest of these was that Man did the deed. At first, and in view of the history of destruction wrought on larger animal life in modern times by men armed with poisons and finally firearms, this would seem to be quite feasible. However, on proper analysis, once again it simply does not hold water. First, between 5,000 and 10,000 years ago, Man was a comparatively rare animal, whereas the Abu were very numerous. Further, the former were still puny and badly armed, for all their corrals, pits, knowledge of fire, stone and bone weapons, and poisons; but the Abu were extremely virile, powerful, and undoubtedly displayed then, as now, an intelligence that, combined with their keen senses and natural instincts, gave them an almost uncanny aptitude for spotting poisons and avoiding hunters. Then, of course, Man, and even most efficient modern man, has still not been able to exterminate the Abu from Ethiopian Africa and Oriental Asia, despite his enormous population therein and even the advent of firearms.

Various suggestions have been put forward as to the cause

of the extinction of these animals, such as sudden excessive cold—which we have seen does not seem to be valid—excessive heat, the onset of widespread aridity, and the clearing of forests and other vegetation to a point where there was not sufficient food for these huge beasts. Any one, or any combination, of such factors would be feasible as the cause but, as with the onset of an "ice-age," none will stand up under critical examination. Further, there is no evidence of any sudden excessive heat; and, although a great swath of land from Morocco to Manchuria did dry up, it did so much later, as we know from the fact that large agricultural communities resided all over it until just before the dawn of history. In the Americas, what is more, neither the forests nor other vegetation suitable to maintain the Abu herds ever did die away and these continents remain today apparently ideal for such animals. Finally, man was not numerous enough or equipped with good enough tools to clear away forests to that extent. Yet, the Abu disappeared and in a surprisingly short space of time; and for this there has to be an explanation. There is only one that I have heard of which seems to be feasible. It may sound very unlikely but it is at least possible.

About the year 1925 it came to the attention of the Brazilian government that cattle in certain of their states were dying in most unusual numbers. Appeals by ranchers were answered by veterinary investigations that diagnosed the cause as paralytic rabies—the form the disease takes in herbivorous animals that have been bitten by carnivorous ones. In the latter it takes the furious form. Since the country

---

Mastodon, of which at least one North American form is known to have been fully furred. (From a fully reconstructed and mounted specimen in the New York State Museum.)

was overrun by packs of feral dogs of the lurcher variety, a campaign was initiated and over 30,000 of these were killed in the reasonable belief that they were the carriers of the rabies. But the cattle continued to die, so it had to be assumed that the carriers were some other wild animal or animals. Hunting all of these out was impossible, and it happened that none of those that were killed proved to be rabid. Then a farmer sent a bat that he had killed while it was biting one of his cows to a government biological station. It was a fruit-eating kind known by the scientific name of *Phyllostoma,* but, on examination of its brain, the damning Negri bodies, invariable indicators of rabies, were found. This presented an appalling problem.

Bats exist in countless millions throughout Brazil and are represented by scores of species. Some are insect-eaters, others fruit-eaters or even fish-eaters, but there are two kinds that can live only on fresh blood, and most particularly that of the warm-blooded birds and mammals. These two bats (*Desmodus* and *Diphylla*) have intestinal tracks that go almost straight through them, so that after lapping a meal of blood from a small gouge that they make in the skin of their prey, they have to go into a hollow tree, cave, or other dark place to digest, depositing cascades of tar-like, semi-liquid, black excrement. Such a bat found biting a cow would have been regarded as quite normal; but what was a pure fruit-eater like *Phyllostoma* doing at this ghoulish practice?

Meanwhile the cattle deaths had continued unabated and had spread right up the east side of South America, finally hitting the British island of Trinidad, where the prize humped cattle permitted to graze on the central park of the capital, Port of Spain, succumbed. These losses were accepted as merely a crashing bore, but not then connected with affairs in Brazil which, as a matter of fact, were not known to the medical and veterinary services in Trinidad. Then, twelve human beings died in a small village called Siparia, in the southern part of the island, and there was a public outcry when it was found that they, like the cattle, had died of rabies. The medical service swung into action and sensibly made a start on a rabies survey (in which I took part) and brought to light three facts: first, that the country was infested with *Desmodus* Blood-lapping Bats; second, that a high percentage of these were rabid; and third, that the local populace had always been and were quite resigned to being bitten, often nightly, by these bats. (One case of a small boy bitten fourteen times in one night was discovered!) The field work in which I participated yielded further information: in the really wild areas, such as the great uninhabited mountain-forest reserve of the north where I operated, all manner of other bats were regularly bitten in their lairs by rabid *Desmodus* and so in turn took to biting everything and anything, even if they were pure fruit-eaters. (Incidentally, *Desmodus* crossed the United States border about a decade ago and has now spread as far as Mississippi. Some human deaths from the bites of rabid individuals have been recorded; and rabies has now cropped up in insectivorous bats as far north as New Jersey.)

The researches into this menace initiated in Trinidad in 1932 brought to light some astonishing things. First, it was discovered that *Desmodus* carried several other diseases, worst of which was Chagas' disease, and second to that, murrain, both of which attack hoofed animals. Second, it transpired that *Desmodus* can carry rabies for weeks or even months without becoming rabid. But probably most unexpected of all was the uncovering of some early Spanish documents that stated that the Amerindians of Panama and Venezuela had told the first white men to arrive in their country that their fathers knew horses and even used them, but that *they had all been killed by bats.*

Palaeontologists already knew that the horse was plentiful in the Americas in bygone times, and there are very fine incised petroglyphs of horses' heads in caves in Haiti and Trinidad. Also, there were still several droves of truly wild horses in Haiti in 1939, the year I obtained a specimen, the skin and skeleton of which are now in the Chicago Natural History Museum. These wild horses were all strawberry roans with a unique coat pattern, one side of the neck under the mane being pale, the other side dark; and they attacked runaway feral domestic horses on sight. They were completely nocturnal and lived only in the upper pine forests. The point here is this: if every single last example of a whole group of animals so widespread and numerous as the horses once were all over the Americas—possibly until only a few hundred years ago—could be utterly exterminated in a generation, and possibly by some disease, in this case carried by bats, why could not all the Abu likewise have been eliminated? Like every other aspect of this problem, however, this leads us to a further quandary.

This might well have been so in the New World, but what of the Old World, where the Blood-lapping Bats are not now and never have been (in a fossil state) known? Could other bats or other animals have effected the same results there? If so, was rabies the cause or was some other disease? Murrain and Chagas' are common to both hemispheres. Then again, could there have been interchanges of animals which could carry these diseases from the Americas to Europe or vice versa? Was bat-borne rabies the origin of the vampire myth? To these questions we have no answers; but once again the earth's shifting-crust theory does supply a possibility that at least one of these suggestions is true, namely: the passage of disease-carrying animals from one hemisphere to the other. Moreover, if the shifts were as rapid and drastic, and as recent as some have now suggested (notably glaciologists and experts on radiocarbon dating), there could have been connections between eastern North America and western Europe later than the classic one between northwestern North America and eastern Asia.

If we suppose that a disease that exterminated the Abu in the New World got to Europe about 5000 B.C., it would explain almost everything. There, if coming from the west, it would probably "roar" through Europe to the open plains of Russia; then it would probably slow down because of the constriction of the forests about western Siberia, before getting into eastern Siberia: and one should note that this is just how the extermination of the Abu proceeded—i.e., progressively from west to east, so that mammoths remained in Siberia long after they were gone from Europe. Also, the Mediterranean, being flooded by then (the ocean only broke through the Straits of Gibraltar at a comparatively late date), formed an effective barrier to the south of Europe, so that Abu lingered on in North Africa, from Morocco to the delta of the Nile and in the old forests of Syria, till Roman times. At the same time, the great swath of super-arid deserts had also by then been created from just south of Morocco all the way across North Africa and through the Middle East to the vast barrier of the Siberio-Mongolo-Tibetan Plateau, beyond which lie the sea-like Tarim and Gobi deserts. This swath formed a more definite and unsurmountable barrier to the spread of anything to tropical Asia and Ethiopian Africa than any sea or ocean.

That Abu existed almost all over the world before, up to, and even during the last "ice advance," and that they may have continued to do so after its retreat for some thousands of years, there can be no question; and that they ceased to exist over an enormous area (often most suitably supplied with their previously preferred food) thereafter, is even more obvious. What is more, an enormous number of them—along with other animals both large and small—somehow got themselves killed and instantly preserved sometime during the past 10,000 to 100,000 years; and, specifically and uniquely, in the two areas of the far north that were *not* glaciated.

These animals are found frozen in a strange material that is called *muck*, in Alaska and in Siberia. Hundreds of millions of mammals are so preserved over an enormous area, and in various degrees of perfection, ranging all the way from complete and perfect corpses with blood, hair, lymph, and even eyeballs intact, to scraps of torn limbs and flesh, half rotten, or completely putrid specimens, and mere skeletons. Not all of these remains are deep-frozen, or even frozen, which is something different. Some are "pickled" in peat bogs, either *in toto* or in part, while the skeletons are often piled together in all sorts of peculiar matrices—sandstone, dried clay or mud, and so forth, in now dry desert areas, or in phosphate beds way down in the lower temperate regions (*vide:* Florida), or in lime-filled chasms, as in the West Indies and South America.

A particularly odd feature of these preserved masses is that they contain specimens of many species of all ages, from infants, the immature and adolescents to the mature in the prime of life and the old and senile. Most of them are grossly mutilated: nay, rather, literally torn apart—and to tear apart a large Abu requires almost unimaginable power. The muck of Alaska, as washed out by gold-mining outfits using high-pressure hoses, is in many places choked also with masses of *bits* of mammoths and other animals such as Woolly Rhinoceroses, giant lions, bison, wolves, and beavers, and also pieces of large treetrunks of types that do not—and cannot—live at those latitudes today for purely biological reasons. The same goes for huge areas in Siberia. These are not just bits of rotten or rotting corpses: they are bits of fresh bodies literally torn apart. And the whole lot, along with the vegetable materials, silt, boulders, and all manner of other detritus are piled together, higgledy-piggledy, in one great sort of pudding, often for mile after mile.

This is no normal process of "fossilization." It can only be the result of special events. This is more especially borne out by the findings of the engineers who have, during the last decade or two, been bulldozing in our far north through the Yukon, the Canadian Northwest Territories, and Alaska, to lay down the first roads to the Arctic Ocean. In these areas the land surface alternates between two very different types of surface. The major part is very firm, the soil being permanently frozen a little way below the surface, and is clothed in a continuous and extremely dense forest of closely packed, small spruce trees with some aspen. These northern spruce forests are called in Siberia the *taiga*, and this term is rapidly gaining acceptance also in Canada. That which stretches unbroken from northern Europe to the Bering Strait is the largest forest in the world: the other—which starts along the feet of the great mountain barrier that runs right down our continent from the mouth of the Mackenzie River, on the Arctic Ocean, to Vera Cruz, in Mexico, on the Gulf Coast —continues right across Canada to the Atlantic in Labrador. However, meandering through these forests—both of which lie on lowlands that are more or less flat—are uncountable channels, great and small, and endless self-contained lake-like areas of another kind of growth to which the Canadians have given the name *muskeg*. These are swamps, devoid of trees, covered with a thick mat of mosses and lichens on which grow a fair profusion of small willows and other bushes. These muskegs freeze solid in winter, but during the summer they unfreeze to a considerable depth, due to the hot sunlight and their "open" nature. The plants of the taiga do not grow on the muskeg, or vice versa. This combination of plant growths continues north to the limit of tree growth and then gives way, rather abruptly, to an entirely different kind of country, open and treeless and covered with a mat of tiny dwarf willows, mosses, and lichens, which is known as the tundra.

In northern Eurasia and around Alaska this continues right to the Arctic coast, but in northern central Canada, on the Keewatin and Ungava peninsulas, it gradually becomes a patchwork, growing in the depressions between bare rock surfaces and stones, and then it peters out altogether and we are in what is appropriately called the Barren Grounds. These taiga, muskeg, and tundra lands are not, it must be emphasized, permanently covered with snow; and during the brief summer months they are actually extremely hot. There is a profusion of vegetable food (other than the coniferous spruce) all over them, even in winter, under the snow, and they used to (and in some areas still do) maintain vast herds of herbivores such as Caribou. These creatures are able to earn a living by scratching down under the snow in the winter, for, curiously, these northern lands have a very low precipitation rate and the snow is never very deep. Other beasts, of lesser number but still individually of some size, such as the Musk-Ox and the Barren Grounds Caribou, can maintain themselves all year round at the far northern edge of the tundra belt and even out onto the Barren Grounds. It must be understood that there is every difference between these lands and those covered with (a) ice-caps, (b) glaciers, and (c) mountain ice-fields. These three ice-structures are permanent, and there is *no* food—or even soil—beneath them; herbivorous animals cannot live on them, and when the ice-caps covered North America down to St. Louis, all the animals had to move out of the north.

Now, this ice-cap stretched from the Great Barrier in the west to the Atlantic. Northern Eurasia, east of the Urals to the Bering Strait, and Alaska were not so covered. Thus, whether they then lay farther from or at the same distance from the north-polar ice-cap than they do today, they always had an ample food supply for large herds of large herbivores. However, unless a lot more of some kinds of plants now found thereon, and/or many other kinds that do not occur there today, existed in those regions previously, these lands could not have supported huge herds of mammoths—and especially all year round. As we shall see later, an Elephant requires between half a ton and a ton and a half of food a day to maintain itself in the wild; also it is very doubtful that mammoths could scrape down through snow, or even if they could do so, subsist on frozen tundra or muskeg mosses. Then again, it is a strange and little-known fact that the precipitation on these northern lowlands is actually lower than that in most true deserts. Abu require a lot of water, so if Siberia and Alaska had a climate such as they have today, there could have been *no* water there for nine months out of the year, since it was all frozen—and we cannot conceive of mammoths getting along by eating snow. All these factors combine to convince us that Siberia and Alaska were not only not glaciated when Europe and the rest of North America were, but that they had a very much milder climate than now. (I may add that forty-foot tree trunks with large leaves and bearing soft fruits have been found in the muck of the Siberian Islands still farther north, which are today barren lands and in part semi-glaciated.)

Nevertheless, it is possible that the mammoths migrated south in the fall and back again to these lands in the late spring, *in Siberia.* But what of those in Alaska, for they were cut off by the sea on three sides and by a solid montane ice-cap on the fourth? They could not go east over that ice-cap, and, anyhow, it led only to the main ice-cap covering the lowlands beyond; they could not go south down the Yukon coast, because even today the glaciers come right down to the sea along that coast. The last remaining suggestion is that they lived there only during what is called the inter-glacial periods, when the ice-caps went off somewhere, and then cleared out to the south before the return of the ice. In Alaska they might have been caught each time the ice came back, and thus were repeatedly exterminated there, while the country was repopulated from the south in the next interglacial period with the return of the vegetation and warmer climates. This is all very well and would be wholly satisfactory were it not for one fact. This is the little matter of the frozen mammoths (and countless other animals, like the giant bison, lions, beavers, the musk-ox, and even tiny ground-squirrels).

These dead animals are not found frozen in ice but in the permanently frozen muck, which is as solid as granite and is, in point of fact, actually a form of rock. How did they get into it, and so suddenly that they did not have time to rot? (I speak now of the complete specimens that have been found.) And this is where the findings of the bulldozers come into the picture.

The first theory about this enigma was that the animals fell into gulches and got stuck in the (admittedly) highly adhesive type of northern clay called *gumbo,* which, in certain cases, can actually hold a man. However, no such gumbo has ever been found under, around, or on top of any of these mammoth or other corpses. They are always in muck, which is quite different. The next idea was that the animals wandered onto muskegs and, due to their great weight, became bogged down and eventually engulfed, as they are alleged to have been in the La Brea tar pits of Los Angeles. This sounded splendid until the bulldozers discovered that: first, the muskegs are seldom if ever deep enough to engulf a mammoth, having permanently frozen bottom layers; and, second, that not one single bone, let alone a whole modern animal, is ever found in them. There are plenty of big animals that cruise about on them, such as the very large Woodlands Bison, the huge Moose, the Woodland Caribou, and deer; and, mark you, all of these have tapering, pointed limbs, albeit with rather widely spreading hoofs, for the express purpose of negotiating such ground (not snow). I very much doubt that *any* Abu ever got bogged down in *any* swamp, or bog, for they are well-adapted to live on, or in, just such country; and, what is more, even animals that sink in water can*not* do so in any swamp or even in the notorious quicksand for the very simple reason that they, being denser media than water, cause everything to *float*. A man stepping into quicksand will sink only to just about his waist. It is his panic that dooms him; and if only he can get horizontal, he is perfectly safe and can roll over any quicksand. Abu float very well, and living ones can adjust their buoyancy by swallowing air. I fear that gumbo in gulches with subsequent landslides and bottomless absorbent muskegs as graveyards of the frozen mammoths have to be abandoned.

So also must the notion of sudden flash floods that drowned them and then rolled them along the bottom of, or floated them down the tops of, rivers to their mouths and then buried them in delta mud. Abu are terrific swimmers; they bloat rapidly after death, and they are then very buoyant. Being washed about in rivers would not leave their pelts in perfect order, and, also, anything of such a nature as buttercup flowers would at least have washed out of their mouths. Yet, in the case of the famous Beresovska Mammoth —found whole near the Siberian river of that name early in this century, and dug out by trained palaeontologists and transported to the St. Petersburg (now Leningrad) Russian Academy of Sciences—fresh buttercup flowers and delicate grass stems were found between the teeth of the corpse. And it is these buttercups that finally upset the whole cart. The reasons are several.

First, they indicate, unequivocally, that it was not winter when the mammoth died and that the temperature was at least over 40°F., because buttercups don't flower in winter or survive at lower temperatures. Also, from these buttercups and the other plant remains found in the stomach of this specimen, the actual time of the year of the mammoth's death was pretty closely pinned down as being September. Second, it is manifest that the ground was not then frozen; that it was not tundra; and that it was not taiga forest. Third, the mammoth had been so suddenly killed that it did not have time even to swallow its last mouthful of food; and, fourth, it had not been overwhelmed in a flood. Yet it was frozen solid, and stuffed, *in toto,* into permanently frozen muck.

This is all very well, but it necessitates some not only bizarre but seemingly inexplicable procedures, for you cannot stuff a mammoth into what is virtually solid rock. If, on the other hand, it was already sunk in a bog, it would at least have swallowed its last mouthful of food while going down. In that case, decomposition of such food would have taken place long before the whole thing got frozen solid. It takes an enormous amount of "cold" (which means extraction of heat) to freeze even a rabbit so that it does not decompose, more especially when its insulating coat of skin and fur is intact. To deep-freeze a mammoth at that speed is a task that would, I am told, be quite beyond the powers of our modern frozen-foods industry (even if they wanted such an object), and the calculations as to the drop in temperature called for to do so, which were computed for me by a technician in that industry, resulted in figures so preposterous that I do not dare give them here. You can, however, also "slow-freeze" meat (and there are frozen gorillas in cold-storage rooms in museums), so you could presumably effect this condition in an elephant if you really put your mind to it. Further, there is a way of telling whether a corpse has been fast- or slow-frozen—by microscopic examination of the cells to see whether they have been burst due to the formation of large crystals from their water content—but, unfortunately, no such examinations of the flesh of any of these animals have been made in the field before the muck in which they were embedded had been melted.

Thus, in view of the monumental and seemingly impossible drop in temperature required to instantly deep-freeze them, we must assume that they were slow-frozen. Yet, even this manifestly calls for some extraordinary and, to us, un-

---

A Woolly Mammoth, one of a group of Abu closely related to the Asiatic Elephant; known to early man in Eurasia and North America. (From a photograph of a complete skeleton unearthed in Indiana.)

precedented occurrences. Whatever killed these animals must have been sudden. If it was not the "cold" itself, then it must have been followed almost instantaneously by an appalling drop in temperature, for the creatures were munching on delicate herbs in a meadow at a temperature of some 40°F. and in the next instant must have been enveloped in air at least many degrees below zero.[1] Drops in temperature of a lot more than 40°F. within an hour are known, especially at the beginning of winter along the southern edge of the Arctic regions, due to cold fronts rolling south. So perhaps the mammoths stayed too late in the fall before migrating south, got hit by a sudden drop of, say, 80 or even 100 degrees, succumbed due to this or some other cause (though standing upright or kneeling in some cases, be it noted!), and were then slowly frozen, from the outside in, until they were wholly preserved. Perhaps they were covered completely in snow and remained so during the following winter. So far, so good: we have our frozen mammoth with his last meal still in his mouth.

But come the next spring, the animal will emerge from the snow as it melts under the powerful rays of the spring sun. As it does so, its back will, of course, unfreeze first and immediately start to rot, while doubtless wolves and other carrion feeders will start to work on it. This process will, moreover, go on progressively till the ground is snow-free, and by that time the corpse will also be mostly unfrozen and/or eaten, and will either topple over or crumble (actually "melt") through decomposition. You can't have deep-frozen mammoths, or anything else, standing about on subarctic or Arctic plains once the snow has melted; the sun is like a furnace up there in the summer, and the temperature regularly rises to disagreeable heights. The notion just will not work. Nor, of course, does it in any way explain how the

[1] The use of the Fahrenheit scale is herein implied, though it is a misleading and in several respects completely invalid method of expressing comparative temperature. A drop of some 50° *Centigrade* is here envisioned.

vast corpse got into solid, permanently frozen muck. In fact, we can only suppose that once the animal was frozen, it must have remained frozen ever since.

This requires that the muck be piled up around and over it, *while itself still soft* and therefore *unfrozen.* For this to happen, the removal of the covering snow must have been virtually contemporaneous with the arrival of the *unfrozen* muck. How does one arrange this? Further, the muck must then in turn also have been frozen solid, as a whole and very rapidly, otherwise decomposition of the corpse would have proceeded automatically.

It has been pointed out that large corpses actually cook themselves from inside out due to the great rise in internal temperature as a result of decomposition by bacterial action, as in compost heaps. I have observed this personally with a long-dead Sperm Whale, fifty feet in length, on a tropical beach: the insides still looked edible, and did not stink; however, the *outside* had completely disintegrated and sloughed off. Our mammoth's skin would long since have gone if the freezing processes took too long or unfreezing periods occurred. So we are right back where we started, while the wretched animals still stand there entombed in their icy casts as plain and irrefutable evidence. That they were hit by terrific and permanent freezing, and that they were then somehow transferred into solid muck, cannot be gainsaid, but we are no further toward solving the problem of how either of these processes was accomplished.

Both were obviously gentle processes in the areas where complete and undamaged corpses are found, and it would look as if the arrival of the muck was gradual. Several theories have been advanced, but, frankly, we still remain much baffled. The idea that the beasts were first entombed (frozen) in snow that covered them and that was then possibly increased, to such an extent that it compacted to ice, seems sound and reasonable. But then other difficulties arise. Did the corpse later sink into the muck, or was the muck deposited on top of the snow or ice? (There are great strata of fossil ice buried deep in the earth between layers of muck in Siberia.) If the latter took place, both muck and ice must subsequently have melted together—i.e., at the same time—but only just enough for the latter to drain away as water and be replaced by unfrozen muck. This could have happened in fits and starts or all at once, but in either case the corpse must then have been unfrozen too. But it so happens that there is a limited range of temperature between which a corpse, although unfrozen, will not decompose (*vide:* that of our household refrigerators). Something such as this could, and in point of fact must, therefore have happened *after* the animal was first frozen.

Millions of mammoths were frozen in eastern Siberia alone, for the Chinese ivory-carving industry has been mostly dependent upon mammoth ivory for millennia. Ivory, being an animal substance, can both dry out and splinter, or rot, and the greater part of the mammoth ivory does one or the other; yet, over 20,000 perfectly preserved tusks reached China alone in one ten-year period. Tons more flowed to Moscow and other centers and it is still doing so, and the muck in large parts of Alaska is still stuffed with it. Then there are the other animals. These were obviously mass extinctions and on a monumental scale. And they also represent mass preservations, but also in a manner that we cannot explain. Then, also, there are the torn-up remains to be explained and the monstrous piles of flesh and bones in bogs farther south, and, finally, the endless bone beds still farther away. (In Florida almost solid bones have been mined from the phosphate beds for over a century, and the supply shows no signs of being exhausted.) Something very odd and very drastic must have occurred over half the earth; and more than once. And it would seem to have been concentrated each time in eastern Siberia. What could this have been, and what effect did it have on the Abu of those countries?

At this point we are forced to consider something that

has been anathema to scientific orthodoxy for a century, now —namely, the idea of cataclysms. It is generally agreed that there were periods in recent times (geologically speaking) when ice-caps covered vast areas of land that are now fully vegetated and even temperate. But it has also always been believed that, regardless of whether this came about due to the movement of an ice-cap or to a shift in the earth's crust, they were gradual and cumulative. However, there is a fifty-mile-long fjord in Alaska that is today ice-free and has a glacier twelve miles inland beyond its head but which was completely filled with ice to a depth of some thousands of feet right to its mouth only 150 years ago. This is a pretty rapid dissolution of what was virtually a little ice-cap; so, we may ask, just how fast can one form? But the real question is, can a whole "ice age" come on in an hour—that is to say, can excessive cold hit one autumn, and then the climate stay so cold for millennia afterwards that the snow never melts off the ground in the following summers until the "age" is over? This is a distressing thought, perhaps, but, frankly, it would seem to be the only feasible explanation of some of the observed facts. Even then, how are we to explain the "smashings" of huge animals, the floods, the corpses in bogs, and the piles of bones along coasts, in deserts, and in caves far to the south? For a sudden freeze followed by a great snowfall is actually a gentle process.

It appears fairly plain, therefore, that the muck was created at another time, which is to say that it was not contemporaneous with the sudden freeze-ups. Both may nonetheless have been parts of a single process and one that included the great piling-up of bones in lower latitudes. The next question is, therefore, what could have caused *this?* As Hibben said, when discussing the condition of the torn and mangled bodies that he unearthed from the Alaskan muck, the only force known that could have torn a head off a mammoth in one wrench would seem to have been explosive. (It could not have happened under water, but it could just possibly have been accomplished under ice.) The most likely suggestion is that, since belts of volcanic ash are found in the muck of Alaska and as it is a highly volcanic area, vast volcanic explosions were the cause. However, torn corpses are spread all over Siberia as well, and this area does not contain any volcanicity or show any evidence of such in the past. This leaves us with wind.

Super-hurricanes could well lift mammoths off their feet and roll them along, smashing them and everything else loose, against large trees or rocks, where they might get wedged for a time, and then other stuff coming along would literally smash bits off them. I have seen this done to turkey buzzards and a large dog in an ordinary Caribbean hurricane, while people, larger animals like cattle, and more solid things such as cast-iron rain-water tanks are today likewise often demolished by these great winds. Hurricanes do not occur in Siberia or Alaska, but if the earth's crust does shift, and drastically, those areas might have got into hurricane zones. On the other hand, the whole climate of the earth may have gone wrong.

The latter seems the more likely, so we naturally inquire why, and how. A mere cold front, however monstrous, could not produce the observed effects, while it, of itself, needs explanation. Such a front could bring an excessive snowfall up north and torrential rains farther south, while the roiling atmosphere might promote hurricanes and coastal floods at the edge of the tropics. However, there would have to have been some much greater force to have initiated these manifestations and also the vast *tsunamis,* or seaquakes, that appear to have accompanied them. So this leaves us with the problem of what was the force that caused these sudden periodical and dastardly cold waves.

Should the so-called ice ages be due to crustal shifts, either in part or as a whole, there would almost certainly be one drastic concomitant to their initiation. This would be the squeezing of the great cracks that run all over and around the whole earth's surface—as have now been brought to light by the IGY. It is along these cracks that almost all volcanoes are strung. Whether these phenomena are vents leading to the molten lower layers of the earth or are merely outlets of "carbuncles" of molten magma in the second layer down, is not yet determined for sure. However, any squeezing of the reservoirs that lie beneath them causes their eruption. There have been some super-eruptions of volcanoes within living memory—the island of Krakatoa, between Sumatra and Java, in Indonesia, Mount Katmai, in Alaska, and Mount Pelée, in the West Indies, in particular—and each of these, alone, produced marked and recognizable changes in world-wide climate for some time. If a dozen of these really big, slumbering giants all went off together, our climate would be very seriously affected; and if a score of them did so at the same time, the whole earth might be blanketed with dust in the upper atmosphere so dense as to exclude most, if not all, of the sunlight and otherwise interfere with the reception of radiation from outside and the dissipation of heat from the inside—such as are normal processes when all is quiet as of today. Any upset of this order to our atmosphere would so distort normal meteorological processes that even our imagination boggles at the possible consequences. Sudden super-cold fronts would be the least of the "plagues" that would descend upon us. We will leave such terrifying thoughts to the meteorologists and geomorphologists.

Nevertheless, something happened several times not too long ago, the results of which were almost universal mayhem over huge parts of the world. These events almost wrote "finis" to the proud Dynasty of Abu, and they seem also to have knocked our own ancestors about to a considerable and alarming extent. After they were over for the last time, both Abu and men found themselves in a very new world.

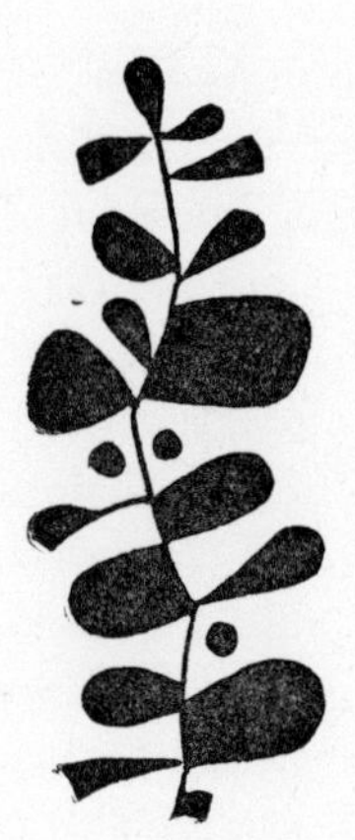

OF A GRAND ALLIANCE

The origins and beginnings of civilization and Man's association with the Abu.

To us 10,000 years is a long time; to a creature such as a mayfly, which spends but one of our days as an adult, it would be an aeon, and it would be as an astronomical age to certain bacteria that live for only a few hours. On the other hand, 10,000 years looked at from the cosmic point of view is absolutely nothing. Certain gnarled little pines growing on the windy sides of a few mountain ranges in the far west of this continent appear to have been growing for thousands of years. Certain treelike Cycads of the genus *Macrozamia* growing in Australia have been calculated by leaf-base counts to be 12,000 years old.

To such old-timers as these, the period since the last retreat of the ice in the northern hemisphere would therefore be but a lifetime. As late as 8000 B.C. the last of the ice age seems still to have been lingering in the Scandinavian mountains. A similar date was assigned by the radio-carbon method to the final retirement of the ice from what is now eastern Canada. And at that time, as we have seen, Abu appeared to have still been living in both Europe and North America. After that date we have no clear evidence of their existence on either continent. That Abu continued to exist in the Old World tropics is manifest, for they are still there today; even so, we have no definite indication of an ancient association of Abu with Man therein at that time. We have to wait for almost 5,000 years; then evidence of the Abu-Man partnership seems to burst out all at once, and all over the place.

It now appears that after the retreat of the ice in the north, man reached the Neolithic stage of development—or he achieved it very soon thereafter—first in the northern climates and then in the tropics. In tropical areas such as the mountains of New Guinea, there are still people living today virtually in the Palaeolithic Period, or Old Stone Age, of development. But since at least 5000 B.C. other peoples in those climes advanced even more rapidly than did the hunters of the cold areas. In fact, between the humid, forested equatorial belt and the temperate belts of the north, man made his most rapid strides, especially along certain river banks. At a very early date, certainly no later than 5000 B.C., he advanced from stone-working by the discovery of how to use metals, notably copper. The beginning of mastery over metals was the beginning of what we call Civilization.

The earliest evidence we have of men living in villages was unearthed in Jarmo in northern Iraq, the date of which is given as around 5000 B.C. The earliest written records that we have so far all appear to have been put down about 3500 B.C. In each of the widely separated places where we have found written records—China, India, Mesopotamia, and Egypt—there is, however, irrefutable evidence (1) that these records were the end-product of a very long development; and (2) that they had evolved in thriving cultures that had preceded them for centuries, if not millennia. But, for all that, we know nothing yet of any association between Man and Abu during those most distant ages. Nevertheless, there must have been such a relationship, because in all but one of these earliest sites of human culture we find evidence of the Abu.

Although these early cultures used mostly stone implements, they also worked in copper, producing novel implements of that material, and they made very fine pottery. They also made many small and useful things of bone and ivory. The ivory, moreover, was of many kinds, ranging from stags' teeth, boars' tusks, and hippopotamus tushes, to identifiable true elephantine ivory.

It appears that this Copper Age began simultaneously (or spread very rapidly) throughout a wide swath across Eurasia, from the Mediterranean to Japan. Its influence also seems to have filtered rapidly down into the populated valleys of the next zone immediately to the south: namely, into the valleys of the Nile, the Tigris and Euphrates, the Indus (and possibly the Ganges and the Brahmaputra), and the Si-kiang, Yangtze, and Hwang-Ho in what we now call China. And it is in these places that we find the first concrete evidence of civilized men being closely associated with Abu.

Nobody knows as yet where the Dynastic Egyptians came from or exactly when. There are wide variations in the dates suggested for their appearance on the Nile, but the radio-carbon method seems to indicate that the remains left by the First Dynasty were buried about 3500 B.C. However, quite an advanced civilization was in existence up and down the valley of the mighty Nile River prior to that time, and this predynastic period was a very long one, as is confirmed by all manner of tombs and other buildings. What is more, it was those unknown builders who developed the language spoken by the later Dynastic Egyptians, and the first hieroglyphs by which they recorded their language. Sometime in that most early civilization loxodonts got a name. This was *Abu.*

"Abu," as stated previously, was very close to another word—*Ȧab*—which meant "ivory" to those people. Now, it appears that at that time loxodonts, possibly of several kinds or distinct races, inhabited not only the Sudan, or what the Egyptians called Nubia, but also many parts of the valley of the Nile itself, and especially its then jungle-covered delta. There were indeed real forests in those days all along the southern coast of the Mediterranean and far inland into what is now almost wholly arid desert, scattered from Morocco in the west to Syria in the east. In these areas there were still either loxodonts or elephants or both. We know that such animals existed in Syria until at least as late as 800 B.C., and in what is now Algeria and Morocco until late Roman times. When they were finally eradicated from the delta of the Nile is a moot point, but they may have lingered there until the time of that famous political witch, Cleopatra.

The Dynastic Egyptians, as we have come to call them, had not only a word for all elephantine creatures and a symbol denoting them but also another, indicating a *trained Abu.* The symbol for the trained animal, which appears in very early scripts, shows a little man riding on the animal's neck just as the oozies and mahouts of the Orient do today. From this it would seem that they, or the Nubians to the south, had by about 3500 B.C. at least caught and domesticated loxodonts. This brings up a very interesting point, for it is stated that it was not until 2,000 years later the Egyptians first encountered the Asiatic Elephant in wars with Syria, and that those animals proved to be in every way superior to their home-grown variety. In other words, they were training *loxodonts* at a very early time, but which type they trained we do not know. There are today two distinct varieties of loxodonts: one large, the Bush type of the savannas; and the other small, the Forest type. What we would like to know for sure is which of these was known and used by the Egyptians; or were there then still other races lingering in the Nile Valley and delta and along the Mediterranean coast?

The ivory of loxodonts was widely used in predynastic times, yet the animal does not appear in Egyptian mythology. Its effigy was used on ships' flags, and the capital of the First Nome (or substate) of Upper Egypt was named Abu, or the "Elephant State." Extraordinarily lifelike representations of Abu done with just a few lines appeared on pottery and on slate palettes. Magnificent ivory weapon handles were carved in the form of loxodonts, one of which shows this animal trampling two snakes. This incident, by the way, seems to embody one of the oldest and most persistent African legends. There are also Egyptian representations of loxodonts trampling mountains, which is also an ancient legend that may have some early connection with a Dravidian Indian myth. In the Thirteenth Dynasty tomb of one Rekhmere, both elephants and loxodonts are clearly depicted bringing their ivory to a temple. Queen Hatshepsut's famous armada, which sailed down the Red Sea to the Land of Punt, brought back, probably from Eritrea, 700 tusks of what is called in the records "real ivory." A tiny ink drawing on a limestone chip, found in the rubbish shoveled out of the tomb of Rameses III, of the Twentieth Dynasty, however, shows very plainly an Indian Elephant, with small ears, arched back, small tusks, and bulbous forehead.

For some reason the Phoenicians, and especially those who colonized the eastern Mediterranean about the coast of Palestine (for they appear originally to have migrated from the Persian Gulf about 2500 B.C.), became the principal ivory workers at a very early date. They fashioned the finest statuaries and other things out of this substance. At first they used mostly hippopotamus teeth for their carvings.

Then they used the teeth of Sperm Whales, and only at a much later period, elephant ivory. But they employed true Asiatic Elephant tusks exclusively, and *not* those of loxodonts. Throughout the centuries the Egyptians continued to use the tusks of the loxodonts.

Moving east, we come next to the great "valley" of Mesopotamia through which, in ancient times, the twin rivers named the Tigris and the Euphrates flowed side by side to the Persian Gulf. Today they unite before they debouch through the fabulous Shat al' Arab. Here in Mesopotamia was nurtured what may still prove to be the earliest of all civilizations, which was maintained by a faintly Mongoloid type of people whom we call the Sumerians. However, this civilization, like that of the Dynastic Egyptians, was preceded by centuries of locally established culture. The Sumerians apparently did not know any Abu, for they have not left behind them a single piece of ivory. Instead they seem to have used pieces of large conch shells. This absence of ivory is the more remarkable as there is much evidence that there was, from the very earliest times, maritime commerce between the early city-states of Mesopotamia and of western India, and all manner of items typical of each of these distinct cultures have been found in the other.

Even so, elephants of some kind seem still to have been roaming wild in northern Mesopotamia as late as 1500 B.C. We have from that year a precise historical record of an elephant hunt by none other than Thothmes III, King of Egypt. An inscription left in a tomb indicates that, while hunting along the bottomlands by the Euphrates in that year, he killed several elephants (properly called Abu), but that one, the vastest bull his party encountered, attacked him and would have killed him had not one Amen-en-Heb been on hand and lopped off its trunk with his sword. But what kind of Abu was it—loxodont or elephant?

The Babylonians, Elamites, Chaldeans, Assyrians, Kassites, and others who filtered into Mesopotamia and built successively various states and empires all used ivory, and sometimes spoke of "elephants." Nevertheless, even though they were consummate artists in sundry media and have left us innumerable statues, statuettes, bas-reliefs, and engravings of all kinds of animals, including even the extinct aurochs, they left us not a single carving or depiction of an Abu itself.[1] Despite the Abu hunts of their nobility, who used tame lions, these people seem to have ignored the animals and to have relied on the Dravidians of India for supplies of ivory. And it is to India and specifically to the valley of the Indus in what is now called Pakistan that we must now turn.

In this great valley of Sind and the Punjab, lying between arid Baluchistan and Afghanistan on the west and the Rajputana plateau to the east, we find evidence of still another of these early civilizations. This evidence has so far become manifest principally at two points—at Harappa in the north, and at a place named Mohenjo-daro in the south. In both, as in Egypt and Mesopotamia, vast cities have been discovered which go back for millennia. Here also is a base level to what we call "civilization," and here once again there is evidence of a culture antedating the use of metal, in this case copper, and of written records. The records are mostly countless masses of small, rectangular, embossed seals made of several different substances. Some are made of elephant

[1] I have endeavored to confirm this statement but have been quite unable to do so. I have been several times told that there are such sculptures and other depictions of Abu, but nobody has been able to refer me to any specific example.

An "Asiatic" bringing ivory and an Abu to Pharaoh Thutmosis III. (From a wall-painting in the tomb of Rekhmere, *circa* 1500 B.C., at Thebes, Egypt.)

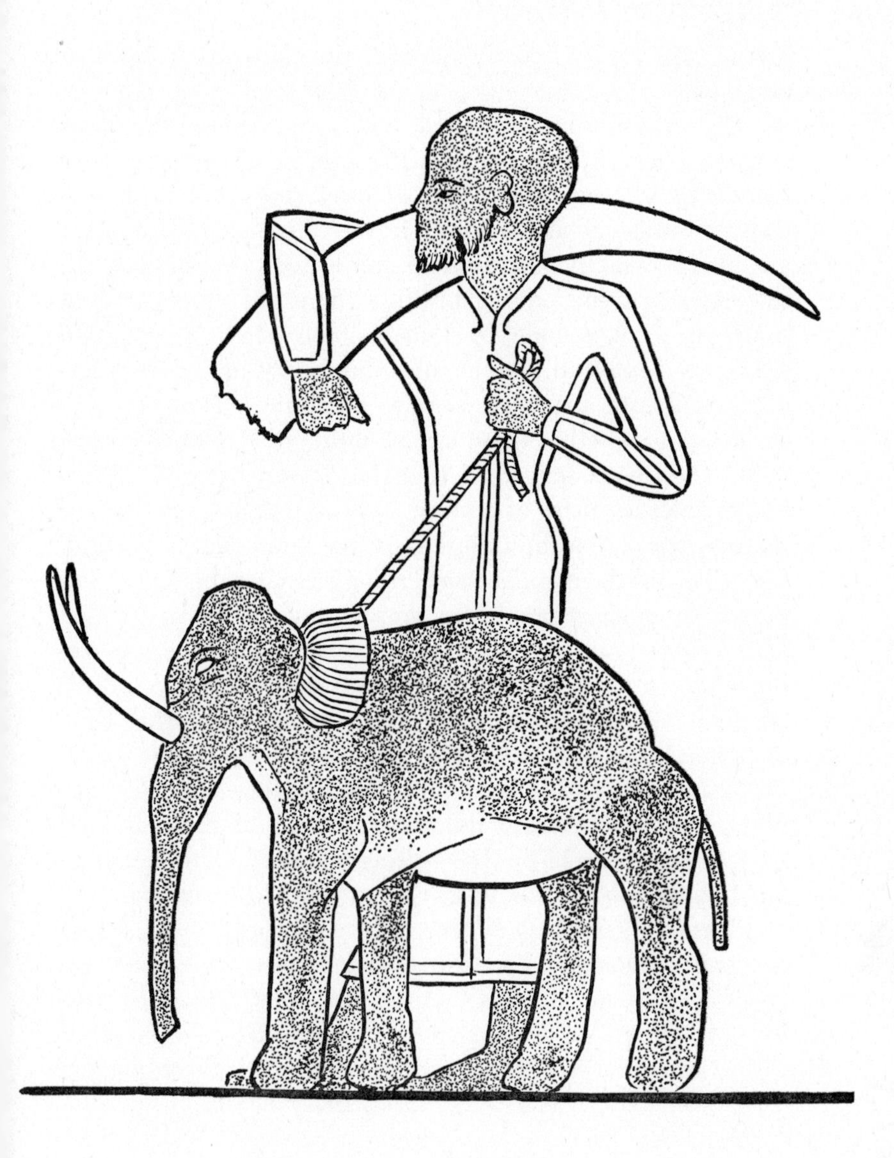

ivory, and, what is more, some of them display effigies of elephants.

This civilization, though it also started about the year 3500 B.C., is not by any means the earliest in India to show knowledge of the Abu. There are cave paintings in north-central India—as at Mirzapur in the Vindhya hills—which are almost exactly like, and in some cases just as fine as, those Palaeolithic cave paintings found in Spain and in southern France done by Cro-Magnon Man. The Indian paintings depict all manner of animals, including rhinoceroses, elephants, and what seem to be giraffes. There is some debate as to whether these are Neolithic or Palaeolithic, and it has even been suggested that they may be contemporary with the latter phase of culture in western Europe. If so, we might have here a direct link between immediately postglacial man and the ancient world, thus bridging the 5,000-year gap in the association of Man and Abu which we predicated at the beginning of this chapter. Nevertheless, the civilizations of Harappa and Mohenjo-daro are obviously indigenous to the Punjab and Sind. There is no doubt that their initiators knew and lived with elephants from the very earliest times. In addition to the seals of ivory and elephant effigies, they also wrote about the animals on the seals in a very strange form of picture writing which can only be paralleled by the most primitive hieroglyphs in Mesopotamia.

Recent discoveries in the valleys of the Ganges, Brahmaputra, Chindwin, Irrawaddy, and Salween rivers, and on the lowlands of Thailand, Cambodia, Vietnam, Laos, and Tonkin, are still inconclusive, but Abu were there in abundance since earliest times and were used by those peoples long before they became civilized. Ivory has been found in those places though not in profusion, probably because, being an "animal substance," it disintegrates in wet, equatorial soils. A similar story may evolve in Malaya and Indonesia, where archaeological delvings are still in their infancy.

The situation is quite different when we move up into what is now China. About forty years ago some scholars, engaged in deciphering and interpreting certain very early Chinese texts, believed they had discovered statements indicating that wild rhinoceroses and elephants were still alive in northern China until historical times. One H. T. Chang, in 1926, himself Chinese and a scholar, re-examined the texts and noted that the same ideographs were used indiscriminately for both these animals and for the products derived from them, notably their skins. The skins were very highly prized for the making of armor, being impervious to the missiles of those days. However, as Mr. Chang delved further into these matters, he found that although Abu seemed to have disappeared from *northern* China before the Neolithic or late Stone Age, they continued to exist in the south.

South China includes the provinces of Hunan, part of Kwang-tung, Kwang-si, and Kwei-chow in the east, and Yunnan in the west. There are definite records of elephants in Kwei-chow in 2350 B.C. The notion that elephants may have lingered on in Shantung, to the north, until a much later date seems more likely attributable to the regular importation of their skins from the south by sea. But most surprising of all was the discovery of several reliable and almost modern reports that rhinoceroses were still quite common in Honan as late as A.D. 1263, and that there were then still wild elephants in Kwang-tung and Kwang-si. This is the more remarkable as the horns of rhinoceroses have, since most ancient times, been highly prized as medicine in China, and those animals have always been intensively hunted.

Abu have been known intimately to the inhabitants of China since the dawn of history. Chinese writing, or ideography, has gone through a prolonged development starting with naturalistic hieroglyphs and ending with the various highly artistic forms of script used today. In the very earliest of Chinese history we find a symbol for Abu which looks like this:

Somewhat later this was upended and simplified and came out like this: Some centuries later it appeared in an even more simplified manner as: Three or four more degenerative stages then followed, ending up with the modern: which also signifies "Prime Minister," which is perhaps in some ways rather indicative.

Besides using Abu as motifs in statuaries, paintings, and architectural embellishments, the Chinese considered the trunk a great delicacy to eat. They used its soaked hide as a "plaster" for severe wounds, and they drank a tonic made of tusk shavings boiled in wine. The Chinese have always felt that the skin of elephants looked like crude, or crepe, rubber. In fact, their word for an eraser (originally Indian or gum rubber) is the same as that for elephant hide. Ivory was always regarded by them as a semi-precious substance and employed in art, and when in Canton, in A.D. 1325, some vulgarians started making chopsticks out of ivory for the wealthy, there was a howl of righteous indignation from the intelligentsia.

Thus, with the exception of Sumeria in the lower delta of the Tigris-Euphrates, all the earliest civilizations that we know of in the Old World made use of Abu. The Egyptians and the Indians—that is, the first settlers of the Indus Valley—had tamed them by the time civilization was established. Once Man and Abu joined forces, the relationship gained importance and spread steadily. First, the Egyptians impressed the world with their loxodonts. But quite early the inhabitants of India were specializing in the capture and training of their elephants.

The civilization of the Indus Valley continued more or less uninterruptedly for some 3,000 years. The rest of the subcontinent of India remained divided and somewhat chaotic until the initiation of the Vedic or pre-Mauryan period by the invasions from the northwest by Aryan-speaking people. Accounts of these early invasions dating about 1500 B.C. mention the trained elephants of the sundry Indian kingdoms. Elephants in profusion appear in stone works throughout that and subsequent periods. Hindu mythology is rife with men, gods, heroes, and elephants in intimate association. For instance, the god Indra rides a vast elephant named Airāvata who represents the thunder and thunderclouds, the lightning and the rains of that god.

The elephant was one of the Seven Treasures of Buddhism—the others being the Pearl, the Golden Wheel, the Gemmeous Maidens, Horses, the Divine Guardians of the Treasury, and the Military Governors. Buddha received sacred gifts offered by the elephant and sometimes rode on an elephant. On one notable occasion Buddha threw one over a wall. Further, Buddha was said to have entered the right side of his mother in the form of a white elephant prior to his miraculous birth shortly afterward. An elephant was believed to carry the world on his back while he stood on a vast tortoise, though he later gained some assistance from two divine partners. Holy Trinity though they were, the three were said, rather logically, to have given the world much greater stability. We must appreciate that for millennia the elephant played a great and often a paramount part in the pantheon of countries all the way from the Indus Valley to northern China and south to Indonesia. Realize, too, that the religious aspect of the elephant extended very far beyond even that area in ancient times. So also did its fame in other, more materialistic matters.

Two Assyrian kings during the eighth century B.C. hunted elephants in Syria. One of them is alleged to have killed thirty. Also, it was in that country that the Egyptians encountered the Asiatic Elephant and found it superior to their own loxodonts, which appear to have been either of the Forest variety or a race akin to it and of modest stature, possibly standing only about 8 feet tall, at the most.

The Egyptians found the Asiatic animal better trained, more efficient in battle, and *larger,* which last would not have been so had they been using Bush Loxodonts. There is no evidence whatsoever that there were ever true elephants anywhere in Africa. It might seem that there had not been any west of the Indus Valley since the drying up of Persia, which began apparently about 7,000 years ago. Yet one small pocket of them may have persisted in the upper half of the Euphrates Valley. Just where Thothmes III hunted his Abu we do not know, but it was probably above Babylon, which might put its location within the borders of the Syria of those days, which was much larger than now. What were the wild elephants that still existed in greater Syria as late as 800 B.C.? Were the *trained* elephants in that country indigenous, or from 2,000 miles away in India, brought there by sea via the Persian Gulf and then marched up the Euphrates Valley?

Unfortunately the latter suggestion is hard to support, because in Babylonian and Assyrian times the passages of numbers of such remarkable creatures would surely have impressed the inhabitants sufficiently so that the event would have appeared in their detailed records. It seems much more likely that some species of elephant lingered on in the general area of Syria until quite late, and this leads us to another conundrum that has not, to my knowledge, been commented upon directly.

It has always been assumed that prior to 350 B.C. elephants (and loxodonts) were completely unknown in Europe. In fact, Europeans, in the form of the Macedonians, supposedly first encountered the animals when Alexander confronted the Indian King Porus across the Indus tributary, the Hydaspes River, at Bucephala in the year 326 B.C.

Arrian's reports repeatedly emphasize that Alexander insisted that his cavalry horses should not be exposed to Porus' elephants, as they would be scared. This belief, though probably untrue, is a most ancient one, and although Alexander may have been apprised of it by Indian allies in his ranks, it is much more likely that he knew about Abu already and had experienced the first shock of encounter with them some time before.

Could it be that the Greeks, and thus their conquerors, the Macedonians, knew about elephants prior to the time of Alexander? If so, where more likely than in greater Syria or the Nile delta, where, it would seem, the Egyptians kept elephants which they later loaned to Carthage on a sort of lend-lease deal in the hope of helping to curtail the expansion of Rome. It is also assumed that the meticulous descriptions of elephants, their structure and movements, and the uses of their trunks and limbs, recorded by Aristotle in his famous *Historia Animalium,* which he wrote in 323 B.C., were wholly derived from information sent back from Alexander's expedition. Alexander died in Babylon in 327 B.C. Aristotle recorded such remarkable facts as that the elephant, alone of all land animals apart from man, has its breasts on its chest, and this alone casts considerable doubt on the idea that he got *all* his facts from the reports of Arrian and others who accompanied Alexander.

His knowledge makes it seem almost impossible that he gleaned it all second-hand or but a scant two years before he wrote. There are dozens of references to elephants in Aristotle's works, and very few of them are wrong. What is more, he observed something that was ignored until today—the elephant's use of its trunk (a matter that intrigued him enough to keep him coming back to it repeatedly) as a schnorkel when it went bathing. That elephants both walk on the bottom of rivers and swim with their trunks elevated for air led Aristotle to observe that the animal was obviously originally partly aquatic.

Arrian, on the other hand, while equally perspicacious,

is compensatingly pragmatic, but he does not give the impression of having known anything about elephants before he saw them across the Hydaspes. His encounters with them make very interesting reading. As we have said, Alexander knew of the potential danger of elephants, and, as King Porus had a train of several hundred of them, heavily armored and handled by expert and specialized crews, he was not going to get his precious cavalry involved with them if he could help it. Alexander therefore divided his forces and engaged in several agile maneuvers up and down his side of the river in the hope of decoying Porus' lumbering elephants to one position while he got his cavalry across at another; but things did not work out quite as he planned. Porus also knew a thing or two; but, even so, battle was finally joined somewhat to Alexander's advantage.

The elephants lined up about a hundred feet apart with archers and spearmen in turrets on their backs, the infantry massed behind them in phalanxes but opposite the spaces between them. On the wings were more massed infantry and, flanking these, the Indian cavalry. By judicious operations and, we suspect, superior horsemanship on the part of the Greeks—or, more accurately, their Asiatic cohorts from the steppelands—Alexander got the main Indian army boxed in so that he could attack the elephants with clouds of arrows from long range and then engage them at close quarters with his infantry. His main assault was upon their mahouts. A dead mahout had the same effect on the charging elephant as a dead driver of a speeding truck. Once the mahout was slain, neither the remaining soldiers on its back nor anyone else could tell the animal what to do. Crazed by the sting of darts and other wounds, they began to tramp about, mashing friend and foe alike. Then they took matters into their own hands and turned on their own ranks. And nothing can stop an elephant in pain when its trusted trainer is gone; the result was a complete shambles in which

Alexander was wholly victorious. He obtained possession of all the remaining serviceable elephants.

It is a very strange thing that no military leader throughout the centuries seems to have stumbled upon the essential aspect of the employment of elephants, namely, the preservation of the mahout, or oozie, or whatever their trainer may be called. If only the leader had armored his animals and given them large swords to hold in their trunks—as was done by one ingenious Chinese general—and then put the mahout, with an assistant or substitute, in some really impenetrable armor on its back and then let the trio go into battle alone, they would have been almost invincible, for elephants can overtake any man running, they can move their trunks and limbs with incredible speed, and they can maneuver with the most unexpected agility in very tight spaces. On the contrary, generals invariably loaded the animals down with huge towers or howdahs filled with soldiers, and left the trainer exposed, and they never seem even to have had substitute trainers accompanying the animals on foot. Time and time again we read of the shock effect on armies of seeing fighting elephants for the first time, and yet read on to find the elephants defeating their own army. It is equally astonishing that despite their very great knowledge of elephants, the ancients seem never to have realized that these creatures are basically peaceful or at least unwarlike. Unless crazed by *musth,* they are normally exceedingly reluctant to exert their strength or to hurt anything. Their whole evolution has been toward the exact opposite, which is summed up in the care with which they protect their own young during a stampede. True, in Rome they were trained—and presumably still could be—to chase nude virgins around an arena, then trample them to death ceremoniously for the edification of civilized morons. But elephants dislike doing battle with anything. What is more, they are really very vulnerable, especially to cold steel, once you know where to pierce them. The ancients were in many respects incredibly obtuse and in no respect did they show themselves more so than in the use of Abu.

Once Alexander acquired elephants, he used them extensively, particularly in India it seems, for there are constant references to elephants by Arrian. Alexander may have transported some back to Babylon, but there he died, and there is no extant record of how they got to Greece. That elephants were marched overland all the way from India we may safely say was impossible because of the vast desert strip between the Indus Valley and Mesopotamia. That they were shipped from India up the Red Sea is somewhat unlikely, though possible. That they were boated to Mesopotamia and then either rafted or marched up the Euphrates is, as we have also seen, only very vaguely possible. But that they were in Greece—and in Epirus, which is opposite the heel of Italy—by about the year 290 B.C. is certain, for ten years later the king of that state, Pyrrhus, transported quite a large number of them over the straits to Italy. There he engaged the Romans on behalf of the city-state of Tarentum, a Greek outpost, at Heraclea, in 280 B.C. He soundly defeated his opponents, though five years later the tables were turned and the Romans drove him out of the country, taking over Tarentum. They also captured and took to Rome his elephants, which they called the "Bulls of Pyrrhus" or "Lucanian Oxen."

The Romans were, from the first, of pretty stern caliber. There is a delightful story of a Roman emissary who was sent to negotiate with Pyrrhus before his defeat, at a time when elephants were allegedly not known in Rome. Pyrrhus, thinking to unnerve the fellow, had the largest elephant caparisoned and hidden behind a screen before the interview. When the Roman became difficult, Pyrrhus gave a signal and the great beast ambled out and stood over the Roman, making unpleasant noises. The Roman is stated to have merely glanced over his shoulder at this interruption and then, turning back to Pyrrhus, continued: "And as I was saying . . ." The Romans were, in fact, from the start, little impressed by Abu. They took the first ones they captured directly to Rome, entered them in an arena, and had slaves armed only with pointed sticks chase them around and finally kill them with lances, to demonstrate to the populace, and doubtless to the upcoming crop of army recruits in particular, that they were not dangerous.

The Carthaginians, who were the descendants of Semitic Phoenicians of Tyre in Palestine, did not seem initially to know anything about elephants, either, and particularly about war elephants. These people had quite a maritime empire established by the time Pyrrhus invaded southern Italy; they held dominion over Corsica, Sardinia, Provence, Sicily, and many other points around the western Mediterranean. There is some confusion as to whether Pyrrhus crossed to Sicily and engaged the Carthaginians there on behalf of his fellow Greeks or whether the Greeks called upon Rome for help. It is certain that there was an engagement between Romans and Carthaginians at Messana on the Sicilian peninsula nearest the Italian shore—the opening gambit of the First Punic War. It is also certain that elephants were used. According to some accounts, the Carthaginians were so surprised and alarmed by the elephants that they immediately went rushing back into their own southern territory and to Mauretania (or what is now Morocco) to obtain elephants for themselves, and soon had great numbers of them trained for war. But this is probably all Roman propaganda. I contend that these latter accounts are complete nonsense.

First, there is no evidence that the Berbers or other indigenous inhabitants of North Africa knew anything about catching, as opposed to hunting, their wild elephants, let alone training them. On the other hand, there is considerable evidence that the Carthaginians already had fully trained war elephants, possibly both loxodonts and Asiatic

Elephants given to them by the Egyptians. There is no doubt that at least by 225 B.C. they had a vast stable of Abu, most of which were loxodonts. The coins they minted at that time show vividly explicit reproductions of these animals being ridden by Africans. These effigies show the familiar long, ringed trunks, sloping foreheads, huge ears, sway backs with a shoulder and a rump-hump, and other features unique to those animals. But a single Carthaginian coin found in Italy depicts just as clearly an Indian Elephant, with arched back, small ears, smooth trunk, and bulbous head, which, incidentally, certainly indicates that the Carthaginians knew those animals also. The point is, the Carthaginians knew about and possessed both Asiatic Elephants and loxodonts long before they encountered those acquired by Rome from Pyrrhus. And the Carthaginians knew how to use Abu in warfare.

And this brings us to an incident that, though really rather minor in itself, might indeed have changed history, and that has certainly received more attention than it warranted: the feat of the Carthaginian general Hannibal in taking thirty-seven elephants on his long march on Rome from North Africa, via Spain, the south of France, and over the Alps. Literally hundreds of books and pamphlets have been written about Hannibal's trek, and dozens of people have devoted a substantial part of their lives to trying to trace Hannibal's route. But for all that, little has been added to the original Roman accounts and especially vis-à-vis his elephants.

The Carthaginians had to do something about the expansion of Rome into the western Mediterranean. And, indigent Greeks in that arena notwithstanding, the two powers had eventually to come to grips. As, in the First Punic War, Rome had most unexpectedly, and with the aid of the maritime Greeks, defeated the Carthaginians in their own natural element, the sea, Hannibal decided to attack his enemy from the rear and by land. So he tramped off for some

1,500 miles around the Mediterranean with a considerable host. That he got over the Alps and waged war in their home territory profoundly shocked the Romans. In fact, when they learned that he had got most of his elephants over that reputedly impassable barrier, they almost gave up.

However, these animals proved to be sitting ducks for the Roman archers, so that when Hannibal reached the Apennines, he had left only one lone magnificent bull named Suru to ride on. Suru meant "The Syrian," which is most significant, for the name and other evidence indicates that it actually came from that country and was an Elephant, not a loxodont. Suru fell to the Romans, was "pardoned," given a sort of honorable discharge, and became a great pet on an estate outside Rome.

Just how Hannibal got his proboscideans over the Alps is most adequately summed up in a small book by Sir Gavin de Beer, who examined all the records by both contemporary and later Romans and by all other authors on the subject. Nobody whose works have survived actually witnessed the crossing, and nobody wrote about it first-hand. We know, however, that apart from trouble on the Italian side near the top of the highest pass, there was nothing much to exploit. Hannibal's whole train was held up for four bad days by a landslide and a huge boulder that impeded the cutting of a new track down the mountainside; during that time the poor beasts were without food and exposed to a blizzard. Elephants, if not loxodonts, are superbly sure-footed mountaineers: they can take a lot of cold and can negotiate mountain trails above monstrous defiles without any sign of vertigo. That Hannibal's "elephants" got over the Alps is not remarkable; that his horses did so is really extraordinary. Horses are excitable and stupid animals, and their spindly, easily breakable legs and single toes were adapted for roaming about on level plains; certainly they were not intended to go mountaineering.

Had his logistics staff planned better, so that Hannibal

had had sufficient men, supplies, and reinforcements to take Rome, the whole continent of Europe might have been a Phoenician province, subject to Baal instead of to Zeus-Jupiter-Votan, and the Mediterranean Basin might have become a Philistine instead of a Roman pond. But Hannibal lost and Rome won and went on to world conquest.

After the defeat of Carthage, the Romans initiated all kinds of animal exhibits, including elephants, in their parades. Then they started promoting spectacles (with elephants as prominent features) in arenas for a fee, so that more people could watch and the promoter make some profit. Later the Romans learned that elephants could be taught or persuaded—albeit rather reluctantly—to fight other elephants, bulls, or Numidian slaves, or to trample virgins. But more of this when we come to the sad history of the Abu in that infamous idiocy called the Roman circus. The ancients, and especially the Romans, were not, history tells us, particularly likable people. It is with some relief, therefore, that we turn to Pliny, that delightful chronicler who, though he doubtless enjoyed the pursuit of nude virgins by elephants in arenas as much as the next Roman, at least wrote with blandness and objectivity. His writings about elephants are, in every sense of the word, classic.

He wrote a whole chapter on elephants in his *Natural History*—a catch-all for everything and anything that he heard or observed which he thought might be amusing to his readers, were it fact or fancy. Interlarded with his brighter records are a large number of very shrewd and accurate observations, some of which are historically signifi-

---

Roman War Elephant bearing tower with armed men. (From a painted Roman pottery dish, *circa* 280-270 B.C.)

cant. He wrote, for example, that the supply of ivory was, in his time, almost exhausted "in the West," and had therefore to be imported, laboriously, from India and the Far East. Does he mean by "the West" Morocco? Then one reads in his introduction to this subject that "the elephant understands the language of its country, it obeys commands, and it remembers all the duties it has been taught." So far very good, but he goes on to say that "it is sensible alike of the pleasures of love and of glory, and, to a degree that is rare among men even, possesses notions of honesty, prudence, and equity." However, he notes also that elephants are often displayed in Rome and that one may see them "frolic through the steps of the Pyrrhic dance." I have inquired about the Pyrrhic dance and must regretfully report that I have not the nerve to publish what I learned! Nevertheless, the Romans must have been delighted by the dance, and the elephants must have been a riot. Pliny claims that an elephant walked a tightrope despite the obvious malconstruction of the animal for such a feat. He reports also that a man rode an elephant that walked "backward *up* a tight-rope." This is a little baffling, for it is hard to conceive of such a device going *up*. However, we may have a clarifying clue in another of his anecdotes which tells of a number of elephants being unloaded from ships at Puteoli; these were alarmed at the length of the gangplank, so they "walked backward over them in order to deceive themselves." This, I contend, is a perfectly splendid idea.

Pliny becomes somewhat extravagant when he records the habits of elephants in the wilds. It must be admitted, though, that his account of the methods by which they were then caught in India and Africa is remarkable for its likelihood. As we will see later, the catching of individual elephants by men riding trained elephants is still practiced in India. Hamstringing, riding down with lances, the use of pitfalls, and even primitive *keddahs* are definitely known to have been ancient African techniques. However, Pliny's notion that elephants know that humans want, above all, their tusks, and that they therefore break them off deliberately and throw them away so that men will pick them up as ransom and let their previous owners go, or that elephants bury their tusks so that men will *not* find them, is just plain *pliniesque.* Yet, he observes that all tuskers have one perfect and well-pointed tusk that they care for, and one shorter, or stubbed, one that they use for work. This is quite true. He is also right in saying that elephants make their young cross rivers ahead of the mothers because the heavy adults, especially the big bulls, tend to break down the banks making it difficult for the little ones to climb ashore. He also gets their breeding cycle right by saying that they mate every other year but his notions about their period of gestation are a little exaggerated.

The amorous activities of animals were always of interest to the Romans, and Pliny may be relied upon to comment on this aspect of any animal. Of Abu he remarks that "adulterous intercourse is unknown to them" but that "one in Egypt once fell in love with a woman; but let no one suppose that he made a vulgar choice, for she was the especial object of the love of Aristophanes, who held the very highest rank *as a grammarian.*" (Italics mine)

Pliny is one of the most interesting sources of information on the introduction of elephants to Rome and thus to the Western world. He states that they were first seen in Italy during the Pyrrhic Wars but that "seven years later Mancius Curius Dentatus [i.e., Mancius with the Funny Teeth] displayed them in his triumph, and three years later 142 of them, captured from the Carthaginians in Sicily, were "transported hence on rafts built on lines of hogsheads [barrels] lashed together." So, elephants may indeed have come from the Carthaginians.

Short of reprinting the whole of Pliny, one can only recommend rereading him in some modern translation, both for facts as well as for pure fun. He says, for instance, that elephants suffer most from the effects of a horse-leech, picked up from a pond while drinking, which attaches itself to the animal's throat or oesophagus, causing exquisite pain. This is the truth, for it is almost impossible to detach these worms from a mucous membrane, and is one of the few operations that may defy the dexterity of the human hand, even with sharp nails. I once assisted at the removal of one of these parasites from an elephant's throat—armed with flashlight, forceps, a mahout, and with my life in my hands. After the removal of the leech, the pachyderm vomited all over both of us in pleasure and relief.

The Carthaginians got most of their loxodonts from the Atlas Mountains region and from the Atlantic coast of Morocco, but loxodonts still lived wild in southern Tunisia in Pliny's time, and as late as A.D. 47 Suetonius Paulinus saw them in the valley of the Guir. As for the traffic in elephants, in 321 B.C. Perdiccas of Syria invaded the Egypt of Ptolemy the First with a lot of Indian Elephants. He was defeated and the elephants captured. Ptolemy the Second sent elephants to Carthage in the Second Punic War, and the coin found in Etruria, Italy (see page 112), shows an Indian Elephant on one side and the head of an African man on the other. In 246 B.C. Ptolemy the Third of Egypt defeated Seleucus of Syria in what the former called the Third Syrian War and captured more elephants.

Although the Romans never succeeded in making good circus performers of elephants, they did use them for psychological warfare. They had the good sense *not* to try them as "tanks." They used them, magnificently caparisoned, as transports or as accoutrements for the parades of the successful conquerors or subduers of outlying provinces. Thus, in 121 B.C., Domitius and Fabius were supplied by the King of Numidia with elephants obtained in Mauretania (i.e., Morocco) and took them on their triumphal entry into the conquered territory of Provincia (Provence) in southern France.

But most significant of all is, perhaps, the fact that Julius Caesar actually got a large elephant over to the then barbarous country now known as England. The Britons were more than just a little peeved by a lot of Mediterraneans landing on their dismal, mist-enshrouded island, and they literally bounded around the invaders in their light chariots, which were rather flimsy but nonetheless efficiently designed for their kind of fighting. They employed guerrilla tactics that confused the Roman legionnaires not a little, so that by the time the latter reached the first real barrier, the Thames River, their morale was very low. Julius approached the Thames from the south and attempted a crossing at a ford where the river was only 5 feet deep. The wretched Britons had ensconced themselves on the opposite bank behind a fence of sharpened posts stuck into the ground. However, Caesar brought up his elephant, armored in silver. He mounted the turret on its back and pounded solemnly into the little stream, whereupon the Britons abandoned their defense works and decamped, "not knowing the nature of this monstrous beast."

Actually, the authenticity of this record is in some doubt, but it writes a suitable finis to the grand alliance of Man and Abu in the ancient world, for not too long after this, darkness descended upon both.

[6]

OF THE DARK AGES

The collapse of Man's ancient civilization. The disappearance of Abu, and their survival in the East.

The ancient world came to an end, though not abruptly, around A.D. 400. During its 5,000-year history Man slowly hauled himself up from the level of a rather rare hunting animal to one of pre-eminence as a new life form on this planet. This he did—at least within a limited compass in the Old World—to a considerable extent at the expense of other forms of life. Although he created vast fertile areas by ingenious artificial irrigation, he also stripped even vaster areas of their natural vegetative cover and cleared them of not only "game" but most other fauna. In fact, he altered the whole surface of the land right across the continent of Eurasia from Britain in the West to the Isles of Nippon in the East, and also set a sort of monstrous bushfire aglow along the latitudes to the south of this belt which changed its whole natural fauna and much of its vegetation. What he was doing meanwhile in Central and western South America, we do not exactly know as yet, but civilization apparently ran a similar course there at equivalent dates.

But Man was not the only influence at work, even in the areas he dominated. The old earth itself had not yet quite settled down from the effects of the final retreat of the icecap. Certain changes of climate took place in Eurasia and Africa during these millennia involving fluctuations in average temperature and rainfall which were sufficient to render large fertile areas into deserts. These changes and the resultant crop failures initiated the emigrations of hordes of animals, including men, from one area to another. The flowering of ancient, or what is called "classical," civilization coincided with a phase of stability and mildness in the climate. Then the climate suddenly worsened again and a Dark Age descended upon the world.

It appears that about 150 B.C. a whole concatenation of such changes began, each dependent upon the other, but all probably initiated by some minor convulsion of the earth itself. What seems to have happened first is that the climate of Mongolia deteriorated rather rapidly. Hordes of human beings living there had to move to milder climes for the sake of their flocks and herds. And as they drifted outward, to the east, south, and west, they encountered better conditions and prospered; they ate better and bred faster. So did their herds and particularly their horses. And, as the grass withered or was overgrazed in their wake, their progress gained momentum until they debouched from the dreary steppes into the settled plains and valleys of civilization. This was the story in the east and the south, but in the west this movement triggered a second train of events.

The climate of northern Europe was also deteriorating, and tribesmen from those parts were also on the move. The Scandians of the southern part of Sweden had already set out east. However, when those Asiatic nomads, the Huns, rolled into the eastern borders of the Mediterranean world of Rome, their impact set a host of other peoples on the move and turned the Scandians in an about-face. The Huns terrorized the Slavs living in what is now European Russia and the Chazars who then inhabited the Caucasus. Slavs and Chazars communicated their disturbances to the Germans on the one hand, and to the Armenians on the other, both of whom began to move away from the on-coming Golden Horde. The Scandians, represented by the Visigoths and the Ostrogoths, were caught in a no-man's land between the now somewhat hysterical Slavs, who were scrambling north, and the invaders from the east. So they turned south and finally west until the Visigoths came to rest in Spain and the Ostrogoths in Italy.

Though the Huns arrived on the scene only in A.D. 375, they thrashed their way through central Europe for seventy-five years before dissipating themselves in Austria. Meanwhile, the Angles and Saxons boated over to Britain, Franks and Burgundians poured into France from Germany, Lombards shoved down into Italy, and the Vandals made a sort of grand tour of western Europe, slashing apart just about everything they encountered. Rome and the world of the ancients retreated, wilted, and finally collapsed under these onslaughts. Then, just when things were settling down, the prophet Mahommet in Arabia launched still another mass movement. The Saracen tide crashed in from the southeast and south and engulfed what was left of ancient Europe and the Near East.

And all the time, behind this symptomatic human flux, the earth itself continued disturbed. Intense cold descended upon northern Eurasia, crops failed in central Europe and arroyos incised the barren lands. Roman armies disbanded rapidly. Rich forests turned into scrub or faded into bare gravel and sand. Copious rivers vanished and instead dry arroyos incised the barren lands. Roman armies disbanded or were annihilated, and silent Roman arenas crumbled or were used as cattle corrals.

Abu became extinct in Morocco, in the Nile Valley, and everywhere else north of Kordofan in Africa and west of the Indus in Asia, though some lingered on in Eritrea until the nineteenth century, as was discovered by a British explorer in A.D. 1868. Nor, as far as we know, was there a tame one left in the whole Mediterranean or anywhere north of the southern fringe of the Sahara Desert by A.D. 500. In their own agony, Western men forgot all about the Abu, and, from being a commonplace item of some local faunas and the playthings of civilized barbarians, the Abu vanished from the Western scene. But they did not vanish in other lands.

In 1835 a modest article appeared in the Proceedings of the American Antiquarian Society by a man who used the name of Colonel Juan Galindo. This was actually the *nom de guerre* of an Irishman, whose real name is not known but who was the Governor of the Province of Peten, the most distant and isolated part of Guatemala, in Central America. There was considerable turmoil in that and adjacent countries at that time, and many military adventurers had gravitated there, adopted Hispanic names, and risen to positions of eminence. Most were outright scallywags, but Juan Galindo had transcending interests. He had stumbled across monumental stoneworks in Chiapas, Yucatan, and Honduras. Up till that time there had been only three accounts of any such things and all pertained to the first-named area, where a vast city was literally buried by jungle at a place called Palenque. One of these accounts had been illustrated by a man named Jean Frederic Waldeck, who, in 1838, published a work in Paris on further ruins that he had visited at a place called Uxmal, in Yucatan.

This book was distributed in America by John Russell Bartlett, who brought both it and Galindo's account to the attention of two Englishmen then visiting this country. One was a famous architectural artist named Frederick Catherwood, who had spent many years in Egypt drawing its ancient monuments, and the other a lawyer named John

Lloyd Stevens, who had turned to traveling and writing. These two men became greatly excited at this disclosure of a vast new lost civilization in Central America, and they organized an expedition. On October 3, 1839, they embarked on the brig *Marianne,* en route to Belize, British Honduras. From there they went to Guatemala, and from there penetrated the rugged Mico Mountains south into the Republic of Honduras, where they were promptly arrested.

But the reception was more or less standard practice in those days, as was also their release forty-eight hours later for a modest consideration and after an impassioned but highly diplomatic political harangue by Catherwood. The party then continued to a valley resting at an altitude of 3,000 feet. The valley, named Copan, contained, just as Juan Galindo had said it did, a vast series of ruins. Among other things, there were two huge pyramids, a vast acropolis, and five plazas, the largest of which was 800 feet long and was surrounded by great tiers of stone seats. In the plaza stood several huge stone monoliths, two of which weighed about 30 tons each. But all of them were carved all over in a manner that somewhat nonplussed Catherwood, for the individual items of the higgledy-piggledy designs were all undercut, like the finer Chinese ivories, so that they were all but three-dimensional. In fact, despite his experience recording the intricate ancient Egyptian designs, and even using a camera lucida to copy what he saw, Catherwood almost gave up. Even Stevens cautiously stated of Catherwood's results that he was not "quite satisfied with the outcome, although I have no right to express an opinion." Here was a complex culture that was not only new but completely unlike anything ever seen before. And if you have ever viewed a Mayan stele, you will readily appreciate both the artist's and the lawyer's confusion. At first the writhing, open-mouthed, multitoothed, and seething mass of plant, animal, and human figures, all with their baroque adornments, make one's vision reel, so that one is unable to make any sense of either the whole or any part of it.

The expedition at first encountered a lot of trouble with the petty local authorities, but everything was settled to everybody's satisfaction when the two Englishmen purchased the whole of Copan for $50. With the help of local labor they cleared the site, most of which was overgrown with a scrubby jungle. But they were unable to clear off the pyramids because of the big trees that grew on them. Finally the two men settled down to study what they had brought to light. It was not until Catherwood had almost completed his painstaking, laborious, and frustrating drawings of the two largest steles that he realized that one of them was topped at both edges by something very remarkable.

These steles are of a peculiar and hardly explicable shape. They apparently started off as tall, rather slender, rectangular slabs, like elongated shoe boxes set up on end. The ancient artists had carved the whole of their surfaces except the back—where they incised only bas-reliefs—but cut so deeply on both edges and on the front that these became almost one rounded surface. There is no symmetry in the design and no two sections are precisely alike. Yet the one side—let us call it the left—tends to mirror the other—or right—in general subject matter. The two top and dominant figures on each edge of one stele are most perfectly and naturalistically represented heads of elephants—not loxodonts, mammoths, or mastodons, but obvious *elephants* richly caparisoned in the manner well known in India and Cambodia. One of these figures carries on its neck a mahout, wearing a typical Oriental turban on his head and holding in his hand a traditional square elephant hook!

When Catherwood's drawings were published, these elephant heads blew up a storm of speculation, controversy, and acrimony which lasted for eighty years. During this time several books and innumerable papers were published upon the subject but no real conclusions were drawn, and several misleading side issues were raised. The fury still goes on, though there has been little sound since the publication, in 1924, of a book entitled *Elephants and Ethnologists* by the famous anthropologist G. Elliot Smith. He reviewed all these works, propounded his own theory, and gave the arguers a rough going-over.

To summarize the arguments, we may say that because elephants in ancient Central America did not then and still do not yet fit into the prescribed scheme of history, but because these carvings were undeniably authentic, everything possible and impossible was immediately put forward to "explain them away." They were *not* elephants at all, said some of the learned, but the enlarged heads of the great parrotlike bird of that country known as the macaw; or representations of turtles, or of a "bat-god" wearing a symbolic headdress, or such forth. All of these things are well known from Mayan carvings, but each is invariably *quite distinct*, for the Mayas were very accurate in their animal representations. Anything seemed acceptable as long as it was not an elephant.[1]

The Copan carvings are of elephants and they are perfectly executed, with their trunks slightly curled to one side and backward, but nobody was prepared to admit the fact. What clinched the matter, however, was a careful search for and reappraisal of the extant original Mayan codices—hieroglyphic texts on scrolls, done in many colors, a few of which survived the wholesale burnings by the Church in the early days. Brought to light were several dozen quite obvious elephants, elephant symbols, and figures of men wearing elephant headdresses, and, what is more, exactly like those shown on the coins of certain Asiatic kingdoms of the first century B.C.

[1] These "reasonable" explanations were, in fact, almost as silly as the everlasting belief that the dragonlike creatures in so many Mayan motifs are "plumed serpents," when they are quite clearly careful representations of the large local Iguana Lizards.

The Late Mayan civilization has been variously dated as of the first to the fourth centuries A.D. by American ethnologists, the sixth to the ninth by the British, and somewhat later by the earlier German investigators. What, then, were the Mayas doing carving and drawing true elephants in the New World at about the beginning of the Dark Ages in the Old World? There are several possible answers. Either, as the German zoologist Stempell suggested and himself believed, the Mayas had their own species of living elephants; or they brought the animals (or carvings or drawings of them, or at least intimate knowledge of them) across the Pacific from Asia; or they got these from across the Atlantic and from Africa or the Mediterranean; or there were still Abu in either North or South America. Let us take these possibilities one at a time.

That there were living Abu in Central America in the first centuries of this millennium is improbable, though not by any means impossible. We know of no true elephant ever having lived in this hemisphere or of a mammoth or a mastodon here that had a head so like that of an Indian Elephant, as displayed on the Copan stele. Further, we have to contend with the most precisely carved trappings of these Copan elephants and the mahout with his turban and hook. That the animals, or drawings, or at least a vivid memory of them came from across the Pacific is possible, and this is Professor Elliot Smith's notion. But Smith is a leader of the school that taught that everything in the Americas came from Asia either over the Bering Strait or by boat across the Pacific. Another school today, led by Thor Heyerdahl, just as fervently believes that more things originated in Central and northwestern South America than ever came from Asia. However, there is now considerable evidence that for centuries, and from even as early as 2000 B.C., there was a constant coming and going across the Atlantic between the Mediterranean Basin and what is now Brazil and possibly the Antilles and even southeastern North America.

Heyerdahl, like others, has noted the existence in South America of a tall, bearded, straight- and long-nosed, pale-skinned race among whom red hair was very common. That race, Heyerdahl claims, built with monumental stones both on the mainland of the Americas and on the islands, such as Easter Island, in the Pacific. He keeps asking, in his books, who they were. Yet several Brazilian ethnologists in extensive monographs about numerous relics, monuments, and even inscriptions in two different known Mediterranean scripts carved on rocks found throughout eastern South America, present us with the fact that these scripts were used by just such a tall, bearded, long-nosed race of seafarers —namely, the *Phoenicians.* The Phoenicians were a Semitic people, and red hair is more common among Semitic peoples than among any other. In fact, the Phoenicians so greatly admired the color that they often dyed their hair red. The very name "Phoenician" is of Greek origin and means "blood red," probably derived from their discovery and manufacture of *Tyrian purple,* a deep red dye made from a small marine shellfish.

The Phoenicians used several forms of writing, and their original alphabet gave rise to two dozen scripts, among them the Latin, the Greek, the Hebrew, and the Arabic. About 1200 B.C. they themselves were using two scripts: one an Aramean form, the other a Hellenic; and they used them for two different purposes—trade on the one hand; religious and heraldic records on the other. One of the inscriptions found in Brazil even gives the name of one of their kings who reigned in Tyre in 1200 B.C.—*and* in *both* scripts. Furthermore, Phoenician coins have several times allegedly been found at various points all along the eastern seaboard of the Americas.[2]

[2] If all these "Phoenician remains" were deliberate hoaxes, will somebody please tell me *where* the hoaxers got the Phoenician coins? I have been trying for a year through the biggest numismatist commercial firms to obtain just one genuine example, but have not been successful.

The knowledge of elephants could thus just as well have been brought to the Mayas over the Atlantic as over the Pacific. The Phoenicians inhabited Palestine, which was the coastal strip of Greater Syria; they traded with India; they had tame elephants; and they were the great ivory carvers of antiquity, using elephant, as opposed to loxodont, tusks. They sailed all around Europe and Africa and yet they never divulged the sources of their gold and other precious commodities. It now appears that they probably had maps of the whole coast of the Americas. Finally, the trappings of the elephants of Copan and the turbans on their riders' heads could just as well be Phoenician as Cambodian; in fact, the turbans are shaped just like the headgear of Near Eastern peoples of that date, as depicted on Assyrian steles.

Nevertheless, Elliot Smith's reasoning is very convincing, provided you accept a considerable and rather rapid commercial route across the Pacific from the region of Indochina. He shows how exactly alike are the elephant carvings and depictions of Cambodia and those of the Mayas. He also points out that the Mayan depictions are in some cases almost exactly the same as the Oriental *makaras*—early Hindu effigies that were compounded of the fore parts of cows, rams, lions, crocodiles, and elephants, and the hind parts of fishes. These often had open mouths with little men in them. As this mythical concept spread east into Indonesia, it developed into mere grotesque heads, one form of which was that of an elephant. Moreover, a small statue of an elephant-headed god, dug up in British Honduras in Central America, was identified as one of the numerous Yucatecan Chacs—of subdeity status, as in Chac-Mool the jaguar—but which is for all the world a representation of the Oriental elephant-headed god, Ganesha.

Despite these very convincing similarities between the Orient and some Mayan art, the possibility lingers that some warm-latitude American civilization tamed and used some dome-browed mammoth or other Abu, or that knowledge of these animals came to Central America from either North or South America.

To set against this, we have a quite astonishing rock carving found in central Brazil, a most perfect reproduction of an Indian Rhinoceros, and specifically of *Rhinocerus indicus,* with its one horn, its typical parrotlike "beak," and all its skin folds exactly in the right places. Astonishing indeed! Why an Oriental, rather than an African, rhinoceros in eastern South America? There never were any indigenous rhinoceroses in South America, so somebody must have carried the knowledge of such a beast there. What is more, this carving is almost perfect and is covered with letters in the Hellenic type of Phoenician script.

Unless this is modern forgery, we are faced with three equally remarkable possibilities: namely, that either most intimate knowledge of the outward form of the Great Indian Rhinoceros crossed the Pacific from the Indochinese region and then filtered down into the heart of the Amazon; or it came from India via the Near East and the Mediterranean to the mouth of that river; or third, that it came directly from Bengal around the Cape of Good Hope. The "forgery" explanation would be the most acceptable were it not for the other numerous and widely scattered indications of Asiatic, and notably of Phoenician, influence in the Americas—particularly the Copan elephants. The current explorations, in the vast Mayan city of Dzibilchaltun in Yucatan have now shown that it was founded between 2000 and 1000 B.C., so perhaps the early Mayas did still have some

---

Elephants wrestling. (From an illuminated Persian manuscript, attributed to Manafi al-Hayawân, on "The Uses of Animals," *circa* A.D. 1200.) Note the decorated "sun-caps."

indigenous Abu to tame. But whatever was going on in the New World at that time, we do not as yet really know.

While Abu vanished from the Mediterranean and western Europe after the collapse of Rome, they continued to play a major role in the civilizations of the Orient, and India was the core of this territory. This subcontinent remained remarkably stable despite its fractionated condition and two major cultural turnovers. What is known as the Maurya period came to an end in the first century A.D. The Kusana period then lasted till the year A.D. 320, when the greatest period of culture, known as the Gupta, blossomed. Then this period tailed off into an early medieval stage about A.D. 600, which in turn blended with the truly Medieval that lasted until the arrival of the Portuguese and other western Europeans in the fifteenth century.

Throughout this considerable stretch of time of almost 1,500 years, Man and Abu grew and worked together in ever-increasing intimacy. The elephant tradition was, as we have already seen, age-old in India as well as in adjacent areas such as Burma, Malaya, Siam, and the other Indochinese states, and apparently also in Sumatra, Java, and Borneo. We have little direct historical information from the last three countries, but in southern Sumatra, about the beginning of our millennium, there was a flourishing culture named the Pasemah, possibly a Chinese colony, which left in profusion stone-relief carvings of ridden elephants.

The Siamese early adopted white elephants as a sacred symbol. Most of these are not real albinos with pink eyes or truly white skins, though there are a very few records of such astonishing animals, but rather semi-albinos of a light beige color with dark or, in a few rare cases, blue eyes. These animals still are sacred and automatically belong to the Royal House, to which they must be taken by their captors, where both are still accorded tremendous ceremonial welcomes and are loaded down with gifts. These sacred elephants were once either painted white or, it is alleged, in some way bleached. Special pavilions were built for them; they were washed by both selected virgins and high officials; stuffed with all manner of queer foods that humans liked but that often made the elephants very ill; and were kept awake for life by caterwauling musicians, oversolicitous priests, Royal visitors, and the hordes of the humble populace. They often did not survive these attentions, especially the fireworks on their "opening night," but in more recent times they have been treated with somewhat more consideration. They have been shielded from the attentions of the masses, so that at least once, about thirty years ago, two of them even mated—this I know because I have a photograph of this glorious event given to me by a member of the Royal family, who was a school friend of mine.

In Java, elephant effigies billow out from every Hindu monument and they even crop up in the much more attractive pre-Hindu, indigenous, animistic religious art of that country and of Bali, and in a strangely Ganesha-like form. Ganesha is thought to have been a creation of the purely Indian pantheon, yet here he is cropping up again just as he did in Central America, and before his time. But he also turns up among the very earliest and crudest statuettes from southern China. And elephants play a very notable part in all Chinese plastic arts throughout the centuries. The Ming emperors in the fifteenth century erected gigantic monoliths of these creatures along the avenues leading to their tombs at Peking and Nanking. Incidentally, it was the custom for women desirous of conceiving to place a stone on the backs of these monoliths, so that at one time a number of them were more or less buried.

During what we here call the Dark Ages, which, from the point of view of the history of the Abu, encompasses the second to the fifteenth centuries of our era, there was a monstrous proliferation of elephant myth and lore, religious and otherwise, throughout the Indo-Chinese-Malayan region. At first this is quite fun to read, but after a time it becomes intolerably boring, and especially because the object of our particular affection itself becomes a symbol and often a hardly recognizable one at that. Nevertheless, the cult of Abu as a sacred creature as well as a symbol spread far beyond the confines of those countries where Abu still lived. Statuettes of elephants appeared upon the altars of Buddhist monasteries in Tibet and in adjacent central-Asiatic lands; they also reached Mongolia and Japan, and in the temples of inner China there were great silver statues of elephantines having as many as six tusks.

With the eruption of the northeast-Asiatic hordes in the first centuries of our era, Europe had, as we have seen, more or less gone under. It was also later cut off from the Oriental or south-Asiatic world by the rise of Mohammedanism. The Prophet was born in A.D. 570 and died in A.D. 632. He was succeeded in the leadership of his new sect by two most ingenious caliphs, Abu-Bekr and Omar, who forthwith set about carving out an empire for Islam with the sword. Led by the Arabs themselves, this religious emigration sprayed west, north, and east until it eventually entered southwestern Europe over the Pyrenees, the Balkans in the north, and central Asia and India in the east. It then filtered onward by proselytization and colonization to Mongolia and to Indonesia. In the Near East it boxed off Europe by the defeat of the Eastern Roman Empire.

Islam then settled down to develop a culture that, led by the Arabs, in some ways approached the competence of the earlier Greeks. It has left us much literature of astonishing variety and erudition which, unfortunately, is scarcely brought to the attention of the average Western student today. The Arab scholars, in fact, were the saviors of the intellectual wealth of the ancient world and they later transmitted this to a reviving Europe. They also acted as intermediaries in all matters scientific between the remnants of European culture in the West and the vast, seething womb of civilization in the East. They alone—during this interim of 600 years from about A.D. 700 to 1300—really knew something about the world; and they left most remarkable records.

Among those records are many references to Abu. For instance, Ibn Quatayba, in his *Uyûn Al-Akhbâr* notes under the heading *Fîl,* which is the Arabic for "elephant"—and specifically for *Elephas* and not for the loxodonts: "I have been informed by one of our teachers that he saw an elephant in the time of Abû Ja'far al-Mansur [A.D. 754-775] which was said to have prostrated itself before Sâbû dhû-l-aktâf and the Caliph." His information about Abu is in part gleaned from Aristotle and in part from Indian hearsay, such as that the tip of its tongue is turned inward, so that: "The Indians say, that if its tongue were not inverted, it would be able to speak." He also adds: "If a fullgrown elephant hears the voice of a suckling-pig it gets frightened and flees." This almost smacks of Pliny, but it is an odd fact that elephants, and especially males, sometimes do appear to be alarmed by the noises made by baby animals, including human and even their own kind.

Ad-Damîrî, properly known as Kamâl ud-Dîn Muhammad ibn Mûsâ ud-Damîrî, professor of Tradition in the Rukniyya in Cairo, born A.D. 1344, died A.D. 1405, composed many works on law and also a monumental lexicon named the *Hayât al-Hayawân* in which he listed in alphabetical order 931 animals mentioned in the Koran. The introduction to this work is worthy of one of our present-day columnists in one of his worst moods, for it records a meeting that he had attended at which all the idiots present spoke more loudly than the erudite and at which both, in his opinion, talked arrant nonsense. He essays, therefore, to write a work in which all the facts regarding animals will once and for all be recorded as per the word of the Prophet and of the Lord himself, and then launches forth into what certainly equals and in some ways even surpasses the works of Pliny.

Ad-Damîrî most shrewdly observes therein that there are two quite distinct kinds of "elephants"—the *al-Fîl,* "a certain well-known Animal" (plural *afyâl, fuyûl,* or *fiyalah*) and the "larger kind," or *Zandabîl,* which "stand in relation to each other as Arabian to Bactrian Camels." This is astonishing in its perspicacity, and is the first written statement of the relationship between the Elephant and loxodonts. He repeats carefully much of the previously published facts about Abu with surprisingly few of the old mistakes. For instance, he knows that they do not drink through their trunks but use them as bellows, and that they have joints in their legs and can therefore—despite the then popular belief to the contrary—perfectly well lie down, as well as perform all kinds of agile gyrations. He knows something of their diseases and the treatment thereof. He is quite knowledgeable about their external morphology and he even seems to hint that their tusks are front teeth and not canines. Then he launches into several pages of beautifully Pliniesque asides. There is the delightful story of one Abû-'Abd-Allâh al-Kalanisi who was going somewhere on a ship when a frightful storm came up, and who prayed; and the Lord put words into his mouth which said: "I will never eat of elephant flesh." In due course this worthy was shipwrecked on an arid coast with a few companions, and all they could find to eat was a small elephant, which they killed, but Abû-'Abd-Allâh refused to eat of it. That night the baby elephant's mother arrived and trampled all of them to death except our hero because he did not smell of her baby. Instead, she took him upon her back and made an eight-day trek during one night and delivered him safely to the nearest human community, which sent him home.

He records also that "an elephant was for the first time brought to Damascus in the time of Mauwiyah ben Abi al-Sufiyan, and the Syrians went out to look at it because they had never seen an elephant before." This would have been in A.D. 664, which is of considerable interest because it proves that any local elephants must have been extinct in that country for a very long time and also that such an animal *could* have been either boated or trekked there from India, at that time. He also gives us the first really clear reason why there is a traditional "Year of the Elephant" in earliest Islamic belief. He tells us that one King Abraha of Abyssinia invaded lower Arabia and marched on Mecca with Abu in the year that the Prophet was born. The King's steed was named Mahmûd. All kinds of things went wrong on the campaign, but eventually someone who obviously knew about Abu grabbed this beast by the ear and made it "lie down on its breast" and told it never to go toward Mecca. They then made it stand up and start off toward Syria, to the north, and in other directions, but every time they pointed it at Mecca, it flopped down again. Ad-Damîrî, however, is more concerned with what he thinks he has spotted as a blatant inaccuracy in this tale—to wit, that Abu can't lie on their haunches. Actually, they not only can, but customarily do so, which shows that he cannot have observed them firsthand.

He tells us also that in the decisive push against the Persians during the first Arab outburst, Rustam of the Persians advanced into the battle of al-Kâdisî-yah on a very fine Elephant, but that the Faithful slashed through its trunk with their long, curved sabers, so that it fell and was killed. Ad-Damîrî attributes the prompt collapse of the Persians to this event. He implies, however, that it was inevitable, anyhow, for various religious reasons, not the least being the regard in which the Prophet held the Elephant. And about this the Prophet seems to have been pretty definite. He forbade eating Abu because they have "canine teeth, or tusks, and were therefore carnivorous animals" (all wrong, of course). He did suggest that "elephant-racing" was permissible if not nearly divine, and that it was one of the few activities in which betting should be allowed. There is a *Chapter of the Elephant* (No. 105) in the Koran.

Ad-Damîrî also observes that in the year A.D. 690 (by our reckoning) a King of India named Yanarus, employing over 700 elephants, clashed with the Muslims. But it was the same old story—the elephants finally retreated upon their own forces. He also writes casually that an elephant was landed at Al-Basrah, in the Persian Gulf, in that same year and it created such a commotion, as nobody had ever seen one, that the whole community went to look at it. The place was modern Basra at the junction of the Tigris and Euphrates, and his statement as to the behavior of the populace once again points up the almost complete lack of popular knowledge of the Abu west of the Indus or north of the Sudan at that time. Finally, Ad-Damîrî observes, when classifying the results of dreaming about elephants, that "if a woman dreams of an elephant, it is not a good thing, in whatever state she dreams of it."

Of an altogether different ilk is the famous Muslim traveler and scholar Ibn Battúta. His astonishing chronicles of travels throughout central and far-eastern Asia, Southeast Asia, India, the Near East, North Africa, and across the Sahara to what is now Nigeria and Ghana, far surpass anything accomplished by even the Venetian Polos. His famous work, *Travels in Asia and Africa, 1325-1354* A.D., is a classic, and has happily been translated into all modern languages. Abu Abdullah Mohammed Ibn Battúta (1304-78), born in Tangiers, traveled some 75,000 miles in twenty-eight years all over the known world and far beyond its then known confines. He records for his chronicler, Mohammed Ibn Juzai, endless facts in a straightforward, lively manner which carry the utmost conviction. He mentions the use of work ele-

---

The upper end of the famous Copan (Mayan) stele, showing the alleged elephant's head and a mahout wearing a Syrian-type turban. (From A. P. Maudslay's plate in *Biologia Centrali-Americana*, 1882.)

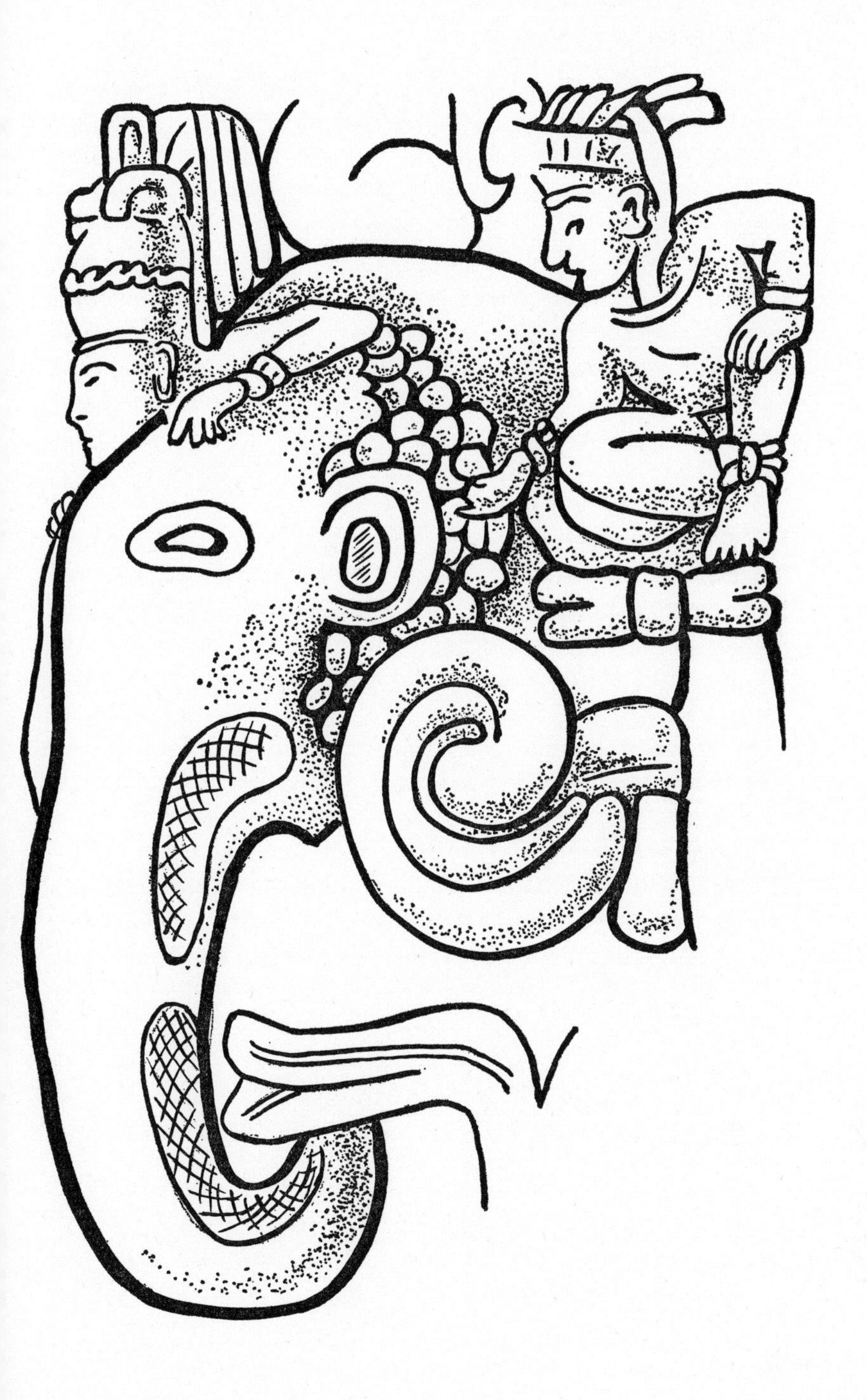

phants in India and the presence of loxodonts in Ghana.

Altogether, the Arab literati, many of whose works are still not translated, were an astonishing breed, and it is from them alone that we learn anything of the position of the Abu in the service of Man during this long, dismal period. But even they become silent about the end of the fourteenth century. Meantime, there were the first European records of some of these matters written by the Venetians, Nicolo, his brother Maffeo, and the son of Nicolo, Marco Polo. These are equally remarkable accounts also of almost as remarkable travels, which started with the brothers in the year A.D. 1250 and ended with Marco Polo's return to Italy in 1295. During this period these intrepid people somehow managed to travel right across central Asia, ingratiate themselves with the Great Khan of the Mongols then resident at what is now Peking, find employment with him, and travel all over his domains, and thence back home via Singapore and India. Marco Polo wrote a somewhat garbled account of all this while he was in prison later, but despite the sloppiness of his chronicle, he reveals a lot of fascinating sidelights on the life of the inhabitants of Asia and incidentally of Abu among them.

It is clear that at the time of his visit to Kanbalu, the capital of the Grand Khan, that potentate had a number of work elephants. Marco Polo speaks of "elephants" transporting trees complete with roots for planting on an ornamental hill in the palace grounds. He describes a parade of these beasts during the great annual festival, called the White Feast, when "on this day it is that all his elephants, amounting to five thousand, are exhibited in procession, covered with housings of cloth, fancifully and richly worked with gold and silk, in figures of birds and beasts. Each of these supports upon its shoulders two coffers filled with vessels of plate and other apparatus for the court." Kanbalu, now Peking, is at almost exactly the same degree of north latitude as New York, but it has an even viler climate because of the frigid prevailing winds that blow down off the Mongolian uplands in the winter, and the heat and dust that descend therefrom in the summer. Their elephants must therefore have been housed in heated stables for at least five months of the year.

Let us say that a work elephant eats, to be extremely conservative, 500 pounds of feed per day; then, 5,000 elephants must have consumed no less than 455,000 tons of fodder in a year. Such a quantity of food makes things look a bit exaggerated even for the Great Khan, more especially considering all the camels, horses, warriors, eunuchs, women, and waifs that he had to feed just to keep his ridiculous empire going. Then again, the average elephant is about 10 feet long, so that if 5,000 walked on parade even four abreast, all holding the tails of those in front, they would take up a space of 13,500 feet bumper to bumper, or about four miles. We fear, in fact, that like most of Marco Polo's statistics, this supercolossal picture is somewhat imaginary. One fact remains, nevertheless: the Great Khan had elephants.

When Marco Polo tells of the conquest, by the Great Khan, of the provinces that he calls Vochang and Mien, being probably Yunnan and Burma, he gives specific details of the encounter in which the Tartars first apparently met Abu. The Khan had sent an army into Vochang to "protect it," a grimly modern note. The King of Mien assembled an army containing numerous elephants with wooden castles on their backs, each castle holding up to sixteen warriors, and went off to try to block the invaders. The Tartar commander, Nestardin, wisely drew up his ranks between two blocks of tall forest so that his infantry could duck for cover should the elephants charge. And charge the elephants did, the Burmese King leading the attack himself and leaving his cavalry and infantry widely deployed behind him. The first sight of war elephants was too much for even the Mongolian ponies, which turned tail and bolted. But the intelligent Nestardin ordered his men to dismount, tie the horses in the forest, and then attack the elephants, on foot, with arrows. The Tartars pulled a much stronger bow than the Burmese and so kept out of range. They concentrated on the poor elephants, who soon resembled monstrous pincushions and started to give way. Soon the crazed animals were milling around among their own ranks or dashing into the forest, where the branches wiped the towers filled with soldiers off their backs. The Tartars then made short shrift of the unarmored Burmese, and took possession of over 200 elephants with their oozies; "after which," Marco Polo says, "the Grand Khan has always chosen to employ elephants in his armies."

During his prodigious wanderings, Marco Polo heard of two places in Africa, which he calls islands. These he names Madagascar and Zenzibar (sic). He obviously did not visit either personally, and his geography was considerably muddled. His descriptions of the first may *in part* have referred to Madagascar, but he says that it abounded in elephants, vast numbers of whose "teeth" were exported by the inhabitants. There are not now and never have been elephants in Madagascar, and his account seems to refer to the Mozambique coast. He also brings up the Rukh, a mythical bird shaped like an eagle but so large that it could, and customarily did, pick up elephants. This is another story, and an interesting one, for Madagascar was the home of the largest known flightless bird, now extinct, named the *Aepyornis.* It was definitely known to man, and laid two-and-a-half gallon eggs that are still sometimes found in sand banks. The other "island," named Zenzibar, is manifestly not our modern Zanzibar, as it is said by Marco Polo to lie "beyond" his Madagascar and "it is reported to be two thousand miles in circuit." He takes a dim view of its inhabitants, saying that "there are in this island the most ill-favoured women in the world," but goes on to note that "in this island elephants are found in vast numbers, and their teeth form an important article of trade." He adds that "with respect to these quadrupeds it should be observed that their mode of copulating is the reverse of that of the brute creation in general, in consequence of the position of the female organ, and follows that of the human species" (of course, quite wrong).

This "island" would also appear to have been a part of the East African mainland, for it is said to have contained also giraffes, "a handsome beast," and its inhabitants appear to have employed trained elephants in battle, for he says: "They have no horses but fight upon elephants and camels. On the backs of the former they place castles, capable of containing from fifteen to twenty men, armed with swords, lances, and stones, with which weapons they fight. Previously to the combat, they give draughts of wine to their elephants, supposing that it renders them more spirited and more furious in the assault."

This account is interesting in several respects. First, by the whole description, this place was definitely Africa; and, second, it must have been East Africa. Third, it was a dry part of that continent and not tall forest (i.e., not true equatorial, closed-canopy forest, or what is today called "jungle") but open country, or at least savanna, because camels cannot live in wet forest. Now, all the loxodonts tamed and trained by the Egyptians, Carthaginians, and others were apparently of the Forest variety, and there is considerable evidence attesting to this. We have no other record of the mighty Bush Loxodont ever being trained. Yet it must have been this animal, for the Forest race does not and cannot live out on the hot, dry savanna country where camels exist. Unless, therefore, the whole thing is pure fabrication, we have to add to our list of peoples who tamed elephants some Bantu or Hamitic people employing the great Bush Loxodont. This place, Zenzibar, is not Abyssinia, which was known to Marco Polo as "the Second, or Middle, India, also called Abascia." Forest Loxodonts still were found in that country in his time.

Despite all this talk about and description of elephants by travelers and others during the Dark Ages, we must understand that these animals and all *real* knowledge of them vanished utterly from the European world for a full thousand years, and that this black-out extended to northern Eurasia, the Near East, and even to Africa north of the Sahara. The citizens of Basra, Damascus, and even of Marrakesh, in Morocco, were just as ignorant of and filled with wonderment at seeing an elephant as were the Germans at the time of Charlemagne or the British in the reign of Henry the Third.

In fact, it is recorded that "the first elephant" was taken to Morocco in A.D. 1599; yet as late as A.D. 399 a Roman official reports that he observed a great host of them in a wild state in the central valley of that country. During the intervening 1,200 years their very existence had been completely forgotten.

[7]

OF THE REDISCOVERY OF THE BEASTS

The rebirth of Europe.

The expansion of the Portuguese.

The first contacts

with Africa and the Orient.

The rediscovery of the Elephant by the European world was a long and slow process extending over about 500 years. That of the loxodonts was abrupt and, although beginning in the fourteenth century, was not truly consummated until Equatorial Africa was penetrated by the Europeans themselves four centuries later. A dim memory of Abu lingered on in Europe from classical times but almost exclusively among the cloisters, where classical texts were preserved and read. That even the monastic scholars had any real concept of the creatures is, however, open to doubt, as the few crude effigies of them found in medieval tapestries, in some illuminated texts, and scattered in ecclesiastical architecture will demonstrate. It is really an astonishing fact that anything so big and peculiar should have been lost sight of for so long by the population of an entire subcontinent that had once known them so well. It is almost as if we should suddenly forget the existence of bulldozers for the next thousand years.

After the collapse of the Western Roman Empire, nothing is heard of Abu in Europe until the time of the Emperor Charlemagne, when—in the year A.D. 797, to be precise—the Caliph of Baghdad, the famous Haroun al Rachid, sent an elephant by the name of Abou Abbas to that monarch. It was landed in Italy and marched over the Alps *into Germany*, for some reason that is not recorded, and nothing further is heard of it. Then, 400 years later, in the year A.D. 1255, King Louis IX of France somehow acquired one, which he sent as a present to King Henry III of England, and that is all we know of that animal.

We are forced to presume that these two animals were true elephants from India and that they were passed along by the Arab potentates; it is fairly safe to assume also that their mahouts or oozies went along with them. It is also probable that they were given hay as bulk feed and also, being royal perquisites, a fairly wide variety of more fancy comestibles in the form of delicacies by people wishing to curry monarchic favor or by those responsible for the creature with a view to maintaining their jobs or their heads. Gifts en route to potentates were almost sacrosanct, and live ones were very important persons. There is no reason why elephants could not have lived and remained healthy in medieval Europe provided somebody was willing to pay the food bill. Elephants can work happily and healthily in snow, and, like almost all other animals—as progressive zoos have now discovered—they can tolerate a lot of cold if healthy, well fed, and kept away from contamination by humans.

As an art form also the Abu were lost sometime during

the fifth century, but in the eleventh and twelfth centuries they began to crop up again in French sculpture in churches. Some of these are very realistic. In a church at Aulnay-de-Saintonge, the populace is categorically informed: "*Hi sunt elephantes*"—"these are elephants." The sculptors must have had models to copy from in making these, and these may have been designs in Persian rugs and tapestries that were then quite commonly traded into Europe. Abu also sometimes appeared in illuminated manuscripts and as carvings in ivories, which were enormously popular and valuable in Europe and which filtered through to that continent from as far away as China. Thus, at a place named Andlau, in France, there are, among the small carvings at the heads of columns in the church, perfect little Indian Elephants fully and correctly caparisoned and with domed howdahs on their backs. At another place, named Saint Restitut, one carries a mahout wielding an elephant hook, and in several other places, pairs of little elephants facing each other may be seen with their trunks entwined. In fact, this is a fairly common motif. But most exceptional is a small effigy in a church at Souvigny which unmistakably shows a loxodont complete with sloping forehead, enormous ears, cross-ribbed trunk, and long, straight tusks. Where did a French sculptor get a model of an African loxodont at that time?

The account of Ibn Battúta's travels, which was written and composed in what is now Tangier, was immediately studied in both Spain and Portugal, countries that were not only adjacent to Ibn Battúta's homeland but that had a long and intimate liaison with the Arab world, having been subject to it for a considerable time. Also, there was a growing interest at that time, and particularly in Portugal, in the activities of the Arab explorers, and an almost overwhelming fascination with the expositions of such classical Greek and Roman writers as Aristotle and Pliny. As late as 1481 the peoples' procurators were still citing Aristotle's *Politics* in the Portuguese parliament. This interest in the classics was both intellectual and pragmatic, for while the Portuguese were much concerned with what the ancients had to say about the conduct of human affairs, they were especially intrigued by what they had to report about the Oriental world. From a geographical point of view, Portugal is literally out on a limb. Culturally speaking, she was also isolated generally by the xenophobic Arab world to the southeast and she was cut off from the main stream of reviving European culture which revolved around France by the haughty, self-centered Spaniards.

Little Portugal, unlike cold upland and arid Spain, is a mellow land inhabited by people of most ancient lineage. They are a coastal race and have been seamen since time immemorial. Their interests lay westward into the ocean, first for fish and other food, and then for commerce. They had long treatied with the Basques, the Bretons, and the English. Yet, their travels had been confined to the seaward scope of their ships, which, though rugged, were small. Galleys that relied mostly on oars were developed in the closed Mediterranean Sea and were not a success in the Atlantic, though the Basques adopted them for a time. It was the development—and possibly by the Basques—of a type of sailing vessel known generally as a caravel which set the peoples of the western European Atlantic fringe free to roam offshore. Following the Basques, Portuguese fishermen were sailing far and wide upon the open Atlantic by the end of the fourteenth century.

It was at this time that a very remarkable man was born to the royal line of Portugal, who, unusually for those days, abdicated all his hereditary prerogatives and virtually locked himself away to devote his life to study. His interests were in exploration, and although he never went on any of the trips he mapped out, he became known to posterity as Henry the Navigator. He began by studying the reports of travelers since the earliest records, and he collected maps:

also, he for the first time came to grips with the technical problems of oceanic and global navigation.

The earliest mention of the compass in Europe is probably that to be found in the writings of one Alexander Nesham of St. Albans, in England, and is dated A.D. 1150. The instrument is often said to have been known to the Chinese many centuries earlier, but then, when there has been a doubt about the origin of anything novel or notable, there has always been a tendency in the West to assign its discovery to the Chinese. There is some evidence that the Norse knew of magnetic iron and lodestones, and the fact that certain elongated objects made of special materials always pointed one of their ends to the region of perpetual cold, which they learned only later to call the North. Navigation in the ancient world and throughout the Dark and Middle Ages had, nonetheless, been carried on exclusively by a form of dead-reckoning, using the position of the sun by day and the stars by night, and relying very heavily on the known or believed positions of coasts. In the Mediterranean it did not matter much where you sailed as long as you kept going more or less in a straight line, for you sooner or later had to make land. In the Indian Ocean, navigators had the utterly reliable monsoon winds to follow; these blow more or less from northeast to southwest at one time of the year and from southwest to northeast at the other. The Chinese were coast-hoppers. Only the Norse, on their Viking expeditions, appear to have gone boldly out into the great oceans. But if you look at their route across the North Atlantic from the point of their origin, putting Denmark at the bottom and Greenland at the top of the map, you will see that all they really did was to go island-hopping straight ahead via the Orkney and Shetland islands to the Faröes, to Iceland, to East Greenland, and thence, it would now appear, on to the coast of Labrador and perhaps southwest along the coast of North America. The only other open-ocean navigators of the ancient world were the Dravidian Indians of the second millennium B.C., who crossed the Bay of Bengal directly to Indonesia in ships large enough to carry several hundred persons.

Still, the world as a whole, and apart from the incredible Polynesians of the Pacific, had not contemplated true oceanic navigation until Prince Henry of Portugal set about investigating its possibility 500 years ago. Just how much residual knowledge of the oceans he gleaned from perusal of ancient texts and maps we will never know, for much of his source material appears to have been lost forever. It is possible that he stumbled upon and believed in accounts of the wanderings of Phoenicians and Greeks around Africa and to South America. His interests were first almost purely scientific in that he wished to ascertain just how both latitude and longitude and thus true position could be found when on the open ocean. But he always kept an eye on the practical applications of his investigations and devoted much time to encouraging ship-building, the training of master mariners, and the promotion of interest in his country in the discovery of a southern route around Africa to the Orient. And he soon began to get results, for Portuguese ships under royal auspices began to sail outward along the old sea lanes of the humble unsponsored fisherfolk.

The Portuguese did not go directly out into the open ocean. Rather, they followed the known offshore routes, discovering first the island of Madeira, then the Canaries, and next the Cape Verdes. They then pressed on around the bulge of West Africa and along its seemingly endless coast toward the mouth of the Niger and the Island of Fernando Po. The going became ever tougher in this direction because the southeast trade winds blow perpetually on to this coast from the south, and the current that sweeps into this great bight from the South Atlantic finally turns seaward and is replaced by a powerful oceanic river known as the Benguella Current, which runs north and then west straight into the

Gulf of Guinea. The Portuguese ships were of about 200 tons burthen and carried three lateen sails so that they could sail closer to the wind than square-riggers, but still, a combination of a beam wind and a head-on current completely defeated them. Thus, very early, the Portuguese captains took advantage of the west-flowing north-equatorial current and the northeast trades that carried them toward Brazil; then they worked their way south through the horse latitudes off the east coast of South America until they picked up the southern westerlies. These carried them to and around the Cape of Good Hope, and into the Indian Ocean.

The progress of this vast expansion by the Portuguese was amazingly rapid. In 1418 two of Henry's captains discovered Madeira; in 1445 Captain Diniz Diaz reached the Cape Verdes; in 1458 Diego Gómez, on the last of Henry's promoted voyages, reached the Rio Grande. Henry died in 1460, but when his brother, King John II, ascended the throne in 1481, exploration was greatly stimulated. Bartholomeu Diaz reached the Gold Coast in 1483 and ten years later first rounded the Cape. By 1498 Vasco da Gama reached India. Cabral failed to follow in 1500, but hit Brazil instead, only to learn later that Pinzon had already been there. By 1520, or within just 100 years, the Portuguese had expanded Europe to the Pacific both by the east and by the west. There has never been any other exploratory outburst to equal this achievement.

At the beginning of the fifteenth century everybody—Europeans and Arabs alike—held the most extraordinary ideas about the Nile. Pliny had said that the Niger was a branch of it, and as this river flows east through Timbuktu, this seemed possible. When Henry's captain, Azurara, reached the mouth of the Senegal River in 1450, however, he proclaimed that he had discovered the source of the Nile! The original record is very bizarre. The company saw what they thought was a shoal off the coast and took soundings, but a man happened to lick his hand, which was wet from the sounding-line, and found that the water was fresh. They immediately lowered a bucket, and when they found this to be a fact, "Surely," they said, "we are near the river Nile, for this water seems to be the water of that river; its current, which is very strong, cuts through the sea in just such a manner." The logic of our ancestors of even five centuries ago is sometimes very hard to comprehend. Did these intrepid explorers really think they had rounded Africa and somehow jumped over the Isthmus of Suez into the Mediterranean at the delta of the Nile? Or did they imagine that the Nile was a vast river-complex that flowed outward to the oceans in all different directions at once?

Having found the source of this fresh water, they put ashore seven men under Don Estavam Affonso. This party found in a hut a naked youth carrying a spear, and, on searching the hut, came upon a large buckler made of tremendously thick leather from which a central boss had been carved just as if the material were wood. This greatly mystified the men, and they took the object with them. Later, it is stated, when they got to the Guinea Coast, the natives told them that it was made from an "elephant's" ear and that most bucklers in that country were so constructed. Also, Azurara adds: "The same Negroes say further that the elephants are so great that their flesh will suffice to satisfy five hundred men, and that they find it very good, and that the 'bones' are not utilized in any manner, and are even thrown away. But I have learned that in the Levant,[1] on the Mediterranean coast, the bones[2] of one of these

[1] I.e., the Syria-Lebanon-Palestine-Gaza Coast.
[2] I.e., ivory.

Cavemen attacking an Elephant. (From an engraving by Johann Straet [Stradamus] in *Venationes, circa* A.D. 1500.)

beasts are currently worth a thousand dobras." Azurara was aware of the existence of the ivory trade maintained by the Arabs from the Orient and from East Africa to the Palestine coast of the Mediterranean via Cairo. But he was still under the impression that ivory was elephant bone. This notion persisted until Da Gama reached India.

Ivory has played a disproportionate part in history, and it is therefore intriguing to note that Bartholomeu Diaz was, in A.D. 1478, granted exemption from all taxes on the importation of all ivory that he brought from the Guinea Coast. Within forty years, therefore, of the Portuguese attaining to the western tip of the African forest belt, and despite the fact that they had never traded in ivory and were vague as to what part of an Abu it came from, and even more surprisingly in view of the fact that the natives of that coast did not value the material, regular importation into Europe had already been established.

The natives, as a matter of fact, were highly suspicious of the whole business, as they could not fathom the almost wild desire for ivory on the part of these foreigners. In answer to their inquiries, they were told by the Portuguese that the material was wanted for the manufacture of small artifacts like sword handles and so forth, but this the natives never believed, for they could not understand why the white man did not simply use wood. To them it was plain that the material must have great value in Europe, and they assumed that they were somehow being cheated.[3] Once the Portuguese had rounded the Cape, their fleets immediately penetrated to the farthest ports bordering the Arabian Sea

[3] I personally encountered a similar situation when collecting zoological specimens. I learned, to my astonishment, that certain locals believed either that I brought the animals, preserved in alcohol or formalin, back to life when I got home or that my countrymen considered pickled lizards, frogs, rats, and other small fry to be expensive table delicacies. The matter was resolved only when I adopted the practice of explaining that I wanted the little beasts for medical or "doctor work." And, believe it or not, this is just the explanation that the Portuguese gave to the natives of the kingdom of Ba'Kongo for their need for ivory.

and the Bay of Bengal. Then they rapidly pushed on into the maze of the Indonesian Islands and up to the China coast. They also doubled back along the East African coast and, by the beginning of the sixteenth century, entered the Red Sea from the south.

Almost everywhere they touched land throughout this vast area they immediately encountered Abu. The Arabs had long since filtered down the East African coast and established colonies as far south as Madagascar, which they practically controlled. They sent armed expeditions inland to collect slaves, ivory, and other desired commodities. This produce they freighted north into and up the Red Sea to the Isthmus of Suez, where they channeled it through Cairo. Raw ivory went to the Levant and also direct to Europe. They also carried on a vast trade with India, Ceylon, and the Malayan countries, and from there came the ivory of the elephant. However, the tusks of the loxodonts were always preferred to those of the Elephant because of their finer grain and much larger average size.

There was one country in which the Arabs had made no headway, however, and this was the ancient mountainous kingdom of Abassia, or, as we call it, Abyssinia or Ethiopia. Its rulers and paramount people were Christians, and they had warred upon and often subdued the original south-Arabian homelands of the Arabs since before the time of the Prophet. They took a dim view of the rise of Islam, and they welcomed the sudden and unexpected arrival of the Portuguese Christians from out of the southern ocean. There is a most delightful manuscript entitled *The History of Eastern Ethiopia* written by the Reverend Father João dos Santos, of the Order of St. Domingo, and published in Paris. This contains a *Succinct Relation of the Most Curious and Remarkable Production of the Country*, and its first chapter is entitled: "Of the Three Divisions of the World, and the Fourth Added to These by Don Emmanuel, King of Portugal." Emmanuel succeeded John II on the throne in 1495.

Father dos Santos, "learning the praiseworthy design of His Portuguese Majesty (to send out an expedition under Pedro de Naya to 'effect settlements' and 'to toil in the vineyard of the Lord'), offered to sail with the fleet, and take charge of the ghostly health of his troops, administer the sacraments to them during their long voyage, and stimulate them to fight with ardour for the glory of God and the aggrandisement of the Portuguese throne and nation." The expedition landed in 1506 at Abassia, where the perspicacious Father delved mightily into the nature of the country and the habits of its people. He happily has a lot to say about the Abu (actually Bush Loxodonts), which goes as follows: "The number of elephants in this country is prodigious, so much so indeed that the inhabitants are obliged to pursue and make frequent hunting courses after them, to preserve from their ravage the lands they sow with rice and millet, in which lands these animals generally commit great waste; when, however, the chase is inadequate to the sufficient reduction of the elephants, snares are made for them, after the same manner as in different parts of the Continent is done for wolves; when a Caffre[4] discovers that an elephant has fallen into his toils, he assembles his friends and relatives, that they may partake of the sport and consequent feast.

"Had not the Caffres the inducement for pursuing the elephant, which arises from the necessity of protecting their property, they would yet have sufficient in the benefit they derive from their capture, seeing its flesh serves them for food, and its teeth are an object of considerable traffic. Indeed with them the elephant is esteemed of great value; so much, that one being obtained *perfectly white,* many princes of the surrounding country waged war for the possession of the valuable animal; but it was ultimately adjudged to the lord of the soil on which it was taken, as a manorial right.

[4] Early form of "Kaffir," meaning literally a (black) coffee-colored person.

"The Caffres, aware of the risk incurred in hunting elephants, endeavour commonly to come upon them when they sleep, which they are enabled to do on account of their discovering themselves by their snoring so loud as to be heard all over the country; when, getting as near to them as they are able, they lance a javelin into their body; this awakening them, occasions, in proportion to their agitation, a less or greater effusion of blood, and oftentimes their death; for they frequently fall upon the javelin, which in consequence is plunged deeper into their bodies. Many authors describe a different mode of taking this animal: according to these, the elephant after it has passed three years old never lies down to sleep, but leans in taking repose against a tree, the trunk of which at this time is cut near the root, and the tree in falling encumbers and kills the elephant. Were such the truth, ivory would be still dearer than it is, and far more rare; for the danger of this mode of hunting would deter many who now pursue the animal in view of enriching themselves with its spoils.

"Two Caffres happening once to wound as many elephants but very slightly, were, on account of the fall of night, unable to follow the trace of them; the next day they returned to the chase in hopes of finding them dead; but their wounds not being considerable, they had traversed a great distance, and were tracked by their blood: the hunters at length discovered them, one of these elephants had gone into a river, and with its trunk was throwing water over the other, this was lying on the bank, and in consequence the huntsmen concluded it was dead. Approaching now somewhat nearer than was prudent, to the living one in the water, this elephant seized one of the two hunters with his trunk, and cast him with such violence on the body of the dead elephant as to deprive him of life, thus avenging the death of his comrade by that of the person by whom it was occasioned.

"It is related, that at Goa, a capital city in the Indies,[5] there was an elephant nick-named Perico (or, The Sot) on account of its predilection for wine. It was accustomed to halt before the door of the different taverns, and never quit its station until a quantity of wine was poured into its trunk; and if, which sometimes happened, any one out of joke gave it money, it carried it to the best tavern, and readily distinguished bad from good wine; so that indeed those who frequented these wine houses, were used always to ask for the elephant's wine."

History is full of very similar anecdotes both prior to the date that this was written—indeed, since the time of Herodotus—and afterward, up until the present century. The account is, however, particularly interesting to us for several reasons. First, its date, which shows that the loxodonts were rediscovered just as early as, if not earlier than, the Elephant. Second, the countries in which these incidents were recorded as having taken place—particularly the reference to Goa. Third, the mention of a white, or albino, loxodont, a rarity indeed, even if it was only a semi-albino. It is, in fact, the only direct statement I know of such a thing, whether it be true or imaginary.

In Africa, loxodonts are hardly, if ever, to be seen on any beach or near a coast, and it was to be many years after the discovery of the mouth of the Senegal River by the Portuguese before white men penetrated any real distance inland into that vast continent and actually met or saw live loxo-

[5] Goa, on the west coast of Peninsular India, was a Portuguese enclave up to 1962.

An elephant bearing a tower on its back. (From an engraving made in the seventeenth century, illustrating celebrations held for Henry II of France, in Rouen, in 1550.)

donts.[6] All that Europeans saw or knew of them were the accounts of the natives and of Arab traders, and the mountains of ivory that piled up at the coastal ports. In the Orient, matters were entirely different. The most piffling raja, let alone the magnificent maharajas, kept both work and display elephants. The former were used as combined cranes, lifts, drays, and shuttle engines on docks; they plowed fields, hauled heavy freight, and helped build houses: the latter marched in parades, carried the wealthy about town, and took both professional hunters and sportsmen into the field. They were kept in enormous numbers, and they were everywhere from the ports of arid Sind, where they were maintained on food inported from the more verdant south, all around India, Bengal, Burma, Malaya, Indochina, and even north into southern China. All inland states north to the barrier of the Himalayas and the mountains of inner Szechwan employed elephants in great numbers, and they were even in use in Java and in a few coastal areas in Sumatra and Borneo at that time. This made a great impression on the Portuguese, and although they were much more interested in the other riches of the Oriental countries, they repeatedly allude to elephants. The Portuguese speak of the work the elephants did, of their eminence in the economy of these states, and, above all, of their incredible sagacity, which to these people far surpassed that of any other mere beast.

These animals seem to have stirred even more greatly the emotions of the less volatile peoples who followed the Portuguese to the Orient. The Hollanders and the British, despite their reputation for unimpressionability, seem to have been generally much more excited and considerably less objective about what they encountered in the Far East. Perhaps it was because they had less first-hand knowledge of the gaudy magnificence of the Near East, that they were more profoundly impressed by what they saw. Even

[6] In the sixteenth century the Portuguese established a Bishopric in what is now the Congo and recorded wild "elephants" there.

throughout the Dark and Middle Ages life had remained rather elegant, if unprogressive, in the Mediterranean world; in northern Europe it had been rugged and dour, and several hundred elephants caparisoned in cloths of gold, parading for some petty potentate, both astonished and shocked these pragmatic people.

After the initial flurry of Portuguese expansion, our history books concern themselves for some decades almost exclusively with the exploits of the Spaniards in the New World. As there were no Abu in that hemisphere, the Spaniards thus have nothing to contribute to our story. It remained for the Hollanders and the British to pick up the eastward expansion where the Portuguese left off, and this they began to do in earnest at the end of the sixteenth century. Although they had made some tentative forays into the Orient before, it was not till the year 1580 that they became active.

OF POMP AND CIRCUMSTANCES

Abu in the service of the courts

and potentates of the Orient.

The coming of

the British and the Dutch.

After the arrival of the Portuguese in the Orient, the entire homeland of the Elephant except Siam was gradually taken over by Europeans. This homeland reached from Sind in the west to Yunnan in the east and from the Himalaya-Sikang mountains in the north to Ceylon, Java, and Borneo in the south. Domesticated elephants were kept throughout this area, but even then there were already within its confines considerable tracts of country too dry for their maintenance and large areas of wilderness and uninhabited territory where they lived only wild. There were also many "islands" where they were not found at all.

The Europeans at first stood in some awe of domestic elephants and left them completely to their native owners. They abolished staged elephant fights and the killing of humans by elephants. They also made tentative moves toward regulating their capture and handling, but more from economic than from humanitarian motives, and they immediately started slapping ownership taxes on the possessors of elephants. They also made it known, though unofficially, that capturing and killing wild elephants was to be considered their prerogative though not *exclusively* the right of the Raj, or Colonial government. The Portuguese, French, and Hollanders went no further than this and, in fact, seem soon to have lost both their awe and interest in the beasts. They tolerated but did not encourage ownership of the animals, and, although handling ivory like any other trade goods, they otherwise ignored them. Not so the British.

During the years 1583-91, one Ralph Fitch, an Englishman, traveled back and forth about the Bay of Bengal. He is highly illuminating in his account of the then royal city of Dala, now a part of Rangoon, in Burma, where he notes that there were eighteen or twenty very great and long houses where the king's elephants were kept and trained. He says that there were many wild elephants in the adjacent countryside, and then goes on to record that "within the first gate of the king's house is a great large room [i.e., courtyard] on both sides whereof are houses made for the king's elephants, which be marvellous great and faire, and are brought up to warres and in service of the king. And among the rest he hath foure white elephants which are very strange and rare; for there is no other king which hath them but he; if any other king hath one, he will send unto him for it. When any of these white elephants is brought unto the king, all the merchants in the city are commanded to see them, and to give him a present of halfe a ducat, which doth come to a great summe, for that there are many merchants in the city. After that you have given your present you may come and see them at your pleasure although they stand in the king's house. The king in his title is called the king of the white elephants. If any other king have one, and will not send it to him, he will make warre with him for it; for he had rather lose a great part of his kingdom than not to conquer him. They do very great service unto these white elephants; every one of them standeth in an house gilded with golde, and they doe feede in vessels of silver and gilt. One of them when he doth go to the river to be washed, as every day they do, goeth under a canopy of cloth of golde or of silke carried over him by sixe or eight men, and eight or ten men goe before him playing on drummes, shawmes, or other instruments; and when he is washed and commeth out of the river, there is a gentleman which doth wash his feet in a silver basin; which is his office given him by the king. There is no such account made of any blacke elephant, be he never so great. And surely they be woonderfull faire and great, and some be nine cubites in height. And they do report that the king hath above five thousand elephants of warre, besides many other which be not taught to fight.

"This king hath a very large place wherein he taketh the wilde elephants. It standeth about a mile from Pegu, builded with a faire court within, and is in a great grove or wood; and there be many huntsmen, which go into the wilderness with she elephants, for without the she they are not to be taken. And they be taught for that purpose, and every hunter hath five or sixe of them; and they say that they anoint the she elephants with a certaine ointment, which when the wild elephant doth smell, he will not leave her. When they have brought the wilde elephant neere unto the place, they send word unto the towne, and enter into a strait way which doeth goe to the palace, and the she and he do runne in, for it is like a wood; and when they be in, the gate doth shut. Afterward they get out the female; and when the male seeth that he is left alone, he weepeth and crieth, and runneth against the walles, which be made of so strong trees that some of them doe breake their teeth with running against them. Then they pricke him sharpe canes, and cause him to go into a strait house, and there they put a rope about his middle and about his feet, and let him stand there three or foure days without eating or drinking; and then they bring a female to him, with meat and drinke, and within few dayes he becommeth tame. The chiefe force of the king is in these elephants. And when they go into the warres they set a frame of wood upon their backes, bound with great cordes, wherein sit foure or sixe men, which fight with gunnes, bowes and arrowes, darts and other weapons. And they say that their skinnes are so thicke that a pellet of an harquebush will scarce pearce them, except it be in some tender place. Their weapons be very badde. They have gunnes, but shoot very badly in them; darts and swords short without points."

It will become abundantly clear that the connotation we place on a "white elephant" is markedly inaccurate. Such a creature has always commanded a tremendous price, and anyone who caught an example had quite a choice of kingdoms to which to take it, where he would be handsomely recompensed and even fawned upon. You could even start wars with white elephants. Moreover, the cost of upkeep is no greater than that of a normal-colored specimen, and there is no evidence that they are any weaker than other elephants.

Fitch also wandered into Siam via the Mekong River, and notes that there were "many wild buffes[1] and elephants." He also visited Ceylon, which, he remarked, is "a brave iland, very fruitful and faire; . . . the elephants be

[1] Buffalo.

not so great as those of Pegu, which be monstrous huge; but they say all other elephants do feare them, and none dare fight with them, though they be very small."

The most luxurious kingdom in the Orient was then that of the Great Mogul, who was paramount on continental India. A certain Captain William Hawkins, who penned *His Relations of the Occurrents which happened in the Time of His Residence in India, in the County of the Great Mogul, and of his Departure from Thence,* which was addressed to the East India Company, describes life at the court of this potentate and relates: "Of Elephants there bee twelve thousand of shee ones, and yong ones, which are twelve thousand. His daily expense for his owne person, that is to say, for feeding his Cattall of all sorts, and amongst them some few Elephants Royall, and all other expences particularly, as Apparell, Victual, and other petty expenses for his house amounts to fiftie thousand Rupias a day. He hath three hundred Elephants Royall, which are Elephants whereon himselfe rideth: and when they are brought before him, they come with great iollitie, having some twentie or thirtie men before them with small Stremers. The Elephants Cloth or Couering is very rich, eyther of Cloth of Gold, or rich Veluet: hee hath following him his shee Elephant, his Whelpe or Whelpes, and foure or fiue yong ones, as Pages, which will be in number some sixe, some seuen, and some eight or nine."

Thus, the Great Mogul could qualify for the Grand Khan class in the matter of elephants, if not in territory or concubines. And as to this, Hawkins remarks in another version of his report that "the expences daily for his women by the day is thirtie thousand rupias," but John Jourdain, who was in the country with Hawkins, says: "It was crediblie reported to Captaine Hawkins in my presence by the king's Purveyor for his beasts, that every daie in the yeare he spent in meat for them 70,000 ripeas, which is 35,000 rialls of eight. His wives, there slaves, and his concubines doe spend him an infinite deale of money, incredible to bee believed, and therefore I omitt itt!" The cost to the Mogul is thus considerably augmented even if we presume the quaint expression "meats" to include vegetable fodder as well as flesh for hunting-cheetahs and other carnivores. These complacent Britishers, like the bourgeois Hollanders, were profoundly shocked at the extravagances of the Oriental potentates and often quite lost control of their emotions—as well as their spelling, it seems—when reporting on them.

William Hawkins gives us one of the best pictures of the status of elephants in India in the early seventeenth century and of their relations with the human populace:

"This king is thought to be the greatest emperour of the East for wealth, land, and force of men, as also for horses, elephants, camels, and dromedaries. As for elephants of his owne and of his nobles, there are fortie thousand, of which the one halfe are trayned elephants for the warre; and these elephants of all beasts are the most understanding. I thought good here to set downe this one thing, which was reported to me for a certainty, although it seemed very strange. An elephant having journyed very hard, being on his travell, was misused by his commander; and one day finding the fellow asleepe by him, but out of his reach, having greene canes brought him to eate, split the end of one of them with his teeth, and taking the other end of the cane with his snout, reached it toward the head of the fellow, who being fast asleepe and his turbant fallen from his head (the use of India being to wear their haire long like women) he tooke hold with the cane on his haire, wreathing it therein and withall haling him unto him untill he brought him within the compasse of his snowt; he then presently killed him. Many other strange things are done by elephants. My selfe, in the time that I was one of his courtiers, have seene many cruell deeds done by him. Five times a weeke he commaundeth his brave elephants to fight before him; and in the time of their fighting, either comming or going out, many times men are killed or dangerously hurt by these elephants."

The Great Mogul was not a pleasant person, but then, almost nobody had any compassion for man or beast until this century. Elephants are nonaggressive creatures, but they can be trained to commit mayhem on command, and in this practice the Indians succeeded where the bloodthirsty Romans appear on the whole to have failed. Some of the gory details are well recorded by one Edward Terry, who was at the Mogul's court from 1616 to 1619. His account is very illuminating:

"They have many elephants; the King for his owne particular being master of fourteene thousand, and his nobles and all men of qualitie in the countrey have more or lesse of them, some to the number of one hundred. The elephants, though they bee the largest of all creatures the earth brings forth, yet are so tractable (unlesse at times when they are mad) that a little boy is able to rule the biggest of them. Some of them I have seene thirteene foot high; but there are amongst them (as I have beene often told) fifteene at the least. The colour of them all is black; their skins thick and smooth without haire. They take much delight to bathe themselves in water, and swim better than any beast I know. They lye downe and arise againe at pleasure, as other beasts doe. Their pace is not swift, about three mile an houre; but of all beasts in the world are most sure of foot, for they never fall nor stumble to endanger their rider. They are most docile creatures and of all those we account meerely sensible, come neerest unto reason.

From an aquatint (copied in the early 1880's) from Bernier's *Voyage* (1679), showing the Cortege of the Grand Mogul *en passage* in India.

"Some elephants the King keeps for execution of malefactors; who being brought to suffer death by that mightie beast, if his keeper bid him dispatch the offender speedily, will presently with his foot pash him into pieces; if otherwise he would have him tortured, this vast creature will breake his joynts by degrees one after the other, as men are broken upon the wheele.

"The Mogol takes much delight in those stately creatures, and therefore oft when hee sets forth in his majestie calls for them, especially the fairest; who are taught to bend to him as it were in reverence, when they first come into his presence. They often fight before him, beginning their combat like rams, by running fiercely one at the other; after, as boares with their tusks, they fight with their teeth and trunks. In this violent opposition they are each so carefull to preserve his rider, as that very few of them at those times receive hurt. They are governed with an hook of steele, made like the iron end of a boat-hook, with which their keepers, sitting on their neckes, put them back or pricke them forward at their pleasure. The King traines up many of his elephants for the warre; who carrie each of them one iron gunne about sixe foot long, lying upon a square strong frame of wood, fastned with girts or ropes upon him, which like an harquebuse is let into the timber with a loop of iron. At the foure corners of this frame are banners of silke, put upon short poles; within sits a gunner to make his shot according to his occasion. The peece carrieth a bullet about the bignesse of a little tennis-ball. When the King travels, he hath many elephants thus appointed for guard. Hee keeps many of them for state to goe before him, who are adorned with bosses of brasse, and some of them are made of massive silver or gold, having likewise divers bells about him, in which they delight. They have faire coverings, either of cloth or velvet or cloth of silver or gold; and for greater state, banners of silke carried before them, in which is the ensigne of their great king (a lion in the sunne) imprinted.

These are allowed each three or foure men at the least, to waite upon them. Hee makes use of others to carrie himselfe or his women, who sit in pretie convenient receptacles fastned on their backes (which our painters describe like to castles), made of slight turn'd pillars, richly covered, that will hold foure sitters. Others he employes for carriage of his necessaries. Onely he hath one faire elephant, which is content to be fettered, but would never indure man or other burthen on his backe.

"These vast beasts, though the countrey be very fruitfull and all provision cheape, yet by reason of their huge bulke are very chargeable in keeping; for such as are well fed stand their masters in foure or five shillings each of them the day. They are kept without doores, where by a sollid chaine upon one of their hind legges they fasten them to a tree or some strong post. As they stand in the sunne, the flyes often vex them; wherefore with their feete they make dust, the ground being very dry, and with their truncks cast it about their bodies to drive away the flyes. Whenas they are mad (as usually the males are once a yeare for their females, when they are lustie, but in few dayes after come againe in temper), they are so mischievous that they will strike any thing (but their keeper) that comes in their way; and their strength is such as that they will beate an horse or camell dead with their truncke at one blow. At these times, to prevent mischiefe, they are kept apart from company, fettered with chaines. But if by chance in their phrensie they get loose, they will make after every thing they see stirre; in which case there is no meanes to stop them in their violent course but by lighting of wild-fire, prepared for that purpose, whose sparkling and cracking makes them stand still and tremble. The King allowes every one of his great elephants foure females, which in their language they call wives. The males testicles lye about his fore-head; the females teates are betwixt her fore-legges. Shee carrieth her young one whole yeare ere she bring it forth. Thirtie yeares xpire ere they come to their full growth, and they fulfill the accustomed age of man ere they dye. Notwithstanding the great plentie of them, they are valued there at exceeding great rates; some of them prized at one thousand pounds sterling and more.

"An English merchant of good credit upon his owne knowledge reported this of a great elephant in Adsmeere (the place then of the Mogols residence), who being brought often through the bazar or market place, a woman who sate there to sell herbs was wont usually to give him a handfull as he passed by. This elephant afterward, being mad, brake his fetters and tooke his way through the market place. The people, all affrighted, made haste to secure themselves amongst whom was this herbe-woman, who (for feare and haste) forgat her little child. The elephant, come to the place where shee usually sate, stopt, and seeing a child lie about her herbs, took it up gently with his trunke, not doing it the least harme, and layed it upon a stall under a house not farre off: and then proceeded in his furious course."

This account is a delightful blend of straight reporting and dubious hearsay and should be taken with the proverbial amount of salt, but it gives a very clear picture of the state of affairs in India before the British moved in. This infiltration, which was by no means an outright conquest, brought many changes in the lives of both elephants and men, and it was the existence of elephants that predicated not a little further conquest and annexation, for the British quickly noted that these animals were essential to the exploitation of a most valuable product: namely, teakwood.

There are many things about the Elephant which particularly intrigue the British, and especially the English. Perhaps basically it is psychological, for the two certainly seem to have some aspects of character in common. More important, though, the Elephant has many traits the Englishman greatly admires and is often at pains to emulate.

It displays a certain calm magnificence that is exactly the ideal of the Englishman, and along with this it shows a considerable condescension to all other creatures. Elephants make good mothers, and their menfolk are aloof, practical, and sometimes rather roguish. They tend to be very brave in a stubborn, unreasonable sort of way, and they certainly understand discipline. Except when in *musth,* they are rather placid about everything. All of this the English appreciated, though it never stopped them from hunting the Elephant for sport. But the English, and in this the ubiquitous Scots also joined most heartily, noted above all that the Elephant was a magnificent machine that ran on low-cost fuel and that could perform works of a nature that neither man nor any other animal and no machine known at that time could accomplish. Also, there was the all-pervading question of wood. This was not only a matter of importance; it was almost *the* matter of importance to the British just then.

Since late Neolithic times the peninsular-insular peoples of the western fringe of Europe had been ship-building, and one and all, from the pre-Norse inhabitants of Scandinavia to the Portuguese, had employed the wood of a certain closely related group of trees—the oaks. Other woods were also employed for planking, finishing, and other specialized purposes, but when it came to laying down the frame of a ship, and, in larger boats, providing the planking, European shipbuilders chose oak and heart oak, if possible. Oaks are slow-growing; however, little seedlings were carefully bent and tied over to grow in all manner of natural curves so that one day, when they were old enough, they might be cut and with a minimum of shaping be used as naturally curved timbers for shipbuilding. The strength of a naturally curved oak timber compared to one adzed from a straight trunk is almost unbelievable to those not acquainted with shipbuilding. Then there was another characteristic of oakwood which was of primary concern to the shipwrights.

Every kind of wood has what is called a different coefficient of expansion in water. That is to say, if you put a number of logs—cut from different kinds of trees, all equally seasoned, and all cut to exactly the same length—into the same water bath at the same time, all will absorb water and expand and thus increase in length, but each to a different extent. This fact is of ultimate importance in boat-building because boats are necessarily built in the air and of dry lumber. If you mix up planks of various different woods in sheathing a boat, caulk it well, and then launch it, all sorts of dire things may happen. Some of the planks may swell more than the others, and, if butted, may have no place to go and so bulge outward, drawing your best-placed nails or trunnels.[2] Others that expand too little may actually appear to draw back from their neighbors, thus loosening the caulking and creating leaks. I have seen mis-selected decks on new yachts rise up like waves on a lake after a rainstorm, and I have seen newly engraved boats fill and sink the first night off the slips because of foolish or dishonest workmanship in the yard. As all ships were built of wood up till the nineteenth century, and as the ship worm (or *Teredo*) and other wood-boring molluscs were just as active then as now, and as the ships of the Europeans took years to make worthwhile round trips to far places, repair work had to be done away from their home ports and with "foreign" wood. If that wood did not have *exactly* the same coefficient of expansion as the original material, the ships were doomed to fall apart and sink.

Few tropical woods matched the European and especially the English oak. Of those that did match, most were so dense that they sank even when dry, and this made it almost impossible to get them out of the forests and down to the coast in sufficient volume, because the only way to move lumber in tall forest is to float it down rivers. Only two kinds of woods which would float and which grew in suitable form

[2] I.e., "tree nails," or slightly tapering wooden pegs, as used in olden days.

were found in sufficient quantity. These were Central American mahogany (*Swietenia macrophylla*) and Burmese teak (*Tectona grandis*).

The expression "suitable form" needs explanation. The same species of tree may grow in a wide variety of physical environments ranging from hot moist to cool moist, and hot dry to cool dry, and so forth, and in most cases—particularly in mahogany—the texture of the wood will vary from very light, porous, and even pithy to close-grained, rigid, and dense. Heart oak is very rigid and dense; therefore, it was essential to the maritime powers, and especially to the British, that sources of woods of similar qualities be found at the other end of their trade routes. This, as much as any other consideration, prompted them to cast more than a casual eye upon any country that might provide such lumber. Burma was one of these, for that country had an abundance of teakwood, and, moreover, the natives there already were expert foresters and used this wood for building. Some eighty-five per cent of all teakwood still comes from Burma despite the establishment of teak plantations that are now over a hundred years old both in India and in Java.

The teakwood tree is widely scattered in the natural forests of Burma—but on an average of only about one tree per acre—and it tends to grow in patches. To get it out, logging trails are not only uneconomical, but impossible, owing to the terrain and the great distances, and it thus has to be floated out. To get the huge timbers to the streams, the Elephant and the Elephant alone has proved successful, and has been used for this work since very early times. Despite the coming of the bulldozer, tractor, and other mechanical power units, the Elephant is still the only really practical means of extracting teak logs.

From the very beginning, the East India Company had its eye on the Burmese teakwood and on the Elephant. Observant men like Ralph Fitch had remarked the value of the wood and the Burmese competence in extracting it and employing it in both house- and boat-building. Moreover, it was soon found that teak was even better than oak, especially for tropical warm-water cruising, as it contained an oil and lacked the tannic acid contained in oak which corrodes iron, so that nails rather than wooden trunnels could be used.

The British moved slowly and cautiously in this matter. There was some teak in India itself, but most was imported from Burma, and ships began to be built in both countries to European designs. The Hollanders were already trading with the Burmese, but they proved to be a little too abrupt in their dealings with them. By the middle of the seventeenth century they were exporting gold, tin, lac, ivory, pepper, copper, and what was called "earth-oil" from that country. Earth-oil was crude petroleum! Various other countries also established diplomatic missions in Burma, but it was not until 1795 that a firm move was made toward annexing the Kingdom of Ava, as it was then called. In that year, one Major Michael Symes was sent by the Governor-General of India to parley with the Burmese and to look into matters.

His report, printed unofficially in London, appeared in 1800 and makes rather astonishing reading. It is brutally frank, and if anything like it were published today, it would set the United Nations in an uproar. Its theme was simply that the Burmese were building very good ships to French designs; that this enterprise was dangerous to British maritime standing; that it should be suppressed at any cost; and that either the teak or the whole country should be annexed. In this report, elephants figure very prominently. Symes

---

An Indian Parade Elephant. (Howdah, trappings, and decorations from a mid-nineteenth-century engraving by an unknown artist.)

notes that all the Abu were owned by the King, who had about 6,000, and only privileged persons were allowed to ride them.

At this time there was much discussion in England about the dwindling supplies of lumber at home and the consequent importation of teak from India. Had it not been for the building of warships in India with Indian and Burmese teak, the British would have been in a sorry plight in the Napoleonic wars, and they therefore moved steadily toward monopolizing the trade thereafter. This brought them face to face with the necessity of learning about the Abu.

[9]

OF THE TAMING OF THE BEASTS

The Oriental and ancient methods of catching Abu; of taming and training them; and their uses.

It took the British almost a century to learn about the Abu, but they plunged into the business without any silly preconceived notions, and they learned fast and well. During this time the British, from regarding the Elephant either as a game animal to be hunted or as an expensive toy for princelings and potentates, came to regard the animal as an essential to the economy, not only of India, but of the whole British Empire. They learned a great deal about them and they employed hundreds of them in various capacities in India both officially and privately; and they ended up in Burma at the outbreak of World War II with several thousand in the care of the five great lumber companies that controlled the export of teakwood. (One company owned 2,500.)

The British government of India strictly protected all Abu throughout its territories; even the killing of alleged "rogues" required a special license. In time they made trapping of wild elephants their sole prerogative and placed the exercise under the Forestry Department. They gave Abu a status that was equivalent to warships or tanks today, which can only be "made" officially—though they are actually manufactured, just as the Abu were "caught," by private groups under license. Abu could be owned by subsidiaries of the government or be sold to private individuals, just as surplus war stock is sold today. There were some work elephants in Dutch East India, French Indochina, and considerable numbers in Siam, but the vast majority were, for 200 years, British-government property and were regarded as animated locomotives. Hunting of the Abu was at first indulged in but later somewhat frowned upon, and finally so regulated as to be virtually stopped. Elephant catching was taken over from the natives and also controlled. Several methods were employed.

As Pliny remarked, various ways of catching Abu were already known to the peoples of the Orient and Africa in ancient times. Those used were sometimes the same in the two continents and most of them have continued until today. When Europeans reached the Orient, they found that the *catching* of Abu was done almost exclusively by professionals. *Hunting*, on the other hand, was carried on by the more primitive tribesmen, who treated the Abu like any other game and killed it as best they could, sometimes the whole tribe co-operating. The catching business was a highly skilled profession, and elephant catchers did not bother with other game. In most places the avocation was hereditary and often licensed by the local authority. The catchers were very proud of their abilities, usually formed a "closed shop," and were very jealous of their rights. In many cases they were employees of the King or other local potentate. As a whole, they regarded themselves as "hunters," rather than "trainers," of elephants and they seldom did more than track down, catch, and break in the animals, after which they either passed them on to their employers or sold them to professional trainers. In Burma, matters were somewhat different in that whole villages made a specialty of elephant catching and then kept and trained their prizes. Baby elephants were often given to young boys of the same age, so that the two grew up together and spent their whole lives in each other's company. In Ceylon and some wild areas the Hindu and Muslim princes employed professional *hunters* to catch, rather than to kill, elephants.

That there were large numbers of elephants in domestication at the time of the arrival of Europeans in the Orient cannot be denied, and that they had almost all originally been caught in the wild can likewise hardly be disputed, but even so, the means by which they were alleged to have been captured often sound highly improbable. Elephant catching is, if you come seriously to consider the matter, really quite extraordinary. Just suppose for a moment that you live in a settled farm community, and you receive a phone call from, say, your local police department asking you to assist in *catching* a wild bear that has been reliably reported as wandering about your vicinity. What on earth do you do? Anybody with enough powder and shot and even a modicum of nerve can presumably blast away at the bear and kill it, but to *catch* the brute alive calls for altogether other procedures. The average person would be completely stumped, and if any of the unlikely-sounding methods used for capturing elephants were suggested, they would be immediately dismissed as wholly impractical, and probably with much derision.

One of these methods was capture by drugs. The idea was to put out choice fruits and other food that elephants were known to relish in places where they were known to go, but to insert drugs—mostly opium in one form or another—into some of the morsels. The elephants were then supposed to eat the doped items, get groggy, lie down, and go to sleep. They were then shackled to trees with ropes. The idea is a good one, and it is said to have worked, but this we accept with considerable reservation. Elephants have a perfectly uncanny skill in detecting anything that has been tampered with, as many carnival men have learned when they have tried to poison elephants that had been condemned to death. In one case a creature ate every bag of peanuts, out of the trolley from which she was accustomed to steal such delicacies every day, except the few that contained the tasteless and odorless poison planted therein to kill her. These she hurled aside with rage and contempt. There is usually an abundance of food in the jungles, so that elephants have no cause to test, let alone eat, morsels that have been handled by men whose smell they abhor.

The second method was the most successful but the most inefficient. This was the pitfall. The idea of the pitfall was developed in the Stone Age all over the world. It is still used for the live capture of the most valuable large-animal specimens (rhinoceroses, for instance), but many improvements in the technique have been added by modern collectors. A large pit is dug on a path known to be used by whatever game is desired. This is covered with light timbers of some kind, and these are strewn with the normal trash and litter that cover the surrounding ground, and then the whole is smoothed over. The quarry comes along, marches on to the device, which gives way under its weight, and falls through into the pit. This sounds very simple, but it seldom works. First, the whole device reeks of humans and is therefore avoided by most animals at least for some weeks—by which time small fry and the elements have usually in part demolished the structure. Old male elephants tend to wander about alone at some distance from their herd and they are extremely cautious, often testing every foot of ground before they tread upon it. Nonetheless, it is quite true that elephants *do* sometimes fall into pits. These pits used to be made in the shape of a wedge so that the animals that fell into them could not gain any headway with their legs. The pits were also often floored with a lot of sharpened posts, on which the wretched beasts impaled themselves. Later, the pits were made like elongated boxes and were dug very deep so that a bed of springy branches or other material could be placed in their bottoms to break the fall of the animal. Of course, all manner of unwanted beasts, like buffalo, tiger, deer, domestic cattle, and even dogs, have a habit of plunging into these traps and fouling up the whole business, but if an elephant does fall in, it is apt completely to lose its nerve and whatever initiative it may possess. Instead of grubbing away at the wall facing it and trampling under foot whatever material it can loosen, and so make a ramp to gain its freedom, it usually thrashes about for hours and then more or less gives up and awaits the arrival of the men, who either worm ropes around it and hoist it out or dig a ramp for it to walk out into a prepared cage or compound.

A somewhat better method was one that was little used but that is very effective in the catching of many wild animals. This was to dig a comparatively small pit or depression on the wild-game path—just enough for the animal to half stumble on—and lay in this a strong wire snare with an automatically holding slipknot attached at the other end to a large log. This was very effective with elephants, whose feet are larger than their "wrists" or "ankles" and who are not concerned with small irregularities in the surface of their paths. Once so entangled, even the biggest elephant cannot go far or fast, and usually he will spend hours trying to rid himself of the encumbrance, wrangling with the wire, heaving the log about, and fussing with the knot about his leg.

The fourth and fifth methods of capturing wild elephants seem in several respects to be distinctly unfair. Nevertheless, they probably do less harm to the animals concerned, and may even provide a certain amount of unwonted solace to some. These revolve around the use of tame females—all tamed elephants are known as *koomkies* —to inveigle wild bulls into positions in which they can be ensnared by men. One, and the most painstaking method, is to tether a nice female in a stockade in the bush and leave her there to mumble and "stink" in her inimitable proboscidean way, until her little cries and body effluvium, wafted over the evening air, reach the trunk of an ardent young bull. From then on the procedure is obvious: the "dope" enters the enclosure, a waiting human cuts a rope, a log door drops, and the wanderer is enclosed.

The other method of using female decoys is more exciting, more dangerous, and a little bit more sporting. They are ridden out by their mahouts, who lie on their backs. The mahouts are often smeared with elephant dung to disguise their own odors, and they are provided with mats with which to cover themselves. They meander off into the jungle and contact a wild herd of elephants, whereupon they may take days maneuvering to surround a lone young bull. The men lie quiet for hours on their charges' backs while the wild bull's attention is obtained by the female koomkies. Slowly the koomkies move in, making passes at him, and finally approaching and even caressing him. At this point the men slide quietly off their elephants' backs and slip a rope around the wild animal's hind legs and attach the other end to stout trees. This method is traditional and it must work, but the whole process sounds highly improbable. Although it is true that you can with infinite patience walk right up to many wild animals, and especially the larger ones, there is no other animal I know of that will allow you to tie a rope around its back legs, or that can become so wholly preoccupied with something else, even love, that it would not notice your doing such a thing. Nonetheless, this is alleged to have been a recognized method of catching elephants and was in vogue in quite a number of areas.

It is also stated that intrepid elephant hunters would

actually creep up on the great beasts, on foot, when they were standing at rest under a tree and, after attaching a rope to said tree, would then quietly tie a slipknot around the animal's leg. I have seen completely wild diurnal animals taken thus at night by Africans using a noose on the end of a pole, but to creep up on a creature so wary and fidgety as an elephant in broad daylight is something quite different and hardly credible; yet, it is widely reported also to be quite a common practice, and I know one man who says he watched the performance through binoculars.

Another method of catching really is rather sporting; in fact it is one of the very true "sports" that I know of, and it might well be encouraged. In this, three teams are organized whose duties are those of beaters, captors, and fighters. The men may go on foot or ride koomkies. If the latter, the wild quarry is literally run down by the captor team while the beaters deploy to head off the particular animal selected. When an elephant is alarmed and in a hurry, it rolls up its precious trunk to keep it out of harm's way, and this makes it possible for a skilled and experienced operator to slip a large noose attached to the end of a long pole over its head. Then the fun begins.

Riding an elephant in thick bush is hazardous enough in itself, what with tree limbs sweeping overhead and unexpected pitfalls all around, but when you also have some 5 to 10 tons of highly efficient, fast-moving "machinery" on the end of a pole to cope with in addition to the other perils, you require exceptional skill and fortitude. The noose line is carried coiled behind you on your koomkie, and simultaneously with the noosing you have to release this; then either your assistant, who is riding behind you, or you yourself have to slide off your mount and throw a half-hitch around some sturdy tree before you come to the end of the rope. If you fail in this, you have to start running and, like the whalers of old when they were fast to a Sperm Whale, try to take up enough slack by outrunning the elephant so that you can make a pass at some future tree as it flashes by. When you succeed in this, your troubles really begin, for your monster "fish" is brought up sharp and then may very likely, after a few moments of amazed disbelief, waltz about and come right at you and your tree. If you want your elephant, you then have to stand your ground till the fighter teams come up; and dodging an elephant is not easy, because its trunk can reach around most trees. If you are lucky, the fighters arrive in time and set to work subduing the crazed beast, which they do by simply bashing their koomkies into it from both sides until it is punch-drunk and exhausted. You then throw cables around it, fore and aft, lash it between two koomkies, and march it home.

The last method is probably as old as the pitfall. It is mentioned throughout history and was the commonest and most efficient. It is still the leading method of elephant capture and is known as the *keddah*. Both the idea and the procedure are obvious, but the execution of the operation is sometimes almost unbelievable. Not only is the organization and the labor involved herculean; the final achievement of its objective seems altogether illogical in nine cases out of ten. Still, it works.

The keddah derives from one of the three oldest methods of fishing. Apart from trout tickling and the new underwater spear fishing, aquatic animals have been taken since time immemorial either by harpoons, by hooks on lines, or in nets. The keddah is the end-product of the net system. Game can be caught in large quantities, and alive, by laying a net

---

Burmese "Logger" rolling teak. The semi-domesticated Elephants of the Burmese lumber organizations are trained for only one of a variety of specialized operations.

around an area of forest or grass, or simply in the open, and then driving the quarry into an opening, preferably a funnel-shaped opening at one side of the net. The practice is pursued in many forest countries today and was once used for rabbit drives. The proposition of catching a herd of elephants in a net is intriguing, but the size and weight of the net required precludes putting it into practice. Men therefore early conceived the idea of making a semi-permanent net in the form of a stockade and then going to fetch the elephants and drive them in. To do this, however, requires an enormous amount of hard work.

Upward of a thousand laborers may be needed. A suitable area is then selected in country where wild elephant herds roam. This is often in a fork between rivers or in a valley running into steep hills, but it often has to be built, *in toto,* on level ground without any natural barriers because elephants are excellent swimmers and great mountaineers. The stockade has to be made of fairly large and sturdy logs or giant bamboos, and within this a ditch several feet deep and at least 7 feet wide has to be dug. An elephant cannot negotiate such a ditch and is thereby prevented from simply marching through the stockade, which it would otherwise do if it had a mind to—though, strangely, it seldom does. Then a platform has to be built all around the outside of the stockade for men wielding guns, rattles, and other noise-making devices and torches. The stockade may be of any shape, but it must enclose undisturbed bush. In it a gate-sized entrance is left and a portcullis-type door is constructed over it. This can be dropped when but one rope is cut. From this gateway the stockade is protracted for a considerable distance in the form of a widening funnel.

While all this construction work is going on, another small army is widely deployed through the adjacent forest. Its instructions are to surround widely a herd or herds of elephants that have been pinpointed by hunters. When this is done, a great curving line is formed of widely separated pairs of beaters who move slowly inward making some but not too much noise: in fact, just enough, combined with their smell, to keep the quarry moving undisturbed ahead to some selected area where there is ample food for several days. When the elephants have been thus maneuvered and compressed into manageable compass near the mouth of the stockade funnel, a loose fence of bamboos, saplings, and smoky fires is thrown up all around, and the beaters then take turns cooking, eating, sleeping, kindling the fires, and making a noise until the word is given by the headmen.

Then the keddah crew takes up its several positions hidden on the platform outside and behind the stockade; a very special man hides himself aloft by the gate; and the army of beaters begins to move inward again, pressing the elephants ever onward to the mouth of the funnel. Once the leading female of any herd is in this mouth, the procedure is hurried up so that she does not have time to change her mind before she sees the stockade on either or both sides. Once she is far enough into this funnel it does not matter if she does turn, because of the press of her tribe behind her, and as soon as most of the lot are in the funnel, the beaters set up the ultimate in infernal dins, shouting, letting off guns, beating on anything noisy, whirling huge rattles, and stampeding back and forth on foot and on elephants. Sometimes even dogs are brought up, which, by their yapping, annoy the elephants while the men scare them; and then the men stationed at the outermost points of the funnel rise up and join the chorus. The elephants rush headlong at and through the gate, and as soon as the last is in, the special man cuts the rope and the portcullis falls.

In a successful drive you may have a couple of hundred crazed titans in your trap. Then the real work begins. The animals have first to be sorted, then individually noosed, then subdued, and finally walked away to captivity. Females too old to be worth-while training are released along with crusty old bulls and usually any tuskless males. These males, or mucknas, though often more powerful than tuskers, are disturbing to other elephants. In the past, suckling young were also released because the cost of keeping them until they were old enough to work and earn money was excessive while they got in the way of their mothers' training. To sort out the mass and take them, experts go into the stockade with koomkies, select one animal at a time and, working in teams, separate it from the rest, and then bully it into partial submission or exhaustion, whereupon a man slips to the ground and either shackles its hind legs together, nooses one foot, or passes ropes around its body. It is then left to flounder around for some time and sometimes for days until it has lost its spirit, when it is marched away between two koomkies and tied to a tree. There it is fed and watered by its future mahout for some time. When all are sorted and shackled and those not wanted driven off into the wild, the prizes are lined up and marched off. By this time they are usually pretty docile, so that, amazing as it may seem, one koomkie can usually handle two wild-caught animals.

After elephants have been caught, they have to be first tamed and then trained. Various methods are employed in different countries, but, in the over-all, it is more due to a provision—or might it be an oversight?—of Nature rather than to any skill of man that the first objective is almost invariably achieved in two or three weeks. There is probably no such thing as a truly "wild" animal *as a species* in the sense of being vicious, mean, and untamable, though individuals of all species may seem wild because they are in ill-health, neurotic, in pain, or have been driven to insanity by physical or mental torture. True, some types of animals seem to be more willing or agreeable to being handled and ordered around by men—like the European Polecat, certain monkeys, bats, and other creatures—but there is probably no *kind* of animal, from a snail to a gorilla, individuals of which cannot be tamed and be perfectly happy and reliable in consort with man. The elephant, as opposed to loxodonts, appears to be an extreme example of a species that is not only not averse to being disciplined but that also, on the whole, seems almost to welcome the procedure. Wild elephants may put up a terrific fight at first, but almost all very soon quiet down and become amenable. They then seem to set about learning from us whatever is needed of them and go to work with a will, usually picking up more information all the time, and apparently taking pride in their accomplishments.

There are a few that go sullen and remain stubborn and unreliable, and a very few remain outstanding individualists. Both types are dangerous, but the latter can be either deadly or the most marvelous characters. Were it not for these specific traits, elephants would never have been even semidomesticated, because although you can tame wild-caught rhinoceroses just as easily, they cannot be taught to do anything useful, and a tame rhino is about as valuable as a truck without an engine.

Today the keddah method of capture has been refined, so that instead of a large enclosure the gate leads to a passageway just wide enough to hold one elephant at a time. They enter in a long line, bumper to tail. The animals can thus be roped quickly and then marched out one by one and put directly into individual structures called "crushes" where their taming begins at once.

The crush is a cagelike device made of round timbers lashed together; it is just large enough to admit the animal. It is built against and lashed to the base of a large tree. Correctly, there are four upright posts and three long horizontal bars on each side. Other bars can be placed horizontally across the inside at various levels to prevent the animal from butting at the tree ahead, or to hold it up under chin, chest, and groin so that it may sleep, or to hold it immovable when medical treatment is called for. Crushes have been standard equipment for the training of calves for some time, but they are now employed also during the preliminary taming of wild adults. Wild elephants resent this confinement, and the older they are, the more they fight their fate; bulls are more stubborn than cows or calves. It is almost useless to attempt taming those over twenty to twenty-five years of age, and nowadays most over that age are released.

Calves born in captivity and youngsters caught wild of from four to six years take about ten days to become obedient, but they usually become used to being shackled and unshackled and learn to raise their feet when ordered in seventy-two hours. Older animals become submissive in about a month, but it takes up to eighteen months to *train* a young adult for actual work, and they are not worked at all until they have thoroughly recovered from the shock of capture and are again in perfect physical health. In olden times taming was accomplished by simply tying the Elephant to a tree and then talking to it incessantly or dancing around it chanting endlessly; by alternately starving and feeding it; and by gradually handling it. The procedure was both risky and often harmful to the animal, which in its frenzy—particularly when first touched, because the Elephant is extremely ticklish, especially about the rear half of its body—often dislocated its hip or broke a leg, and it usually developed the most appalling rope sores that permanently crippled it. Incidentally, the crush is not applicable to loxodonts, which are much more nervous and can be rendered permanently untamable by so much as the unexpected click of a camera. Nor can loxodonts be caught by drugs, decoys, lassoing, or the keddah. They have to be taken when babies by killing the mother and separating them from the herd.

There are infinite variations on the two methods of taming—i.e., confining and tethering—but whatever the physical methods used or the psychological aids employed, the business has but one end in view: to make the animal understand clearly and once and for all that men are its superiors and that certain men are its absolute masters. This means that the animal has to fear man, and to instill true fear, very firm and sometimes harsh measures must be taken. Just like a recalcitrant child, so with an elephant! The quickest and in the end the best way to do this is by the infliction of physical pain. This does not mean *damage,* be it clearly understood. It is very easy to damage an elephant if you don't know what you are doing, for many parts of its body are very vulnerable; on the other hand, you can hurt it very readily if you know how, *without* harming it in any way. Its trunk is very sensitive but very tough, and a whipping on that organ which does not even bruise it will bring even an angry elephant up short.

In taming, and later in training, an elephant must never even in part be allowed either to get away with a refusal to comply with an order it understands, or to make any untoward move of its own volition which is undesirable. Elephants can be individually stupid or slow to learn, and even the most intelligent and willing may be absolutely unable to grasp some things. Due allowance must be made for these variations in temperament, both in taming and in training. Careful judgment must be exercised in assessing an elephant's every action, because they are past masters at faking and they are often very playful and naughty. Fortunately, they can learn a considerable vocabulary of commands and this makes training much easier than with other animals, for actions learned in association with spoken commands can be pyramided, as it were, to achieve complex multiple actions at a single command.

Training elephants for lumbering is highly specialized and very complicated. Lumber camps are run on military lines and with absolute precision around the clock and on a month-by-month schedule. The animals feed at large at night, are rounded up in the morning by their own trainers (called *oozies* in Burma), are bathed, harnessed, and marched off to work for a specified number of hours. Each is trained to a special task such as hauling logs, clearing jams in rivers and streams, piling logs, and so forth. Once learned, the work is performed with a minimum of commands by the oozie and with absolute precision by the elephant.

Training of parade elephants is much simpler, while transport animals require little but evidence of absolute obedience and knowledge of about two dozen commands, such as "go forward," "go backward," "turn right," "kneel down," and so forth. Elephants used for hunting, and notably for hunting tiger, have to be carefully selected and usually from among sturdy young bull tuskers, and then very assiduously trained to the noise of guns, the cacophony of beaters, the smell of tiger, a large number of specialized commands, and, above all, to stop all movement on command and then to stay absolutely motionless even in face of grave danger. Most of this is much harder for a bull to do than for a cow, as the latter by nature lead and defend the herd while the bulls customarily take to flight. Elephants have vile eyesight and only fair hearing, but an extremely acute sense of smell; they are also highly sensitive to small vibrations transferred through the ground to their feet, and they can in some circumstances sense a moving tiger at considerable distances up-wind and long before any man, so that training them to control their actions when they thus sense danger is extremely difficult. The training of show or performing elephants is a much more exacting and laborious business, and is highly specialized. We shall have more to say of this later, but it should be mentioned here that while work, transport, hunting, and parade elephants have to learn a greater or lesser amount, show animals have first to learn how to learn and then be forever ready for the unexpected. Much of their performance in a circus appears purely mechanical, but there is always a disturbing factor that the audience does not realize. This is that elephants are par excellence creatures of habit and very conservative, and the one thing that throws them off is a change of environment. Show elephants are constantly on the move from one environment to another even in circuses, and today in film-making and, above all, in television, they are expected to do many things outside their normal, learned routine, at odd times, in different sequences, precisely on time, and in the midst of novel surroundings. A whole new technique for training show elephants has grown up. This is in some respects a re-creation of the training methods of the ancients. An already-trained work elephant will *not* submit to this technique.

Elephants, simply because of their size, are very strong animals, but compared to other animals, weight for weight, they are rather weak. They are ten per cent weaker than a man, while a horse is twenty-five per cent stronger than a man. Elephants, as opposed to Bush Loxodonts, are forest animals and so require a moist atmosphere and shade. Their mere bulk necessitates a large amount of food, which takes them a long time to gather and masticate, so that in the wild, to keep truly healthy, they eat for about twenty hours out of the twenty-four. Under normal conditions they do this, sleeping only for about three hours after midnight or in two or more briefer periods during the night. They are more active at night than by day. These facts have to be taken into account in work elephants as also must be the absolute necessity for regular and preferably twice-daily bathing of the animals. For this, shallow running water is best, and the animals should be made to lie down first on one side and then on the other and then be briskly scrubbed all over for about twenty minutes with particular emphasis on all such crannies as the groin, behind and in the ears, and around the base of the tusks, where ticks and other parasites may gather or lay eggs.

Sites for elephant camps should be carefully selected on level ground and cleared to admit sunlight and keep down flies, and all the buildings should be widely spaced. Camps should never be too far from the work area and must have nearby running water and an abundance of natural forage for the animals. The elephants are never marched through the camp but around it, and their harness is kept under a special shelter near their bathing place. Lumber elephants are not worked at all during the hot-weather months and, on resuming their labors, they are at first worked only for four hours a day. This progresses to six hours, and finally to the limit of eight hours per day. They are worked only when their health and food are fully satisfactory, the country is not too difficult, the lumber not too big, the weather not too hot, and the drag paths are easy. They work a five-day week from Monday through Friday, and rest on Saturdays, Sundays, and the days of the full and change of the moon, which in Burma are religious festivals. They thus work on an average of only 150 days per annum in the timber forests.

The procedure in teak logging is for a camp to be set up in an area where the teak trees have been ringed three years previously, so that they are dead and partly dried out. The trees are then felled and the main trunk cut so as to harvest the utmost footage. The trunks are hauled by relays of elephants, each specializing in one phase of the job, to the nearest stream. This hauling is done along rough paths cut from each individual tree; rollers are used where necessary, and one, two, or more elephants may work in tandem or abreast, if possible, in moving the logs. On long hauls or on roads, the logs are balanced on low, heavy, two-wheeled dollies. The streams are usually either dry or have too little water to float the logs throughout most of the year. So the

---

Young tusker Elephant in a "crush." Newly captured wild Elephants are placed in this device, anchored to a large tree bole, while they become used to ankle-chains and human contact.

timber lies until the rains come and floods bear the timber downstream. The streams are usually clogged with fallen trees and other growth and have first to be laboriously cleared; but even then the logs, when once on the move, usually get jammed. Rises in the streams and rivers come suddenly and are often of short duration but may sometimes be predicted by rain over distant mountains. Then all other work stops and all elephants except pregnant females and mothers with very young are assembled at key points along the stream, be it night or day. A few of the best elephants are fully harnessed and have drag chains to extract the key logs in jams when found; the rest wear only a halter for their oozies to cling to. The streams are regularly patrolled, and as soon as any sign of a jam is seen, the elephants set to work to try to get the logs moving again. This is called *aunging* and is the most important feature of the whole tedious logging procedure.

After a flood the logs are often scattered far and wide in the forest or up side creeks, or are jumbled into great masses in narrows or littered over sandbanks. Those that are half buried have to be winched or dug out before the elephants can push or haul them back to the stream; the others have to be dragged or rolled back. The elephants work systematically and ponderously but intelligently, and they often know better how to extract the logs than do their oozies or the *singoung* or headman, or even the officer in charge, known as the *chaun gookie*.

The elephants will often, if allowed, overwork and overstrain themselves; thus, they have to be watched very carefully. A sudden freshet is the signal for furious activity and great excitement in a lumber camp, and if it takes place at night it provides a wonderful sight. Everybody, including the elephants, is seized with a great enthusiasm, and under the glare of bamboo torches and usually in a torrential downpour, they all flounder about for hours in the flood, tugging and pulling like ants. Yet in a well-regulated camp there is no confusion and no shouting other than staccato commands, the rush of water and rain, the clank of chains, and occasionally a strange ululation of ecstasy on the part of an elephant. Unlike the men, who may become overenthusiastic, the elephants seldom take undue risks but work with deliberation; yet they are apt to give vocal expression to their satisfaction when the jam begins to move.

If the aunging is successful, and it always has to be in the end, the logs finally reach a large river. There they are made up into huge rafts on which fairly substantial houses are built for the men who travel with the valuable material. Once these rafts used simply to be floated downstream; now they are usually imparted some headway by small pusher tugs and are thus to some degree steered. Yet they often still take several weeks to reach the ports, because most of the lumbering is now done far inland.

It takes on an average of about seven years for the stem of a standing teak tree to reach the great lumber mill at the coast. Most of the work all along the route, from the time that the tree is ringed until it comes out of the mill shaped or as planks, is done by elephants, for even at this end stage specially trained pairs of elephants may carry out the timber and stack it for shipment and then move it once again into the slings that hoist it aboard ship.

Lumber camps also employ elephants specifically trained solely for transport. These have to be very carefully treated and managed; they cannot be walked too fast or too far, or pressed in any other way; they require 800 pounds of fresh fodder per night; they must rest a day every three days if the going is hard. Over flat country a fully-laden but long-legged elephant may keep up a pace of four miles an hour, but this is exceptional. A little under three miles an hour is the average over all types of terrain and in all seasons. A man can outmarch the best of them even when carrying his normal maximum load, and a man can continue both longer at a single stretch and for more consecutive periods, but elephants have been known to make prodigious marches. There are those who state boldly that even baby elephants, which are customarily ridden astride with a soft pad and stirrups, may keep up a pace of from fifty to sixty miles a day in rough country (and doubtless the poor creatures could be pressed to do so); but the very idea would make any true elephant man cry out in horror. Twenty-one miles is a good trek, and, if possible, the animals should be rested for a time every seven miles or so. During World War II, elephants (as told by Lieutenant-Colonel J. H. Williams in his now classic book *Bandoola*) made forced marches over trackless mountain terrain with overloads (and on short and uncertain rations) in a final dash to safety in Assam with women and children refugees. These elephants kept going for twenty days with only one day of real rest and sometimes marched from sunup to sundown.

The handling of trained elephants is today a highly developed discipline, and their care, equipment, housing, feeding, and health call for a far greater experience and wider knowledge of several specialized practices than does the management of any other domesticated animal. There are textbooks on the subject, and new techniques are constantly being added. The Indians, Singhalese, Burmese, Siamese, and Cambodians still probably know more about these animals than we do, but the handful of Europeans, mostly British, who have spent their lives with these wonderful creatures, starting with G. P. Sanderson, who was in charge of all "Her Majesty's Elephants" in the mid-nineteenth century, have added much original information and have systematized all that is known upon scientific lines.

When Burma gained her independence, all her elephants were "nationalized." This meant the end of a long regime and the withdrawal of most of those Europeans who had dedicated their lives to the welfare of these animals in the great private teak companies. However, Burma, with or without teak to cut and sell, must still have elephants for a long time to come despite the arrival of the bulldozer and the tractor, and nobody knows better how to handle them or is more solicitous of their welfare than the Burman of the forests and the elephants' own oozies.

In the other newly independent Oriental countries, the status of the Elephant has not changed except that fewer will spend their lives henceforth as toys and parade spectacles. They can still do work that no machine can do and there are still areas where they live and breed in comparative safety. Their homelands are shrinking and will continue to shrink, but some fifty per cent of the work elephants in the Burmese camps before World War II were bred in captivity, and there is hope that at long last the species may sustain itself in true domestication. There is no new grand alliance between Man and Elephant, but it seems that the two may at last have settled down to mutual co-operation.

OF SLAVES AND IVORY

The Arabs in Africa. The trade in "black ivory" and white ivory. The history and uses of ivory.

When Captain Azurara's men lowered their bucket off the mouth of the Senegal River in the year A.D. 1450, they could not have imagined that their action would constitute a major pivot of history. Yet this was actually a turning point of far greater significance than the first sighting of Trinidad by Columbus some forty-two years later, for it signaled the true beginning of the expansion of Europe, and the end of a millennium of cultural debility in that continent. It marked also a geographic turning point, for by it Europeans had reached the bulge of Africa beyond which lay the way to the Orient. The dropping of this bucket is also significant because almost the first thing found thereafter upon landing on the adjacent coast was the buckler made from a loxodont's ear. In fact, the Portuguese that day took back to their ship *two* items that grew into dynamic symbols—the elephant-ear belt and the naked boy in whose hut it had been found. Little did they realize what these items symbolized, for although both slaves and ivory had been valuables since before the dawn of history, both commodities had been at a premium in Europe for a long time. The discovery of either in any quantity, and at a price that impoverished Europe could pay for them, was of the utmost significance.

Slavery had up till then been an accepted aspect of life throughout the world. Individuals of every race and of almost every nationality known have at one time or another been enslaved. But slavery was not always a dire estate or a human indignity. For millennia slavery was simply a status in a caste or class system. And the slaves were not at the bottom of the social pyramid by any means, for they were valuable chattels and they cost money, and thus were the perquisites of the rich. They were relieved of all responsibilities except obedience. Theirs was actually a privileged position although akin to that of our pedigreed cattle, which are housed, fed, and pampered in contrast to our small farmer, day laborer, or even some skilled industrial workers who are often enough left to face alone and unaided the brunt of natural disasters and economic depressions. I am not saying that there was no brutality or abject misery inherent in slavery; there was in almost all walks of life in olden days. On the whole, slaves were a pampered class as long as the slave culture remained solvent.

In the fifteenth century slavery was known by other names in Europe, but most Asiatic and many African countries were virtually slave states, and the slave trade was of high economic importance to those countries. Most of this trade was in Arab hands, and, as always, the African was the preferred commodity. There are Arabic records wherein the desiderata for a slave are listed—honesty, fidelity, stamina, health, strength of mind and body, courage, and a godly demeanor. These are splendid qualities indeed! The wealthy bought slaves for their protection as well as for service and often because they could not trust their own people, and for thousands of years it was to Africa that they turned for the supply of the best of these, their personal bodyguards. And it was from the Africans themselves that they bought and traded this precious commodity until a new necessity and a new avarice arose, mostly in expansionist Europe. The concepts of human dignity and freedom only came much later.

The history of ivory followed a strangely parallel course. We can only assume that early Stone Age man possessed slaves; we know definitely he collected ivory. In the rubbish of caves all across Europe, Asia, and North Africa inhabited by Aurignacian man after the last retreat of the northern ice, there are found worked pieces of ivory, incised in patterns or carved into little figures. There are ivory implements like needles, combs, and other items. Some of the ivory statuettes have facial and bodily features clearly indicative of what are called the Proto-Negroes—or those "who went before" the Negroes—whose descendants we know today as the Bushmen of South Africa. Most of the artifacts were, moreover, of true ivory, namely the tusks of Abu of one sort or another. All the early cultures, with the exception of the Sumerian, collected ivory and made much both practical and artistic use of it. Since earliest times, ivory appears to have been valued almost as a gem and to have been the particular delight of the sculptors. Two millennia before the birth of Christ there were wealthy collectors of ivories, and, like gems, the material has never lost its intrinsic value.

Ivory, however, means several different things, as we shall see in a moment. It appears that of all of these, the tusks of the Forest Loxodonts were always the most highly prized except by the Africans themselves, who for centuries esteemed ivory only as a durable material for door lintels, stockades, and as fences for graves.

The appearance of the Portuguese in Africa and then in the Orient wrought a profound change in many ancient trades and unbalanced the economy of almost the whole world. No sooner did they reach West Africa than ivory began to stream to Europe, and directly instead of by the long and circuitous route through the Middle and Near East and the hands of numberless middlemen. Slaves at reasonable prices also began to appear in Europe, and this proved to be a terrible new menace to the continent and especially to its economically depressed serfs, peasants, and bondsmen. The effect of this new Portuguese business was profound, first in Europe and Africa, and then in Asia and America. The real clash, however, arose between the Christian and the Islamic worlds, an uproar that lasted for four centuries and which to a certain extent still continues today, though it is not specifically recognized as a distinct war—either hot or cold.

At the end of the fifteenth century the Arabs held the ivory and slave trades, most intercontinental transport, and several other world enterprises firmly in their hands. When the Christian Europeans arrived upon the scene, the Arabs struggled valiantly to retain control of these trades in face of this invasion from a reviving West. But they lost out on two counts—first, to the new navigational aids and ocean-going shipping of Henry of Portugal, and, second, to the discovery of the New World, with the production of which they could not compete. Port by port, tribe by tribe, and kingdom by kingdom, Islam had to secede before the irruption from the West; and the economy of the Orient, which had previously been the hub of the universe, crumbled and fell into the hands of Europeans.

As we have seen, Europeans as a result took over the Asiatic House of Abu *in toto* and ruled it for two centuries, but at first they by-passed Africa. The Portuguese established trading posts all along the Guinea Coast and along other stretches of the West Coast of that continent; they made treaties with the Kingdom of Ba'Kongo, who even sent delegates to Rome; and they built forts in Mozambique, on Madagascar, and all up the East Coast of Africa in the sixteenth century. However, they did not push far inland, establish colonies, or take over kingdoms. Perhaps it was against their hereditary coastal nature to do so; in any case, they stayed in their forts, and on offshore islands, and on the sea. It was left for the Hollanders to make the first colonizing move into Africa and this they did in the cool temperate zone of what we now call the Cape. The U.S.A. of the Dark Continent (The Union of South Africa) has a longer history than the U.S.A. of the New World, for the Hollanders were pushing up on to the Karroo before the Pilgrims landed in Boston Bay. What is more, the Dutch actually got there *before* the Bantu Africans, against whom they later fought for possession of the country. They entered a land inhabited only by lowly Bushmen and countless hordes of animals, among them huge numbers of loxodonts.

At that time Africa south of the Sahara was divided into five parts. The Guinea Coast was the homeland of innumerable Sudanese tribes, some of which were organized as autonomous states of considerable size like Dahomey, Benin, and Bagirmi. Related peoples held dominion right across Central Africa to the Nile Valley in the eastern Sudan. South of these, in the Cameroons, Gabun, and Congo, there was a great mass of unassimilated tribes ranging from primitive Pygmies to proud Bantus, Nilotes, and even Hamites in the eastern regions. Farther to the east still, the uplands and savannas were inhabited by Bantu peoples with, to the north in and around Abyssinia, Hamitic peoples. In the deserts of the south and on the temperate coastal belt below that dwelt the remains of Africa's earlier inhabitants—the Bushmen, Hottentots, Herero, and the vanishing *Strandloopers.*

All of these peoples, with the exception of the primitive Proto-Negroes of the far south and the little Pygmies, were rather proud warriors though mostly, apart from the West Africans, still living in very primitive communities and backward about such things as arms. For their lack of weapon knowledge, however, their country made up in violence of climate and in virulence of diseases that were fatal to non-Africans. Even the Arabs who had penetrated farther into the continent than any other foreigners and who had been present longer there than any other intruders were not immune to these diseases.

Weather and disease were Equatorial Africa's first line of defense. Its second was its vegetation. Historians talk blithely of "slave raids" in Africa, implying that raiding was the method by which cargoes of both white ivory and "black ivory" were obtained and especially for shipment of the latter to the New World. Such myths can be shown up even by a tourist today. If a well-organized army landed on an African coast and tried to catch so much as one of its indigenous inhabitants against his will, it would come away panting and empty-handed. In forested Africa, all the natives would have to do as the invading army approached the shore would be to take a few paces to either side, whereupon they would simply vanish into the forest. The whole population of large villages can do this even today. No slaver ever *caught* a slave; he bought them.

The Portuguese learned early that if they wanted anything out of Africa, they had to trade for it with the natives. The Spaniards, then the Hollanders, then the French, and later the British learned that if they wanted slaves, they had to buy them from the African chieftains and princelings. The Arabs long before had learned the same. And so it was with ivory. No elephants were down on the coast, and even if you went into the forests you seldom saw them. Only on the open savannas could you encounter them, but there the tribesmen were also rather tough. Only in the extreme south of Africa were foreigners able to amble inland and meet loxodonts. And that is just what the Hollanders did. On the rest of the continent, Europeans had to be content with trading with the natives or bartering with the Arabs who had already traded with the natives. Equatorial Africa thus remained for almost four centuries after its *rediscovery* by the Portuguese just a great and aggravating bulge of land on the way to the Orient.

The Negroes[1] themselves, and especially the Bantus, enslaved whole peoples as they spread west and south over the continent of Africa from their original home, which seems to have been about the upper Nile Valley. This movement appears to have taken place about 1000 B.C. The original, subjugated peoples were often then maintained apart as second-class citizens: hewers of wood and drawers of water. The Negro chieftains were quite willing to sell their surpluses of these subject peoples, but when the supply began to dwindle, they started to sell captives of their own race taken in tribal warfare. Later still, they even sold their own subjects. Finally, when the population was depleted and food production fell off, they found themselves facing the Arab slave traders with nothing to offer. And that was when real misery descended upon the continent. Meanwhile, their other stand-by had become ivory, and ivory led them into even more trouble and woe.

Although most Africans had not originally placed any particular value on ivory, they had found it just as satisfactory to carve as the harder woods and to be somewhat more durable than most woods. As it came in fair-sized and gently

[1] All Africans are not, of course, Negroes. The true Negro peoples—or Sudanese, as anthropologists call them—seem to have originated somewhere between the upper Nile and the Congo, comparatively recently. Thence they spread west, south, and east, conquering and eliminating or absorbing the previous ancient inhabitants of the continent, such as the Bushmen, Hottentots, Pygmies, *Strandloopers,* and others, which is to say those little yellow-skinned and tall brown-skinned races known collectively as the Proto-Negroids. In the east they met Semites and formed, by mixing with them, the Nilotes, Hamites, and Bantus. These last only reached South Africa at the time of the first European invasion. To the west, the Negroes found and subdued all manner of non-Negroid peoples still living at a Palaeolithic stage of culture. These the Negroes often enslaved, instead of absorbing, and they retain today in certain parts of Nigeria and the Cameroons their original identity. They are perfectly free but still "hewers of wood and drawers of water."

curving pieces, they also used it for building and for a few other utilitarian purposes. Loxodonts were good "beef" and one of them fed a lot of people; their skins were tough and made good shields. The Africans therefore hunted the Abu as and when they could, and the chiefs made a habit of piling up the tusks behind their houses as they were brought in by their hunters. For many centuries the Nubians, the Ethiopians, and the Arabians had been able to satisfy their needs for ivory by trading for it around the upper Nile, and there had been no necessity for them to penetrate inner Africa. Thus, when the Europeans arrived on the coast, there was a monumental store of old ivory piled up all over Equatorial Africa waiting to be traded.

The Europeans brought not only the incentive to collect ivory but also new weapons—guns—and with their guns they eventually joined the tribesmen with their primitive spears and poisoned arrows. Together, white and black slaughtered the loxodonts wholesale until ivory flowed out of Africa in unbelievable quantity. But we get ahead of our story.

So wild was Africa that until only some hundred years ago only a few trade routes led out of the heart of the continent. Apart from the short routes to the coast from inland Guinea, the only other outlets from Central Africa were via the mouth of the Congo; southeast via the Zambesi; directly east across what is now Tanganyika to Zanzibar; southeast from Uganda to Mombasa; and northeast via the upper Nile. At the time of the arrival of the Portuguese, the Arabs controlled the last four routes, as they had controlled the whole East Coast for centuries, and they were not disposed to give up their holdings. The Europeans might take black and white ivory from the West Coast—they could not be prevented—but on the East Coast they had to buy it from the Arabs. But the Europeans sailed round *behind* the Arabs, as it were, and cut off both their best sources of supply and their markets in the Far East, and this drove them into

Africa on a rampage that lasted two centuries, so that Stanley, writing as late as 1850, stated bitterly: "Every pound weight [of ivory] has cost the life of a man, woman or child; for every five pounds a hut has been burned; for every two tusks a village has been destroyed; every twenty tusks have been obtained at the price of a district with all its people, villages, and plantations."

The enhanced demand for slaves is comprehensible. It was caused by the discovery of the New World and by the strange and proud character of the Amerindians, who just would not work as serfs. This attitude resulted in an acute labor shortage in the New World. The violent scramble for ivory seems, on the other hand, one of history's inexplicables. Gems are pretty, portable, and rare; gold does not tarnish and is heavy; uranium is now very useful; but ivory cracks, warps, changes color, is eaten by rats, and breaks easily. Yet it has intrigued men throughout the ages. People who did not know what it was placed a high value upon it, and even now, long after the discovery of dozens of other substances that do everything it does, people still pay a high price for it.

This regard for ivory may be partly mystical and have originated in early Stone Age times, when it seems to have acquired a religious connotation bestowed upon objects (notably sculptures in the round) made from this substance which seemed to have qualities of half-life. Ivory, be it Abu, Hippopotamus, Walrus, Sperm Whale, or even Narwhal or Wild Hog tooth, was derived from the biggest and most impressive local animals. Being the material of which teeth are made, it seemed alive; early man suffered from toothache just as we do and he knew only too well that teeth grow and die. Teeth are the least destructible parts of an animal and they are an animal's ultimate weapon. When a wondrously powerful animal died, you might wear its teeth around your neck not only because they were pretty and durable but because, not being yet wholly dead, they might retain some of the strength and power of the animal. Then too, at various times and in many places teeth have been used as currency. The mighty hunter had many teeth, and lesser folk would trade with him for these teeth in an endeavor to acquire some of his valor. Certainly ivory has always figured prominently in ecclesiastical prestige. The throne of the Pope was once made of Narwhal and elephantine ivory, and even today we have the Elk's clubs with their ivory symbol of an elk's tooth.

The word "ivory" means two quite distinct things. Derived from the stem *ebur*, as pointed out, its first and more basic meaning is simply "a heavy substance." In this respect it came to denote any hard white animal product, including the dense parts of large bones and the homogeneous parts of any animal teeth and particularly their dentine and enamel. However, ivory also includes the dried "meat" of the nuts of a South American plant known as the Tagua (*Phytelephas macrocarpa*), indigenous to the hot tropical valleys leading down from the Andes. And the strange inorganic substance known as *Meerschaum*[2] has often been called ivory too. But for us the word "ivory" is restricted to the substance of which the incisor teeth or tusks of the elephants, loxodonts, mammoths, and in exceptional cases of a few other extinct forms of Abu are composed. True ivory has a readily recognizable structure—best seen in a cross-cut of the tusk—composed of concentric circles caused by its continuous growth from the inside. These circles enclose curvilinear belts of little "eyes" arranged more or less radially. Only Sperm Whale-tooth ivory, among all the other ivories, has a structure in any way comparable; but despite the resemblance, Sperm Whale ivory is in other ways quite distinct from true elephantine ivory.

Prehistoric man worked for the most part in true (elephantine) ivory, but a very high proportion of Dynastic Egyptian ivory artifacts were made from the tushes and

[2] A hydrous magnesium-silicate, also called *sepiolite*, and a natural mineral.

front teeth of the hippopotamus, which, although smaller than the tusks of the Abu, are even finer grained, harder, and more durable. The outstanding ivory carvers of the ancient world were the Phoenicians. In fact, most of the raw ivory was handled by them, and most of the art objects collected by wealthy Egyptians, Assyrians, Babylonians, and later by the Greeks were made by these people. The Phoenicians were seafarers and they had a flourishing whaling industry centered, it would appear, upon the Sperm Whale and the Common Dolphin. They did a brisk trade in the small teeth of the Common Dolphin. Dolphin teeth commanded an extraordinary price in Persia both as ornaments and as charms. They also preferred the huge teeth of the Sperm Whale to those of any other animal—loxodonts and elephants not excluded—for carving their choicest ivories.

Other ivory was obtained from the larger kinds of wild swine such as the Wart-Hog, and this is still in some demand in Germany, where the tushes, having just the right curve, are used as handles for beer steins. In the far north, both in the Atlantic and the Pacific, two other kinds of ivory have been prized since before the dawn of history. These are the tusks of the Walrus and the strange, spirally twisted "horns" of the Narwhal. The Narwhal is a small whale the males of which bear one or two such structures sticking straight forward out of their heads sometimes to a length of 12 feet. Walrus ivory is very dense and pure, and although individual tusks seldom surpass 24 inches in length, all kinds of

---

"Black Ivory" toting White Ivory. The slaughter of the Loxodonts finally merged with the slaughter of Africans in the latter days of the slave trade conducted by the Arabs from East Africa.

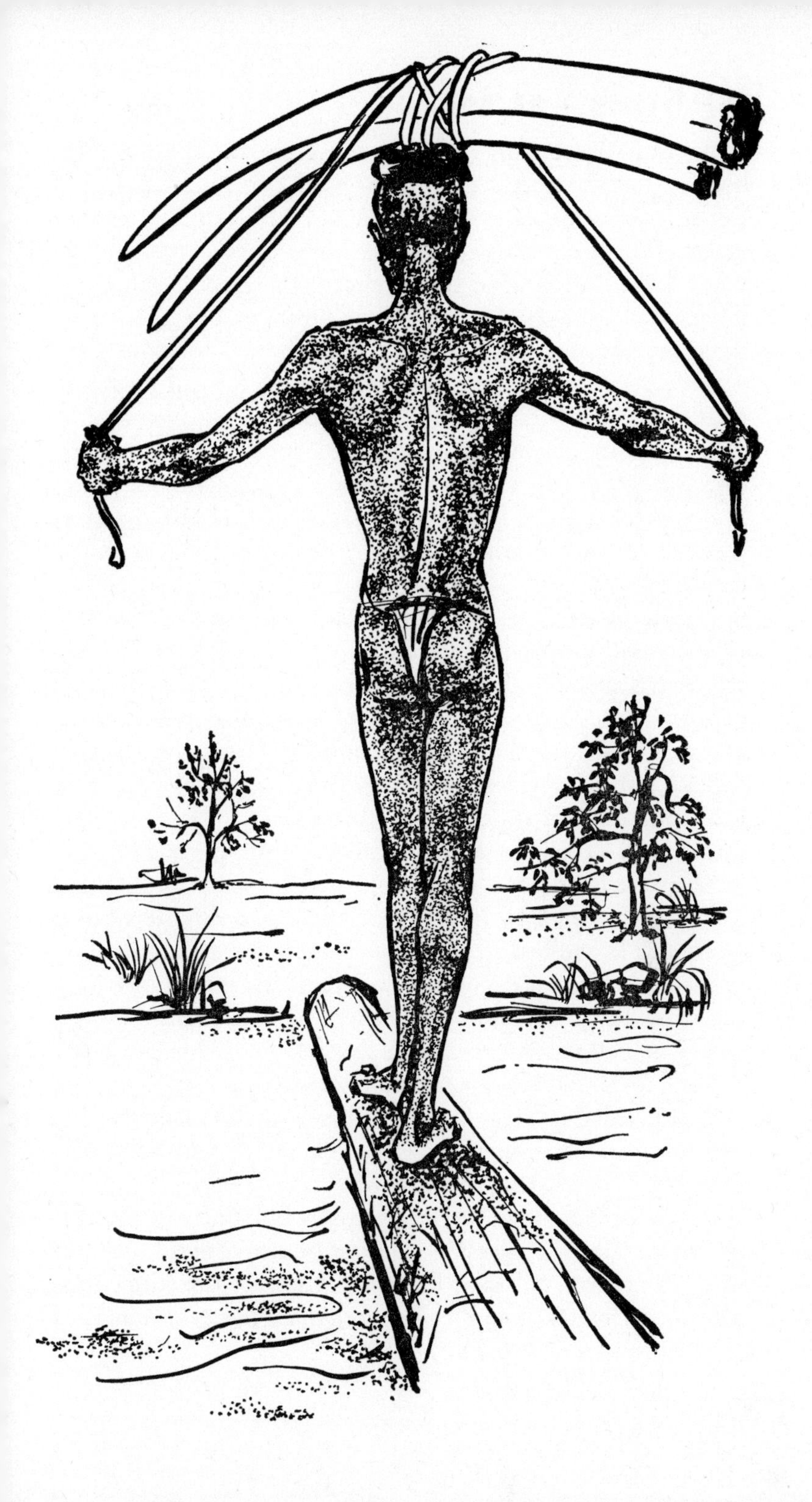

artifacts and art works were made from it. The Narwhal horns, spears, or tusks, though used for many practical things like sword handles, early acquired a religious connotation. They were marketed as the horns of unicorns, are still depicted sticking out of the foreheads of rampant horses on the British coat-of-arms, and the Church in the West used them as legs and struts for episcopal thrones. Walrus ivory was used for sculpturing, and in the Orient it went mostly to China, where it was used to make armor.

Abu ivory comes in innumerable colors, consistencies, forms, and conditions. That of female loxodonts is the finest. It is yellowish and oily when first cut, but dries out to a clear white. The best grade is almost transparent with a bluish cast when fresh cut. Elephant ivory of the best quality starts out pure white when fresh but in time degrades in color to yellow and eventually to dark brown. Mammoth ivory, which is scattered all over northern Siberia and Alaska and of which hundreds of thousands of tons have been dug up and exported to both the Orient and the West over the centuries (until it mysteriously ceased to appear on the Moscow market in 1934), being "dead" and very ancient, is mostly full of cracks and is friable. However, some mammoth ivory is as pure, white, and dense as that of any Elephant. But not all ivory is white or yellow. Almost all of it while still borne by its rightful owners in the wild has a thick brown overcoating called the "bark" which must be scraped off to disclose its true color. The tusk inside may be any shade of yellow, olive, brown, mauvish, or even jet black. Sometimes also it may be naturally mottled.

Also, the tusks of both Elephants and loxodonts vary enormously in shape and size. Both sexes of both species of loxodont bear tusks, but those of the males are larger. The Bush Loxodonts have the larger tusks, but those of the Forest Loxodonts often are much larger in proportion to the size of their bearers. Further, the longest Forest Loxodont tusks are much longer, though slimmer, than those of the Bush species. The tusks of elephants are much smaller and lighter than those of the loxodonts and are borne only by the males; those of the females, if developed at all, just reach the overfold of the lips and are barely visible. Strangely, today, the Elephants of Ceylon are almost exclusively tuskless though they are a sturdy breed, and it is recorded that, like their mainland relatives, they once bore tusks.

Perhaps the oddest tusk form is known in Burma as *kyan zit,* in which both tusks are regularly ringed, constricted, and ridged throughout their length and right up to their roots, like a bamboo. Another form is that of a corkscrew, which in extreme cases forms such a compact twist that the tusk is almost straight and bears a "thread" like the Narwhal's spear or the tusks of the extinct *Cordillerion* (see Chapter 2). Loxodonts and Elephants may be born with only one tusk or none at all, yet three- and four-tuskers have been found. Most curious of all, perhaps, were the skulls of two young elephants—one with tusks growing downward and backward, the other having a bifurcating tusk—which were once on display in a small hotel in Penang.

The first multi-tusk Abu was described in 1865. It has now become recognized that the condition occurs in both loxodonts and elephants with regularity. Some of these are really remarkable. One killed in 1868 in South Africa had five tusks on one side and four on the other. In 1952 one was killed in Uganda with eight on one side and a normal one on the other. In 1947 in the Kasongo a bull was shot that had two perfectly formed tusks on both sides, each weighing fifty pounds.

From here on I will speak of ivory in its restricted sense, being that of the living Abu. It must be borne in mind, though, that there was probably as much mammoth ivory about in bygone days as there was loxodont or elephant. Ivory is an organic substance known as dentine, of which the bulk of our own teeth is made. Like our own and all other teeth, a proboscidean tusk contains a central pulp cavity reaching almost from its tip (as a tiny canal) back to between a half and two thirds of its length and then swelling out in the shape of a cone until it forms the whole base of the "tooth" and merges with the soft parts lining the socket in the upper jaw. The hollow basal part of the tusk is called the "bamboo" for obvious reasons, and its extent varies considerably in proportion to the length of the whole tusk. The tip beyond the central apex of the pulp cavity is called the "point" and generally is more solid and of finer grain than the rest of the tusk.

Ivory is highly elastic but as strong as spring steel, and a riding crop made from a lengthwise strip of it is as supple as a willow switch. Cut to the thickness of ordinary typing paper, it is so transparent that standard print can be read through it, and at the same time its structure of concentric rings and small lozenge-shaped whorls, which look like engine-turning on the back of a watch, become visible. The concentric rings are called "laminae," and the Elephant has about a dozen per tusk to the mammoths' two dozen. Dentine is akin to cartilage but is "solidified" with phosphate of lime and other minerals, including fluoride of calcium (the chief ingredient of tooth enamel), the percentage of which gradually increases in "dead" ivory to as much as ten per cent. At the same time the gelatinous component gradually dries out, so that very old ivories tend to crumble. Ancient ivory statues are restored by boiling in albumen or gelatin. Ivory is about two and a half times as heavy as water. Hippo and Walrus teeth are covered with an immensely hard, flint-like dentine that will strike sparks from iron. It can hardly be cut and blunts files and the hardest-tempered steel.

The finest ivory is translucent and comes from West Africa—from between 10° N. and 10° S. of the equator. A belief is that the nearer the equator, the better the ivory is, and the farther away, the less desirable, except in East Africa. However, a glance at the map will show that these latitudes exactly enclose the range of the Forest Loxodont, from Gambia to Ruwenzori, and it is the ivory of that species which is the finest. The average size of tusks brought to the market today (which is still in London for "soft" ivory, and in Amsterdam for "hard") is about 50 pounds in weight and 5 to 6 feet long. This ivory is almost all loxodont; the Elephant has not been hunted for some time for ivory, and very little ivory now comes from the Orient. Before protective measures against poaching and the killing of young animals were introduced, the average weight of tusks was about 20 pounds. The French once placed a 4½-pound *lower* limit on the size of tusks in Equatorial Africa, but hunters still persuaded the authorities that there was a Pygmy Elephant the tusks of which never reached even that size, and hundreds of smaller tusks duly turned up on the market, but all of them were patently those of immature Forest Loxodonts.

The amount of ivory coming on the market today remains about the same year to year, and it averages in price about $3 per pound. Prices in the past are hard to calculate, as they were quoted in sterling and of course at various rates. About 10 tons of ivory per year now reaches the market, which, at about 20 Abu per ton, means only some 200 Abu now killed annually. However, a lot of "dead" or hoarded ivory still reaches the market. In addition, there are also the trophies carried away by modern licensed hunters and tourists. A certain amount of ivory goes direct to other markets, notably to the Orient ex Africa, but most of this is the "bamboo." In 1893 over 60 tons valued at £62,391 reached London from the Orient and 150 tons valued at £142,078 from Africa. In other words, the price has a little more than doubled. During the period 1870-81, 5,286 tons were imported into England, and from the known number of tusks represented, their average weight was only 40 pounds *per pair*. Small—10- to 20-pound—tusks are called "scrivelloes." Going backward still farther we find only 40 tons imported in 1850, 25 in 1848, and 15 in 1827. Thus, we are more or less back where we started when the great invasion of Africa began and the ruthless slaughter of the loxodonts started.

A rather curious feature is the number of tusks which contain bullets, shot, or even spearheads embedded in them. The number would seem to be quite disproportionate were it not for the fact that the average hunter aims for a head shot, and the tusks go far up into the head near the best point at which to aim. A bullet hitting a tusk will shatter it, but one penetrating the pulp cavity at its head will lodge there and then slowly sink down into the pulp and eventually be enveloped in the new ivory that grows outward layer inside layer. Objects are moved around during growth, so that they come to lie with their long axes parallel to the surfaces of the tusk.

Ivory is cut with very thin circular saws that have to be wetted constantly. It may even have to be cut under water for very delicate operations. Oil is seldom used, as it is absorbed and stains the finished product. Ivory is also, of course, sawed by hand and cut and carved with everything from a machete to a dentist's drill. Every scrap of the tusk is used. From the points come billiard balls, chessmen, and other hard-used utilitarian objects. The main shaft is delaminated and the plates cut for such items as the handles of cutlery. In fact, this was once ivory's greatest use and a quarter of it at one time went to Sheffield in England for that purpose. Another quarter went to the towns of Ivoryton and Deep River in Connecticut and to a few other American cities where the keyboards of pianos were made. The little bits and pieces went and still go to button manufacturers. The sawdust is used as fertilizer or is boiled down to make gelatin or a light sizing for use by the weavers of straw hats and lace. The scraps have always been distilled to make ivory black, the process having been invented by the early Arabic alchemists.

The list of other things that have been and still are made from ivory would fill pages. Combs with as many as seventy teeth per inch were once made of it and were much in vogue; and brushes made of solid ivory into which clumps of hog bristles were directly inserted in holes by a process of softening and expanding the ivory and then drying it closed. The farther back in history you go, the more items you find made of this substance and the more highly it was esteemed.

Attempts to resolidify ivory dust have been made for centuries, but all have failed. Recently, scientists have discovered how to pulverize ox bones, store the material, and then build parts of living human bones with this. The human body takes over, infiltrates the mass with blood vessels, and in time replaces all the material with new human bone-growth. False teeth used to be made of ivory, and work is now proceeding on techniques for pulverizing dentine for building up human teeth, just as we can make machine parts with powdered metals. Perhaps the Abu will thus make still another contribution to the welfare of their old rivals.

It has always been in the arts, however, that ivory has figured most prominently. We have already several times alluded to the ivories of the ancients, but we have not discussed the utterly amazing art of the Chinese in this material, who still remain, after some four thousand years, the arch ivory carvers. Their genius has for the most part been displayed in the miniature—the exquisite statuettes, models of temples and pagodas, animal statuaries, and in those mysterious series of carved hollow spheres, one within the other, that take years to execute but only a few dollars to purchase.

Incidentally, I recall a gift given my mother by the last Manchu Emperor, Pu-yi. It was a sculpture of an ordinary clam shell and of life size, but within its half-opened shell was a complete scene of a Chinese summer pavilion set among trees and shrubs and with a garden sloping to a pond. On the pond were five ducks and each bore a collar. A man wearing a big straw hat stood on the bank and held a string attached to each of the collars. I recall with what amazement I first saw, with the aid of a very strong magnifying glass, that each of these strings was carved into the twisted form of a rope and that all were separately gathered into the minuscule right hand of the man! The ducks were about a millimeter long. How the artist could have done such work, even aided by powerful eyeglasses, is really incomprehensible.

Allegedly there were once enormous ivory statues—or rather, statues covered with ivory—in inner China and in India during early periods, but it was apparently the Greeks who perfected this larger-scaled art. Ivory was known and used at the time of Homer in 600 B.C., but it came into its real glory at the hands of the great classical artists. Even though its use was gaudy, ivory was not beneath the dignity of some of Greece's greatest sculptors. Theirs was an art form known as *chryselephantine* in which ivory was mixed with solid gold, cedar and other woods, gems, and other materials. With these materials the Greeks made statues rising up to forty feet in height, like that of Minerva in the Parthenon in Athens. According to Pausanias, such colossi were numerous, and he mentions a Venus at Megara constructed by none other than Praxiteles, and also a Hebe by Naucides, and a vast work in gold and ivory by Phidias at Elis. The Romans later learned the art and erected hundreds of such effigies.

It seems that the Greeks learned from somebody how to soften ivory. The Jews had long before made much use of

---

A bull Forest Loxodont with four well-developed tusks, each weighing about 50 pounds; shot near Kasongo, in the Congo, in 1947; the skull is now in the Musée du Congo Belge, in Brussels.

this material for thrones, couches, beds, and other furniture and many of these were paneled with solid sheets of ivory. The Phoenicians even made covers of this substance for the seats of the rowers in their galleys. Wherever the softening method originated, the Greeks perfected the art. Unfortunately they have not left us any technical details as to how they did this, but there is a fifteenth-century recipe in a manuscript in the British Museum which states that ivory can be rendered as soft and pliable as wax in muriatic acid, when it can then be molded; after which it can be hardened again in white vinegar. It is believed that the ancients first somehow softened the whole tusk, then straightened it out and either cut it in half longitudinally and separated the laminae and flattened each out, thus obtaining "planks" up to 2 feet wide; or that they slit it down to the central pulp channel and then flattened the whole out, thereby getting planks up to 4 feet in width. Then, it is also supposed, they either had wood molds prepared or, alternatively, had the whole statue already completely in hardwood. On to this they laid the sheets of pliable ivory, covering all those parts representing exposed skin, and then hardened it on with some adhesive beneath. Clothing was then represented by gold sheet or leaf, while the thrones, bases, and other appurtenances were left bare in the appropriate materials.

Ivory can be both dyed and etched, and it is known that the Greeks and Romans colored their statuaries. The ivory was apparently given perfectly natural skin tones. The eyes were painted in, and eyebrows, mustaches, beards, and so forth added in real hair. The jewelry was real gems; fingernails were made of cow horn and polished; scepters were of bronze, and sandals of leather. In fact, it is little wonder that the ancients were awed by the colossal statues of their gods, for they must have been utterly lifelike. Ivory will take a very fine polish with chalk and wet leather, and it can be made to resemble the grain of flesh with rouge, sponge, and sand.

The Romans, as we pointed out before, were basically pragmatic gadgeteers. They absorbed the arts of others as sponges suck in water and they got most of their initial culture from the Etruscans. The Etruscans seem to have worked ivory, though where they got the material from is a mystery unless they killed off the last European mammoths or retrieved buried caches of tusks. Ivory was a symbol of power to them, and they transferred this symbol to the Romans, who held the material in the highest esteem, even using it as currency. Roman magistrates sat on thrones made of ivory, and consuls had chryselephantine chairs made in Etrusca. They used ivory for dagger and sword hilts and they used it on the harness of their steeds. Their "Congressional Record" was traditionally inscribed on ivory, as were the births, marriages, and deaths of their prominent citizens and their key census figures. They dyed it, encrusted it, etched it, and carved it. They made the first *diptychs* of it.

Diptychs were the standard stenographers' pads of the day, being two slabs of ivory joined together by two or more cord hinges, the inner faces of the slabs being slightly guttered and filled with a thin layer of wax. On this, Roman secretaries took notes with a stylus; the notes were preserved when the two leaves were closed. The outside was carved and engraved with the name of the owner and with various designs and scenes. It became the practice for newly appointed consuls to present a number of these to their sponsors, to local senators, and to other prominent persons on the occasion of elevation to office. A few have been preserved.

Later, these diptychs were adopted by the princes and bishops of the Holy Roman Church. In many cases the head of the Roman consul was merely given a tonsure, the name of a saint inscribed below, and the note pad was ready for use in recording sermons, hymns, and incantations. Some of these also have been preserved. Later came *triptychs,* and carved-ivory (spelled in Old English, *iverey, eivry, yvory, ivery, et al.*) caskets containing the relics of saints and apostles; and then came crooks, pastoral staves, crucifixes, and just about every other church appurtenance made in the same substance. Even the *flabellum* devised in the East to waft flies off the sacrament was traditionally made of ivory in the West.

After the virtual disappearance of ivory in secular circles, after the fall of Rome, it soon reappeared in the form of sets of chessmen and the like which were sent to western potentates by the caliphs. In fact, we have a more continuous record of ivories than we have of any other European art form, with the possible exception of manuscripts, and despite its friability, more of it has come down to us than of any gem or metal, and even of architecture.

[11]

OF THE IMPERIAL AND THE ROYAL

The initial exploration of Africa.

The attitude to loxodonts;

and letters from European residents.

It was a desire for ivory, and thus a search for the Abu, which in the expansion of Europe took second place only to the proverbial search for "spices," which has been given in history books as the principal reason for the quest for a direct trade route to the Orient. It was quite true that in order to preserve food for the winter and make it palatable, spices were needed in Europe, and the sources of those commodities were in the East and had been cut off by the Arabs. Ivory was a precious material in Europe and also had to be obtained through the Near Easterners, so we see why it was much prized by the first Europeans who reached Equatorial Africa.

However, apart from the stolid Hollanders in the extreme south, none of the other powers did anything much about Africa until the end of the eighteenth century. The continent intrigued Europeans, but their only real knowledge of it still came only from the ancients. They read of fantastic empires south of the Sahara which had exchanged consulates with Rome and of vast mountains allegedly visited by Roman captains where the river Nile began. There were also current all manner of exotic stories about Prester John and other fabulous characters. It is extremely difficult for us to comprehend that only a century and a half ago our ancestors knew absolutely nothing of the second biggest continent in the world although they had by then been sailing around it for over 300 years. Then, in 1788 an organization called the African Association was formed in London. Although it did nothing and disintegrated, some of its members gathered funds to send a most remarkable young Scotsman, a twenty-four-year-old medical student named Mungo Park, on a scatterbrained expedition to West Africa. His objectives were various and preposterous. For example, he was to treaty with the "Emperor" of Timbuktu, a place that had become a legend.

This agile young man sailed to Gambia, spent time there learning the Mandingo language, and then meandered into the backcountry. He was the first man really to explore Africa and he brought back the first true accounts of the hinterland of the country's western bulge. Park was born in 1771 and died in 1806, but an account of his travels was not published until 1842 in Edinburgh, by William and Robert Chambers. It is a priceless document and tells us much about the inner working of the ivory trade.

In this, under the heading "An Account of the Country and the Natives," Mungo Park says: "The commodities exported to the Gambia from Europe consist chiefly of firearms and ammunition, iron ware, spirituous liquors, tobacco, cotton caps, a small quantity of broad cloth, and a few articles of the manufacture of Manchester; a small assortment of India goods, with small glass beads, amber, and other trifles: for which are taken in exchange slaves, gold dust, ivory, bees' wax, and hides. Slaves are the chief article, but the whole number which at this time are annually exported from the Gambia by all nations, is supposed to be under one thousand.

"Nothing creates a greater surprise among the Negroes on the sea-coast, than the eagerness displayed by the European traders to procure elephants' teeth—it being exceedingly difficult to make them comprehend to what use it is applied. Although they are shown knives with ivory hafts, combs, and toys of the same material, and are convinced that the ivory thus manufactured was originally parts of a tooth, they are not satisfied. They suspect that this commodity is more frequently converted in Europe to purposes of far greater importance, the true nature of which is studiously concealed from them, lest the price of ivory should be enhanced. They cannot, they say, easily persuade themselves, that ships would be built, and voyages undertaken, to procure an article which had no other value than that of furnishing handles to knives, &c., when pieces of wood would answer the purpose equally well.

"The greater part of the ivory which is sold on the Gambia and Senegal rivers, is brought from the interior country. The lands towards the coast are too swampy, and too much intersected with creeks and rivers, for so bulky an animal as the elephant to travel through without being discovered; and when once the natives discern the marks of his feet in the earth, the whole village is up in arms. The thoughts of feasting on his flesh, making sandals of his hide, and selling the teeth to the Europeans, inspire every one with courage, and the animal seldom escapes from his pursuers; but in the plains of Bambarra and Kaarta, and the extensive wilds of Jallonkadoo, the elephants are very numerous, and, from the great scarcity of gunpowder in those districts, they are less annoyed by the natives.

"Scattered teeth are frequently picked up in the woods, and travellers are very diligent in looking for them. It is a common practice with the elephant to thrust his teeth under the roots of such shrubs and bushes as grow in the more dry and elevated parts of the country, where the soil is shallow. These bushes he easily overturns, and feeds on the roots, which are in general more tender and juicy than the hard woody branches or the foliage; but when the teeth are partly decayed by age, and the roots more firmly fixed, the great exertions of the animal in this practice frequently causes them to break short. At Kamalia, I saw two teeth, one a very large one, which were found in the woods, and which were evidently broken off, in this manner. Indeed, it is difficult otherwise to account for such a large proportion of broken ivory as is daily offered for sale at the different factories, for when the elephant is killed in hunting, unless he dashes himself over a precipice, the teeth are always extracted entire.

"There are certain seasons of the year when the elephants collect into large herds, and traverse the country in quest of food or water; and as all that part of the country to the north of the Niger is destitute of rivers, whenever the pools in the woods are dried up, the elephants approach towards the banks of that river. Here they continue until the commencement of the rainy season, in the months of June or July, and during this time they are much hunted by such of the Bambarrans as have gunpowder to spare. The elephant-hunters seldom go out singly—a party of four or five join together, and having each furnished himself with powder and ball, and a quantity of corn-meal in a leather bag sufficient for five or six days' provision, they enter the most unfrequented parts of the wood, and examine with great care every thing that can lead to the discovery of the elephants. In this pursuit, notwithstanding the bulk of the animal, very great nicety of observation is required. The broken branches, the scattered dung of the animal, and the marks of his feet, are carefully inspected; and many of the hunters have, by long experience and attentive observation, become so expert in their search, that as soon as they observe the footmarks of an elephant, they will tell almost to a certainty at what time it passed, and at what distance it will be found.

"When they discover a herd of elephants, they follow them at a distance, until they perceive some one stray from the rest, and come into such a situation as to be fired at with advantage. The hunters then approach with great caution, creeping amongst the long grass, until they have got near enough to be sure of their aim. They then discharge all their pieces at once, and throw themselves on their faces among the grass. The wounded elephant immediately applies his trunk to the different wounds, but being unable to extract the balls, and seeing nobody near him, he becomes quite furious, and runs about amongst the bushes, until by fatigue and loss of blood he has exhausted himself, and affords the hunters an opportunity of firing a second time at him, by which he is generally brought to the ground.

"The skin is now taken off, and extended on the ground with pegs to dry; and such parts of the flesh as are most esteemed are cut up into thin slices, and dried in the sun, to serve for provisions on some future occasion. The teeth are struck out with a light hatchet, which the hunters always carry along with them, not only for that purpose, but also to enable them to cut down such trees as contain honey; for though they carry with them only five or six days' provisions, they will remain in the woods for months, if they are successful, and support themselves upon the flesh of such elephants as they kill, and wild honey.

"The ivory thus collected is seldom brought down to the coast by the hunters themselves. They dispose of it to the itinerant merchants, who come annually from the coast with arms and ammunition to purchase this valuable commodity.

Some of these merchants will collect ivory in the course of one season sufficient to load four or five asses. A great quantity of ivory is likewise brought from the interior by the slave coffles; there are, however, some slatees of the Mohammedan persuasion, who, from motives of religion, will not deal in ivory, nor eat of the flesh of the elephant, unless it has been killed with a spear.

"The quantity of ivory collected in this part of Africa is not so great, nor are the teeth in general so large, as in the countries nearer the line: few of them weigh more than eighty or one hundred pounds, and, upon an average, a bar of European merchandise may be reckoned as the price of a pound of ivory."

Nothing could better sum up the situation in Africa at the end of the eighteenth century. The second House of Abu now stood face to face with their age-old rivals. After almost 2,000 years of mere skirmishing, open warfare was declared upon them by their native rivals and lethally armed foreigners. But, unlike their Asiatic cousins, they did not submit docilely; rather, they fought, and despite their terrible losses, they were not conquered.

Though Mungo Park was the first true "explorer" of Africa in the modern sense, he was by no means the first person to write cogently about the continent. Europeans resided all around the coast of Africa during the seventeenth and eighteenth centuries, and many wrote reports home. There is a delightful series of books entitled *A General Collection of the Best and Most Interesting Voyages and Travels in All Parts of the World: Many of Which Are Now First Translated into English, by John Pinkerton (Published in London, 1814)*. In this collection appear two very colorful accounts showing what Europeans thought about loxodonts at that time. One is entitled *A Voyage to Congo and Several Other Countries, Chiefly in Southern Africk;* this was written in the seventeenth century by one Father Jerom Merollas da Sorrento, and states:

"Among the variety of numerous quadrupeds, the most wonderful are the elephants, being, as it were, living and moving mines of most curious white ivory, whereof so great a trade is made; but these being vulgarly known to all persons, I will give no other account but only the manner of killing them.

"When these beasts are gathered together in a herd, the hunter anointing himself all over with their dung, gets in slily with his lance in his hand among them; there does he creep about from one to the other, under their bellies, till he sees an opportunity to strike any of them under their ear, by which wound they are easily to be brought to the ground. After the stroke is given, the hunter takes immediate care to escape, before the beast can well turn about to revenge himself; and the other beasts being deceived by the smell of their dung, take no notice of his crying out, and flouncing, supposing it to be only one of their young. By these means the rest of the herd walking on, and forsaking their falling companion, leave him a prey to the successful hunter. If the wounded elephant happens to pursue his assaulter, he can easily baffle him, by taking to many roads, for it is a very difficult thing for this beast to turn his body so often as such a dodging would require. The Negroes are wont to distil a water by the sun from the bones of this animal's leges, which is held to be good against astmas, sciaticas, or any cold humours. Some of the pagans of these parts, particularly the Giaghi, have a kind of devotion for the tail of this beast; for when any one of their captains or chief lords comes to die, they commonly preserve one of these tails in memory of him, and to which they pay a sort of adoration, out of an opinion they have of its great strength. For the sake of cutting off these tails only, they often undertake this hunting; but which amputation must be performed at one blow, and from a living elephant, or their superstition will allow it no *virtue*."

Some of this may sound purely mythical, but it would

appear to be a fact that loxodonts were hunted in this way and that their tails were so cropped.

Also in John Pinkerton's series is another title—*A New and Accurate Description of the Coast of Guinea,* written in 1698 by William Bosman, a Hollander. This document also is in the form of letters sent home and is such a treasure trove of long-forgotten facts and literary *naïveté* that it would be unforgivable merely to paraphrase its contents. He wrote:

"It is but reasonable that I should begin with that wonderful beast the elephant, who is endowed with so many different, good and remarkable qualities, that, to rob him of the first place among the beasts, is a piece of injustice. I shall not recite a great many particulars concerning him; either because I cannot relate them upon my own observation, or that several have done it already: besides which, some authors have allowed themselves to tell us several very strange and ill-digested stories concerning its copulation, pregnancy, bringing forth its young, its age, changing its teeth, and several other follies; and it is not without reason that I call them so. For, as far as I can learn, no man in the world ever saw how they engendered, nor can tell how long they go pregnant, in what separable places they calf their young, or whether they change their teeth or not. These are all wild guesses, of which we can get no information by tamed elephants, and, therefore, this knowledge must come out of the woods; but how they come to converse so long with these wild beasts there as to obtain such an accurate account of them, I can scarce believe anybody, except good

---

A few African tribesmen still hunt the Bush Loxodont with spears and by frontal attack. This was the common practice among Bantu tribes before the introduction of firearms.

old Pliny can pretend to it. At present, several of his relations have been confirmed by the discoveries of judicious travellers.

"We shall let Pliny alone, and return to the elephant [i.e., the Forest Loxodont in this case], whom we find here in Africa to be a beast of twelve or thirteen foot high, and, consequently, much less than those in East India, since the writers concerning that country assure us, that its height there amounts to more cubits: besides this difference, they do not differ in their nature or shape from those in other places.[1]

"These beasts prove very prejudicial to the fruit-trees, especially orange-trees, bananas, and another sort of figs; of the last of which, they eat both fruit and stem.

"The Negroes also affirm, that the elephants, meeting any people in the woods, never offer any violence to them; but that, if the shot levelled at them misses, they grow very wild. But I have observed directly the contrary of one of them in our garden at Elmina the last year. At Rio de Gabon, four, five, and more elephants have frequently passed by me and my company without offering us any injury, but we were not courageous enough to present them with a few bullets, though very well stored; for they are very difficult to be killed, unless the ball happens to light betwixt the eyes and the ears; to which end, the bullet ought to be iron also. Their skin is as good proof against the common musket leadballs, as a wall; and if they hit the mentioned place, become entirely flat.

"The country here where the greatest number of elephants are found, is chiefly that before we come at the Gold Coast, and is, from the multitude of their teeth which are there traded for, properly called the Tooth, or Elephants' Tooth Coast,[2] extending to the Gold Coast, and takes in the country of Awine, Jummore, Equira, Abocroe, Ancober, and

[1] This is, of course, all quite inaccurate.

[2] I.e., previously called the Ivory Coast, now known as Guinea, which gained its independence from France in 1958.

Axim, several elephants being daily killed in the said places; and the wilder and less inhabited the lands are, the larger quantity of elephants and wild beasts are found.

"Ante also doth not want these beasts, there being not only in the in-land country multitudes of them shot, but besides that they come daily to the sea-shore, and so near our forts, that they are in sight of our people, and do a great deal of mischief.

"In the tract of land betwixt Ante and Accra, there are a few, though not so many as in the former countries, because this place hath long been reasonably well peopled, except the country of Fetu, which, for five or six years past, hath lain almost waste; wherefore there is a much larger number of elephants there at present than formerly.

"A great part of the country about Accra lying waste and uninhabited, a great quantity are annually killed here. In the year 1697, one of an uncommon magnitude was killed near Accra, just by our fortress, and no doubt but that he was at least full-aged, his two teeth weighing two hundred and twenty pounds; from which you may infer that he was not very light himself.

"In Ardra and Fida there are none, though in my time one was there killed, and the Negroes affirmed it was what had not happened in sixty years before; for which reason, I believe he had accidentally strayed from some other country; for the in-land countries of Benin (which borders on Ardra), Rio de Dalbary, Camerones, and several other adjacent countries, are so incredibly overcharged with these beasts, that it is to be admired how the inhabitants live there.

"The vast numbers of teeth traded for in these countries, clearly evince the great abundance of elephants here; but whether all those are taken from slaughtered elephants, or some of them are found in the woods, or elsewhere, I cannot determine: though I am apt to think that here they come by them both ways; from whence it should seem that, as some tell us, the elephants change their teeth; but this is utterly contradicted by the great difference betwixt the teeth themselves, some of them weighing one, two, or three pounds, and others progressively heavy, till they amount to above one hundred pounds weight: nor is it in the least probable, that a solid body, composed of such hard substance as elephants' teeth, can, in about twenty years' time, grow from one to a hundred pounds weight: how this happens to increase, I must own I am ignorant.

"I shall now add something concerning the elephant; of which I have in one of my former letters told you that unprovoked he very seldom falls on mankind, but when urged to it falls on with wondrous fierceness. Both which I shall here confirm by a couple of instances; and shew you how difficult it is to kill them.

"In the year 1700, in December at six in the morning, an elephant came here to Elmina, walking easily along the shore under the hill of St. Jago: some Negroes were so bold as to go against him without any thing in their hands, in a sort to welcome and bring him in. He suffered them to encompass him, and very quietly went along with them to just under the mount St. Jago: where one of our officers belonging to that hill, and a Negro which came down with him, fired on him immediately; and the officer's ball hit him above his eye. This and the following shot which the Negroes poured on him were so far from provoking him, that they did not move him to mend his pace in the least; he only seemed to threaten the Negroes betwixt whiles, but still let them alone.

"It was surprising, when he threatened to fall on the men, to see him prick up his ears; which were of a prodigious size: however he went on, and lastly stept into our garden, expecting perhaps civiler treatment there.

"This extraordinary accident, and our own curiosity, drew the director-general and myself into the garden; and we were soon followed by some of our people. We found him standing in the midst of the garden; where, before our coming, he had broke down four or five cocoa-trees; which number, either to divert himself or shew us his strength, he augmented with five or six more in our presence. The strength which he seemed to use in breaking down a tree may very fitly be compared to the force which a man exerts in order to knock down a child of three or four years old.

"Whilst he stood here, above one hundred shot were fired at him, which made him bleed to that degree, as if an ox had been killed. During all which he did not stir, but only set up his ears, and made the men apprehend that he would follow them.

"But this sport was accompanied with a tragical event; for a Negro, fancying himself able to deal with him, went softly behind him, catched his tail in his hand, designing to cut a piece of it off; but the elephant being used to wear a tail, would not permit it to be shortened in his life-time: wherefore, after giving the Negro a stroke with his snout, he drew him to him, and trod upon him two or three times; and, as if that was not sufficient, he bored in his body two holes with his teeth, large enough for a man's double fist to enter. Then he let him lie, without making any farther attempt on him; and stood still also whilst two Negroes fetched away the dead body, not offering to meddle with them in the least.

"After the elephant had killed the Negro (which happened not above sixteen paces from us), and had been about an hour in the garden, he wheeled about as if he intended to fall on us, which made all that were in the garden to fly, each endeavouring to secure himself by getting away; but the greatest part made to mount St. Jago; thinking, indeed, with reason, that if they could reach that, they should be safe: but the elephant followed nobody out of the garden, which was very fortunate; for otherwise amongst such a number of people he had undoubtedly made a great slaughter, since nobody by swift running could have escaped him; which I believe on horseback is scarcely to be done.

"We all flew out of the garden, as I have told you, through

the fore-door, and the elephant took to the back-door; which, whether in his way, or whether it was too narrow for him to pass, I cannot tell, but he flung the door, though a brick and a half thick, a good distance; which I had the good fortune to see a good way off, but could not observe that to do that he very much exerted himself, but rather seemed only to touch it lightly. After which he did not pass through the gap where the door had been, but forced through the garden-hedge, going very softly by mount St. Jago towards the river, where he bathed himself in order to wash off the blood with which he was besmeared, or to cool himself after the heat occasioned by so much shot. After having refreshed himself a little in the river, he came out and stood under some trees where were some of our water-tubs; where he also cooled himself, and broke them in pieces, as he did also a canoe which lay by them. Whilst the elephant stood there, the shooting began to be renewed, till at last he fell down; after which they immediately cut off his snout, which was so hard and tough that it cost the Negroes thirty strokes before they could separate it, which must be very painful to the elephant, since it made him roar; which was the only noise I heard him make: after this he died under the mentioned tree; confirming the report of the Negroes, who tell us, that whenever an elephant finds his death approaching, if able, he always gets under a tree or into a wood.

"For the truth of which, though I will not be obliged to

Mother Bush Loxodont with baby. While both Elephants and Loxodonts are very solicitous of their young, the Loxodonts are more likely to abandon them in a stampede, but more often "readopt" them afterwards than do Elephants.

answer, it hath yet thrice happened at Elmina; and at Gabon I found a dead elephant in a pleasant thicket; of which more hereafter.

"The elephant was no sooner dead, than the Negroes fell on him in crowds; each cutting off as much as he could, so that he furnished a great many as well Whites as Blacks with food enough for that day.

"He was not very large; his teeth not weighing above four and thirty pound. Thus we had the diversion to have a near view of an elephant, and to see him partly exert his strength; and the pleasure had been much greater, if not allayed by the misfortune of the poor Negro, though it was his own fault. Hence we began to reflect to what danger we had exposed ourselves by venturing so near the elephant; for had he but once grown furious, his rage would doubtless have cost several men's lives, and perhaps we should have fallen the first, not being so swift of foot as the Negroes; besides, all making one way, we should have been in the way, and obstructed one another's flight.

"Upon this consideration we resolved never for the future to come so near an elephant; to which I would not advise any man who hath the least tenderness for his life.

"From both these instances it is sufficiently clear, that unprovoked they do not often hurt any body; but that they grow very fierce when shot at and missed doth not so plainly appear, since this elephant suffered above three hundred shot to be made at him, without any sign of being enraged or resistance: but as the same actions have not always the same success, I should be loath from hence to advise any person rashly to fire at an elephant, since this vast number of shot which were thundered at him were not sufficient to fetch him down; and those who pretend thoroughly to understand the elephant-shooting told us, that we ought to have shot iron-bullets, since those of lead are flattened, either by their bones or the toughness of their skin.

"This seems probable; for after his death we found of the

vast quantity of shot levelled at him very few had passed the bone into his head. Some remained betwixt the skin and the bone; most of them, more especially the small shot, was thrown off by his hide as if they had been shot against a wall. The bullets were certainly too small, since what the English factor told me, was confirmed by others, that as he was in river Gamby, in a canoe, he killed an elephant, which pursued him, with one shot only. For to imagine that none of the balls hit him in the proper place is not very reasonable, since in such a great number one must hit right, as appeared after his death."

Slowly Europeans came to know the loxodonts, and their discoveries seem always to have provided considerable surprises. This attitude of marvel and bewilderment lasted until the time of the great explorers in the nineteenth century. We find numerous reports like that written by one Monsieur Adanson, of the Royal Academy of Sciences of France, of a journey he made into Senegal in 1795. He expressed amazement at seeing "a great number of elephants all along the banks of the river." Only in extreme South Africa were conditions somewhat different. There the Hollanders had established themselves, got to know the local game, and set to work to clear it out while bagging all the ivory they could under pretense of "sport." As early as 1772 the famous Swedish botanist Thunberg could write that on a visit to that country he had met "the first sportsman in the colony," who, "by killing elephants and selling their teeth, had acquired a tolerable fortune." He continues: "This man informed me that in its infancy, the colony had so small an extent, and the Hottentots in it were so numerous, that the Christian settlers could not without danger venture as far as Zwellendam. At that time too the elephants abounded so much, even near the Cape, that in travelling to and from the Cape, one might kill a great many of them. Thus he had often shot four or five in a day, and sometimes twelve or thirteen. Twice in his life, when he was out in pursuit of these animals, he had destroyed with his gun twenty-two elephants each day. A good sportsman always kills the elephant at one shot, but, should he hit any of the fore-legs, so as to break it, two shots must be fired; the hunter always takes his aim in such a manner as that the ball shall pass through the lungs. The ball is always mixed with one third of tin, and weighs a quarter of a pound; the piece is in proportion to this, and rather heavy. Each elephant's tooth weighs from thirty to one hundred and thirty pounds. They are bought up by the Dutch Company, at the rate of one guilder per pound."

[12]

OF THE SLAUGHTER OF THE BEASTS

The early settlers and explorers of Africa. Loxodont hunting and slaughter. Conservation and respite.

It was not until 1850—just a little over a century ago—that the real investigation and exploration of the continent of Africa began. The opening gambit was the journey of a German, Henry Barth, south across the Sahara on behalf of the Royal Geographical Society of London and the British government. This was an astonishing feat. Barth was gone several years and wrote a painstaking report, in which he repeatedly mentions the large numbers of elephants he encountered all the way from Timbuktu, in the west, to Lake Chad, in the east, and south to the northern limit of the closed-canopy forest in what is now Nigeria. These were Bush Loxodonts, and in some places they were so numerous that the whole surface of the earth was pitted with their foot tracks made when the ground was soft in the rainy season and hardened in the dry, and Barth complains about them as forming a miserable surface on which to have to sleep. He also makes a curious remark about these animals seen in Adamawa, the open upland territory south of the Benue River in the northern Cameroons. He says: "Of animals, the elephant is exceedingly frequent, not only the black or gray, but also a yellow species." He probably saw a herd or herds that had been wallowing in clay pits.

The final onslaught on the Dark Continent was made by three principal routes: up the Nile to Uganda and the great lakes; west from Zanzibar to Lake Tanganyika and then on to the river Lualaba; and north from the Cape, across the Zambesi, and so on to that same river. The Guinea Coast became a separate operation. The vast triangle forming the central-equatorial, closed-canopy forest block from Nigeria to the Bahr-el-Ghazal and south to Angola was ignored. Not until Stanley had boated down the Lualaba and the Congo and come out at Boma in 1875 was Africa crossed.

This triangle is the home of the Forest Loxodont. All the great explorers speak of "elephants," and as most of them were by tradition what used to be called "sportsmen," many of them avid "big-game hunters," and some of them keen naturalists, their records are of great interest. The "elephants" they speak of are invariably the Bush Loxodont. Two of the best informed were Richard F. Burton, who explored the Lakes region in the years 1856-9, and the experienced big-game hunter Sir Samuel W. Baker, who had spent many years observing elephants in India and Ceylon and loxodonts in Abyssinia.

Burton gives a very clear picture of the horrendous conditions in the territories that were then being preyed upon by all manner of native scoundrels, crooked Indian traders, and predaceous Arab raiders. The Sultan of Zanzibar, although controlling almost the entire export trade, did not administer the interior. Like his predecessors, he organized slave raids, permitted others to conduct them, and made his money from taxes levied on their proceeds, but he was not the arch ogre in the picture. In fact, the Sultan of Zanzibar did more to eradicate slavery at that time than any other person of authority, after signing a treaty with Britain and other powers to that effect in the year 1873. Burton reached Lake Tanganyika, where he noted a singular absence of game, generally caused, he believed, by the tsetse flies, but remarked on the presence of elephants in the bamboo thickets. He says that the mountains of ivory exported from there came from several thousand square miles of country around. Ivory was worth its exact weight in the brass wire prized by the locals for self-adornment. He gives an account of the methods used in hunting the Abu in that area. He states:

"The elephant hunt is with the African a solemn and serious undertaking. He fortifies himself with periapts (amulets) and prophylactics given by the mganga,[1] who also trains him to the use of his weapon. The elephant-spear resembles our boarding-pike rather than the light blunt arm employed in war; it is about six feet long, with a broad tapering head cut away at the shoulders, and supported by an iron neck, which is planted in a thick wooden handle, the junction being secured by a cylinder of raw hide from a cow's tail passed over it, and shrunk on by drying: a specimen was deposited with the Royal Geographical Society. The spear is invariably guarded by a mpigi or charm, the usual two bits of wood bound together with a string or strip of skin. It is not a little curious that the East African, though born and bred a hunter, is, unlike almost all barbarians, as skill-less as an European in the art of *el asr,* the 'spoor' or 'sign.'

"The great art of the African Muinzi or elephant-hunter is to separate a tusker from the herd without exciting suspicion, and to form a circle round the victim. The mganga, then rising with a shout, hurls or thrusts the first spear, and his example is followed by the rest. The weapons are not

[1] Medicine-man.

poisoned: they are fatal by a succession of small wounds. The baited beast rarely breaks, as might be expected, through the frail circle of assailants: its proverbial obstinacy is excited; it charges one man, who slips away, when another, with a scream, thrusts the long stiff spear into its hind quarters, which makes it change intention and turn fiercely from the fugitive to the fresh assailant. This continues till the elephant, losing breath and heart, attempts to escape; its enemies then redouble their efforts, and at length the huge prey, overpowered by pain and loss of blood trickling from a hundred gashes, bites the dust. The victors, after certain preliminaries of singing and dancing, carefully cut out the tusks with small, sharp axes, and the rich marrow is at once picked from the bamboo and devoured upon the spot, as the hare's liver is in Italy. The hunt concludes with a grand feast of fat and garbage, and the hunters return home in triumph, laden with ivory, with ovals of hide for shields, and with festoons of raw and odorous meat spitted upon long poles.

"Zanzibar is the principal mart for perhaps the finest and largest ivory in the world. It collects the produce of the lands lying between the parallels of 2° N. Lat. and 10° S. Lat., and the area extends from the coast to the regions lying westward of the Tanganyika Lake. It is almost the only legitimate article of traffic for which caravans now visit the interior.

"Whenever tusks are used as cattle-pens or to adorn

Uele Pigmy attacking Forest Loxodont. The Pigmy tribesmen creep up on their prey from behind and either hamstring them or drive a spear up the base of the spine, which paralyzes the quarry.

graves, the reason is that they are valueless on account of the want of conveyance.

"The merchants at Zanzibar recognize in ivory, the produce of these regions, three several qualities. The best, a white, soft, and large variety, with small 'bamboo,' is that from the Banadir, Brava, Makdishu, and Marka. A somewhat inferior kind, on account of its hardness, is brought from the countries of Chaga, Umasai, and Nguru. The Wamasai often spoil their tusks by cutting them, for the facility of transport; and, like people of Nguru and other tribes, they stain the exterior by sticking the tooth in the sooty rafters of their chimneyless huts, with the idea that so treated it will not crack or split in the sun. This red colour, erroneously attributed at Zanzibar to the use of ghee, is removed by the people with blood or cowdung mixed with water.

"The second quality is that imported from the regions about the Nyasa Lake, and carried to Kilwa by the Wabisa, the Wahiao, the Wangindo, the Wamakua, and other clans. The 'Bisha ivory' formerly found its way to the Mozambique, but the barbarians have now learned to prefer Zanzibar; and the citizens welcome them, as they sell their stores more cheaply than the Wahiao, who have become adepts in coast arts. The ivory of Wabisa, though white and soft, is generally small, the full length of a tusk being 7 feet. The 'bab gujrati or kashshi,' is that intended for the Cutch[2] market. The tusk must be of middling size, little bent, very bluff at the point as it is intended for rings and armlets; the girth must be a short span and three fingers, the bamboo shallow and not longer than a hand. The 'bab wilaiti,' or 'foreign sort,' is that purchased in European and American markets. The largest size is preferred, which ranges from 45 to 100 pounds.

"The third and least valued quality is the western ivory, the Gendai, and other varieties imported from Usagara, Uhehe, Urori, Unqamwezi, and its neighbourhood.

[2] Indian.

"The elephant is by far the most formidable of all animals, and the African variety is more dangerous than the Indian, as it is next to impossible to kill it by the forehead shot. The head is so peculiarly formed, that the ball either passes over the brain, or lodges in the immensely solid bones and cartilages that contain the roots of the tusks. I have measured certainly a hundred bull tusks, and I have found them buried in the head a depth of 24 inches. One large tusk, that measured 7 ft. 8 in. in length, and 22 inches in girth, was imbedded in the head a depth of 31 inches. This will convey an idea of the enormous size of the head, and of the strength of bone and cartilage required to hold in position so great a weight, and to resist the strain when the tusk is used as a lever to uproot trees.

"The brain of an African elephant rests upon a plate of bone exactly above the roots of the upper grinders; it is thus wonderfully protected from a front shot, as it lies so low that the ball passes above it when the elephant raises his head, which he invariably does when in anger, until close to the object of his attack.

"The character of the country naturally influences the habits of the animals: thus, Africa[3] being more generally open than the forest-clad Ceylon, the elephant is more accustomed to activity, and is much faster than the Ceylon variety. Being an old elephant-hunter of the latter island, I was exceedingly interested in the question of variety of species, and I had always held the opinion that the African elephant might be killed with the same facility as that of Ceylon, by the forehead shot, provided that a sufficient charge of powder were used to penetrate the extra thickness of the head. I have found, by much experience, that I was entirely wrong, and that, although by chance an African elephant may be killed by the front shot, it is the exception to the rule. The danger of the sport is, accordingly, much increased, as it is next to impossible to kill the elephant when

[3] The East African uplands and savannas.

in full charge, and the only hope of safety consists in turning him by a continuous fire with heavy guns: this cannot always be effected.

"The temple shot, and that behind the ear, are equally fatal in Africa as in Ceylon, provided the hunter can approach within ten or twelve yards; but altogether the hunting is far more difficult, as the character of the country does not admit of an approach sufficiently close to guarantee a successful shot. In the forests of Ceylon an elephant can be stalked to within a few paces, and the shot is seldom fired at a greater distance than ten yards: thus accuracy of aim is insured; but in the open ground of Africa, an elephant can seldom be approached within fifty yards, and should he charge the hunter, escape is most difficult. I never found African elephants in good jungle, except once, and on that occasion I shot five, quite as quickly as we should kill them in Ceylon.

"There are various methods of killing them. Pitfalls are the most common, but the wary old bulls are seldom caught in this manner. The position chosen for the pit is, almost without exception, in the vicinity of a drinking-place, and the natives exhibit a great amount of cunning in felling trees across the usual run of the elephants, and sometimes cutting an open pit across the path, so as to direct the elephant by such obstacles into the path of snares. The general elephant route to the drinking-place being blocked up, the animals are diverted by a treacherous path towards the water, the route intersected by numerous pits, all of which are carefully concealed by sticks and straw, the latter being usually strewn with elephants' dung to create a natural effect.

"Should one animal be thus caught, a sudden panic seizes the rest of the herd, and in their hasty retreat one or more are generally victims to the numerous pits in the vicinity. The old bulls never approach a watering-place rapidly, but carefully listen for danger, and then slowly advance with their warning trunks stretched to the path before them; the delicate nerves of the proboscis at once detect the hidden snare, and the victims to pitfalls are the members of large herds who, eager to push forward incautiously, put their 'foot into it,' like shareholders in bubble companies. Once helpless in the pit, they are easily killed with lances.

"The great elephant hunting season is in January, when the high prairies are parched and reduced to straw. At such a time, should a large herd of animals be discovered, the natives of the district collect together to the number of perhaps a thousand men; surrounding the elephants by embracing a considerable tract of country, they fire the grass at a given signal. In a few minutes the unconscious elephants are surrounded by a circle of fire, which, however distant, must eventually close in upon them. The men advance with the fire, which rages to the height of twenty or thirty feet. At length the elephants, alarmed by the volumes of smoke and the roaring of the flames, mingled with the shouts of the hunters, attempt an escape. They are hemmed in on every side—wherever they rush, they are met by an impassable barrier of flames and smoke, so stifling, that they are forced to retreat. Meanwhile the fatal circle is decreasing; buffaloes and antelopes, likewise doomed to a horrible fate, crowd panic-stricken to the centre of the encircled ring, and the raging fire sweeps over all. Burnt and blinded by fire and smoke, the animals are now attacked by the savage crowd of hunters, excited by the helplessness of the unfortunate elephants thus miserably sacrificed, and they fall under countless spears. This destructive method of hunting ruins the game of that part of Africa, and so scarce are the antelopes, that, in a day's journey, a dozen head are seldom seen in the open prairie.

"The next method of hunting is perfectly legitimate. Should many elephants be in the neighbourhood, the natives post about a hundred men in as many large trees; these men are armed with heavy lances specially adapted to the sport, with blades about eighteen inches long and three inches broad. The elephants are driven by a great number of men towards the trees in which the spearmen are posted, and those that pass sufficiently near are speared between the shoulders. The spear being driven deep into the animal, creates a frightful wound, as the tough handle, striking against the intervening branches of trees, acts as a lever, and works the long blade of the spear within the elephant, cutting to such an extent that he soon drops from exhaustion.

"The best and only really great elephant-hunters of the White Nile are the Bagara Arabs, on about the 13° N. Lat. These men hunt on horseback, and kill the elephant in fair fight with their spears.

"The lance is about fourteen feet long, of male bamboo; the blade is about fourteen inches long by nearly three inches broad; this is as sharp as a razor. Two men, thus armed and mounted, form the hunting party. Should they discover a herd, they ride up to the finest tusker and single him from the others. One man now leads the way, and the elephant, finding himself pressed, immediately charges the horse. There is much art required in leading the elephant, who follows the horse with great determination, and then adapts his pace so as to keep his horse so near the elephant that his attention is entirely absorbed with the hope of catching him. The other hunter should by this time have followed close to the elephant's heels, and, dismounting

---

An Eastern Sudanese tribesman attacking a Bush Loxodont. The peoples of the northeastern fringe of the Central African forests either rode their quarry down on horseback or crept up on them on foot, and hamstrung them with huge "crusade-type" swords.

when at full gallop with wonderful dexterity, he plunges his spear with both hands into the elephant about two feet below the junction of the tail, and with all his force he drives the spear about eight feet into his abdomen, and withdraws it immediately. Should he be successful in his stab, he remounts his horse and flies, or does his best to escape on foot, should he not have time to mount, as the elephant generally turns to pursue him. His comrade immediately turns his horse, and, dashing at the elephant, in his turn dismounts, and drives his lance deep into his intestines.

"Generally, if the first thrust is scientifically given, the bowels protrude to such an extent that the elephant is at once disabled. Two good hunters will frequently kill several out of one herd; but in this dangerous hand-to-hand fight the hunter is often the victim. Hunting the elephant on horseback is certainly far less dangerous than on foot, but although the speed of the horse is undoubtedly superior, the chase generally takes place upon ground so disadvantageous, that he is liable to fall, in which case there is little chance for either animal or rider.

"So savage are the natural instincts of Africans, that they attend only to the destruction of the elephants, and never attempt its domestication."

It was not until the turn of the last century, however, that the mighty Bush Loxodont really came under the staccato attack of the white man as well as that of native spears, sabers, pitfalls, fire, muzzle-loaders, and sundry other hellish devices. This pitiless, one-sided war was then opened up on them from Gambia, in the west, to Abyssinia, in the east, and south throughout the continent to the Cape. Only in the recesses of the tall jungle was the little Forest species left more or less alone. Meantime the slave, or "black ivory," trade had happily come to an end, but not without a considerable military flourish. In fact, the European powers had to institute open warfare with the Arabs, who ranged all over Central Africa, in order finally to stamp it out. This warfare and its successful conclusion only made matters worse for the poor Abu.

There was a terrible old ruffian named Hamed bin Muhamed bin Tuma bin Rajab, otherwise known as "Tipoo Tip" (an onomatopoeism for rifle fire), who continued to hold the ivory and most other trade from Central Africa in his hands for years. It was about his ravages that Stanley waxed furious, but this did not stop the two from working together. It is alleged that in obtaining his ivory, Tipoo Tip was responsible for the deaths of over 100,000 Africans, and many of the great ivory houses and those corporations processing the material today were founded on his grisly enterprises. (Tipoo Tip died in Zanzibar after a long retirement, in 1911.)

Meantime also, "big-game hunting" had become widely prevalent. This was and still is regarded as a "sport," and almost everybody who could afford a rifle and a trip to East Africa has indulged in it. It began with the Boers in South Africa in the 1600's and it has continued until today. Its excesses are now happily for the most part curbed by game laws and licensing, promulgated in accordance with sensible ideas of wildlife preservation and over-all conservation, but it still does not qualify as a true sport and is highly obnoxious.

To many people the very word "elephant" still prompts an involuntary mental, if not actual, grab for a gun or other weapon of destruction. To these people I make no apology for the omission of further information on this subject and its results. The almost endless library of literature on the subject of slaughtering elephants adds nothing to our story, and frankly revolts me. I have read just about all of it and have yet to find a worth-while addition to our knowledge of the Abu in any of it. Only men like G. P. Sanderson and J. H. Williams, who started as "sportsmen" and ended by admitting that they were repelled by the whole business, and who then devoted the rest of their lives to the care and study of these magnificent creations of nature, really tell us anything valuable about the Abu.

Then there was yet another, even more scurrilous clan that arose to harass the wretched loxodonts. These were the professional ivory poachers both black and white. Nevertheless, dastardly as they have been, it must be admitted that they actually added more real facts to our store of knowledge of the Abu than all the sportsmen combined. On the whole also, they usually killed more cleanly and less wantonly because they were in the business, *for business.* They had to think of the cost of their ammunition and of their daily maintenance, so they did not blast off at young and old indiscriminately or waste time on body shots or leg-breaking. They needed as much ivory as quickly and as cheaply as possible. Merely to stay in business, they had to be extremely efficient. Their parasitical trade began at about the turn of the century, when Africa had been parceled out among the European powers and before game laws had been drafted or any glimmerings of conservation had been born, but they have carried on until today. The toll they have taken is appalling, and unhappily all too many native poachers are still at work.

The white poachers were hard-boiled adventurers who weighed all the risks and the costs and then set out deliberately to rob or highjack a specialized field. One of the most notorious was an American named James Ward Rogers. This man was employed by the British government in Uganda for ten years. He then resigned from his official post and, using his extensive knowledge of the country, its inhabitants, and wildlife, went into the ivory-poaching business. He organized a whole territory with his own scouts, spies, and runners, and treated the local chiefs despotically, though any of them could have lopped off his head at any time. He was eventually run down and shot by a detachment of British soldiers under Lieutenant C. V. Fox in Belgian territory after a long trek. Fox wrote, in 1911, that Rogers had a genius for organization and administration surpassing anything the colonial authorities had devised at that time.

Ivory poachers both native and foreign still exist, and a considerable amount of ivory is still smuggled out of Africa, while not all tusks registered with the authorities are submitted by licensed sportsmen, game-control officers, or settlers and natives with a legitimate cause for shooting a loxodont. Not all tusks can be checked, and often men still have to shoot in self-defense in Africa. Also, the Abu are on the increase, and so are banana plantations and other enticing gardens for them to feed on. Official "exterminators" are few and overworked, and a farmer cannot be blamed for defending his crops.

Loxodonts, like Elephants, are still killed every year in some numbers, but the Abu have gained, at least temporarily, a comparative respite. There is no official hunting and little poaching in Asia—it is hardly worth the trouble—and shooting is, as far as possible, controlled and regulated in Africa. Despite the steady encroachment of agriculture and sylviculture, there are still very large wild areas of forest and savanna in both continents where the Abu can lead their peaceful lives. They are not yet a dying race. Almost everywhere they are protected and they are breeding both in the wild and in semicaptivity. Moreover, there are still the uncounted tribes of Forest Loxodonts about which we still know practically nothing.[4]

[4] The sudden, and in many respects ill-advised, granting of "independence" to almost the whole of Equatorial Africa has considerably altered this picture. In many large areas authority and mere administration have themselves broken down, while game laws which were often not understood and seldom approved have fallen into abeyance. The tribal African cannot be overly blamed for the results, for the very simple reason that he is hungry—and notably meat-hungry—and in such circumstances a full and better balanced diet in every way transcends the altruistic motives of conservation. Unless the new African governments make almost impossibly rapid strides in all other fields, any conservation enforcement that may return to the continent will come too late. Meantime, not only the loxodonts but most other large game will have become totally extinct.

[13]

OF BREAD AND CIRCUSES

The origins of performing Abu and of the circus. The Assyrian circus and the Egyptian trainers. Rome; the death of the circus; the great American invention.

We will now retrace our steps for some considerable distance in time to unravel the history of Man and Abu in quite another association. We have seen these two together in the wild and in warfare; we have seen them chasing each other and working together; and we have seen the Abu as servants of men. There is one more relationship, and an astonishing one, between the two which must be mentioned. This is men as servants of the Abu. This singular position actually obtains whenever a mere man has to look after an Abu, be it in the wild, as in a Burmese forest lumber camp, or in a modern zoo. Nor is the situation unique to Abu and Man: it pertains in some degree whenever any man aspires to keep any animal, for he must perforce devote a certain quota of his time to his charge; but with Abu, men become virtual slaves, for they must devote *all* their time to these animals. Such a relationship is inherent in this association in any case, but it becomes grossly pronounced in one particular case: namely, that of performing Abu. In this relationship, man and animal are more closely and perpetually associated than under any other working conditions. An oozie may grow up literally on the back of his elephant, but even he is free of his "master" for a few hours every day and for longer periods during the off-work season. An elephant trainer is never for a moment much more than out of reach of his charge's trunk, and if he is, his mind is never free of elephantine shackles.

This strange relationship seems to have begun professionally about 3500 B.C. in India. Some of the small seals dug up at Mohenjo-daro on the Indus show richly caparisoned elephants in curious attitudes. They do not bear towers on their backs and they are not accompanied by men bearing spears or other warlike devices. Yet, in addition to a considerably resplendent mahout, they are sometimes attended also by a servile-looking little man. These were obviously elephants on parade, or they may have been specifically parade elephants, and some of them appear to be "performing," and this means something quite special. How they may have performed in early Dravidian India we do not know, but we may guess that, from what they were trained to do at a later date in Aryan India, their performances were many and varied.

At a very early date tame elephants were separated into six quite distinct classes for training in quite different fields. These were, as we have outlined above: warfare, hunting, transport, work, parading, and entertainment or performing. As it was found that, with the occasional exception of warfare and hunting, none of these activities was compatible, each called for special techniques. The war elephant had to be brave and aggressive; the hunting elephant brave but passive; the transport elephant preferably long-legged, or what is called a *meergha,* and taught to either carry loads on its back or to haul carts; the work elephant deliberate, ingenious, and strong, for which the *koomerah* type was preferable. The parade elephant had only to be magnificent and docile. The performing elephant had, on the other hand, to display a wide range of aptitudes. It had to have a long memory and be extremely obedient; show agility and imagination; but, above all, it could not exert any initiative until specifically instructed to do so, and this is an extremely subtle demand to make upon even a human being. Performing elephants have ever been the princes among the Abu, and upon their behavior the reputation of all their kind has always rested.

A performing elephant has first to be tamed and taught to comply with a certain number of commands, just like any other elephant (and this naturally goes for loxodonts, too). That there are very few trained loxodonts is not, as popularly supposed, because they are any less tractable, but because so few of them are caught. Actually, once they get over their initial nervousness, they are considerably brighter than elephants and learn much more quickly than the average Asiatic animal.

All Abu, unless they are individually very stupid, never stop learning, and they are constantly figuring out new "tricks" of their own. Performing elephants on the whole are picked from the best and brightest tamed stock. They are usually singled out from the start for show business, but many circus owners have tried to make performers out of work elephants or zoo specimens. The attempts have seldom, if ever, worked out, and it is these animals that have given the most trouble. According to Lewis—and it is my conviction that this gentleman knows more about the business than anybody outside of India—taming elephants is based on pain and can only be accomplished by instilling fear in the minds of the animals.

There are two ways of *taming* animals, which may be called the subjugation and the tantalization methods, but there is only one way of *training* them: this is by the reward method. You can tame some animals simply by putting them in restraint, notably a tight halter. This is like breaking in a young horse. They just give up, and unless they are of particularly vile disposition—in which case they can *never* be tamed—they will be utterly reliable thereafter. You can also apparently tame wild adult animals by pure kindness, by speaking softly to them, and by having a constant supply of food in hand. However, any animal so tamed will never be reliable, because it becomes greedy, pampered, and completely delinquent—a word that actually means "failing in duty." Some of the most gentle, reliable, and capable of performing Abu have been homosexual males, or asexuals like "Old John," the leader of Ringling's herd, who never once in a long life gave any trouble and died of old age.

When you start the training, which is something quite different from merely taming an elephant, you very quickly find out by which method the taming was accomplished. Neither method by itself is wholly satisfactory, because the subjugated animals have often so far "given up" that they have no will to learn. The best animals are those that have been subjected to both: stern discipline and pain combined with sentimentality and overindulgence. Those are the methods used by Nature's parents, and it's the only procedure that is absolutely plain and clear to the animals being trained.

Elephants and loxodonts are very big, powerful creatures and are great individualists. They are very intelligent, far more so than any dog, horse, bat, or even ape or pig. If you start pampering an elephant, you are in for trouble. If you meet a pampered one, you are lucky if you have trouble immediately; otherwise, as time goes on, you will get increasingly off your guard and may then find yourself being unexpectedly attacked. In dealing with elephants, it is suicidal ever to let down your guard.

It is permissible to treat a new elephant with all kindness and respect and to talk to it. Remember also that with small elephants, whose eyes are below the level of your own, you must stoop or squat down out of range of their trunks so that they may look you over before you first approach them. Next you should give some commands in a very firm voice, using elephant language, if you know it; if not, use your own language or any vocal sounds that express your wish. Your mere vocalizations are often better than any set language, and if it is singsong but clipped and loud enough, it is quite comprehensible to the animal. This is because he uses some kind of mental telepathy (or whatever less unpleasant word you prefer) as well as sound. If the animal responds or attempts to respond, reward it immediately. If it makes a mistake and does something other than you wanted, then and there make it continue trying until it does do what you want. Then reward it. On the other hand, should it refuse, do something deliberately bad, or attack you, there is only one thing you can do if you want to continue associating with the elephant, stay in business, or stay alive. You have got to go to work on the elephant mentally and physically and *beat it into submission;* nor dare you give up until you have won. An elephant has an enormous amount of physical and mental stamina, and, in addition, a spoiled elephant is devilishly cunning and often a past-master at deception. Many a would-be trainer has lost his life by walking up to reward his opponent too soon, having been deceived by the elephant's abject air of penance. No; not only must the animal obey every command before you let up; it must actually lie down on its side voluntarily and sigh. And once you have seen an elephant thus give up and acknowledge a human to be its master, you will know the symptoms and should then take your life in your hands and go and sit on the beast, soothe it with words, and let it sniff and fondle you with its trunk.

Now, this is where a clear distinction must be made between discipline and brutality, and between the infliction of pain and of damage or harm. In training animals, discipline is not enough; you have to be brutal; otherwise the discipline will not be understood. But you do not have to do bodily harm or injury to the beast. Nevertheless, you have to hurt it so much that it comes to fear you and to such an extent that it never forgets just how brutal you can be. When I say training *animals,* I am being misleading. The term should be *mammals,* for you simply cannot beat a bird into submission, while the best you can do with reptiles, amphibians, or fish is to pamper them and hope for some response.

There are many parts of an elephant which are like the backsides of little boys and the calves of little girls, and it is on these that you should concentrate. A long, light but hard and supple whip applied to the trunk hurts terribly but will not do any damage. A long, heavy pole of wood or metal can be used on the top of the trunk, or rather the bulb of fatty tissue which covers the front of the head. An elephant's backside may also be paddled; its ears are very sensitive and can be prodded, though not near the orifice, and care should be taken not to puncture them. The neck behind the ears is even more tender, and quite a light whack there can make them almost dizzy without doing any harm. On no account should the ridge of the spine be struck, as permanent damage or even death may result, and the regions between the front and hind legs and under the tail should be avoided. You can whip or smack the lower legs but not hard enough to bruise the bone, and the tummy can be whacked but not thumped; in fact, it is better to leave the nether regions alone. Lay about your delinquent without let-up, and shout at him or her as long as he or she shows any sign of aggression. Then give it a command, and if it doesn't comply immediately, start in again.

You may have to go on for twelve hours or more, but if you are going to be associated with that elephant in any way, you have got to outlast it. If you do relent, the more beating you have given it *before* you give up, the more resentment the animal will retain, and the more will it give it back to you. Most likely it will kill you! Once it is over and you have won, the elephant will, unlike other animals, not only completely give in and accept you as its master, but also drop all resentment and completely forget the past as regards what you have done to it. This goes even for elephants that have killed other people. However, an elephant's submission to one human does not carry over to another.

After the argument, training may begin, but you should realize that this is very difficult for the elephant, especially if it has already been trained by somebody else. It has a very good memory, but it is part of you now, and your desires and wishes may conflict with the last trainer's, so that the animal becomes confused. Nevertheless, there is nothing to elephant-training except patience, hard work, and enormous understanding, but it probably should not be attempted unless you were born with a certain as yet undefined "emanation" that animals alone understand.

There are also certain other matters that need your attention. For instance, you must ascertain whether your elephant is left-handed or right-handed, and you have to act accordingly. Most elephants are right-handed. If you are, too, always walk on the left side of the animal just back of its head so you can poke it below the ear before it can turn around (it can't turn its head alone) and get at you with its trunk. If it is left-handed, you should walk on its right side, or it will not understand what is going on; and this goes for both right- and left-handed people. Many left-handed elephants have been trained as right-handed with sorry or dire results; as with children, it can cause long-lasting difficulty. But then again, don't forget that all of us are left-handed for some things; so are elephants, and you must find out in what it is "other-handed," and in what it is naturally ambidexterous.

However much you come to know about Abu or however well trained your animal is, you will remain a slave to it as long as you two shall be together. The elephant will work for you and with you and on occasion, in show business, it will literally lead you through your routine and through life. Almost daily some trained elephant comes to the aid of its human friend, unasked and uninstructed. Many a man has been beaten to a pulp or hurled into the branches of a tree for attacking or even threatening a mahout, a trainer, or a zoo keeper. During the war, elephants faced gunfire to rescue their oozies and smashed down burning buildings to rescue people. More than once elephants have handled hoses at circus fires, but I have never heard of anybody *teaching* one to do so. The Abu think; and they think of *us;* they have compassion as well as a mere desire to protect their human friends. In return they ask only this—*that you devote your entire life to them.*

Under the general term *performing* we include several specialized activities. These may be discussed in the order of their historical appearance. In the beginning, we may presume that elephants were first tamed by primitive tribesmen for work in agriculture or such activities as house-building, transportation, or hunting. A tribal chief would obviously gain much prestige as well as additional wealth by owning such large and competent "machines" in a primitive society, and he would most likely make use of these, his most notable possessions, in ceremonies both religious and political. A village chief arriving for Council on an elephant must have been like a bank president rolling up to his bank in a Cadillac. A tribal chief who owned an elephant probably attracted settlers, and in primitive communities nothing was more important than population and manpower. Eventually, however, a time would come when a chief had so many elephants that he could afford to designate one or more of them to ceremonial duties alone. These parade elephants were chosen for their magnificence, their size, and their docility, to impress the populace.

The minions charged with the care of such parade elephants doubtless then, as today, were rewarded or scolded according to the condition and behavior of their charges on parade. As a result, there must have been constant and deep rivalry between these men to attract the attention of the chief to their particular animals, and very soon indeed some oozie who taught his animal to bow or kneel to the headman would obviously acquire great merit. Elephants are very amenable to learning tricks, and, in fact, they often seem to think them up themselves and to take much delight in performing them. Thus, with comparatively little effort, intelligent parade elephants might turn out to be regular performing elephants, to the delight of their owners. And so the true "show-business elephant" was born.

However, elephants so trained became useless for more menial tasks and much too valuable to perform them. They might still be displayed in parades but they acquired a special status. In very early days princelings and potentates vied with each other in the perfection of their performing elephants, and these animals became quite distinct in value from their solemn, trudging, patient, panoplied parade confreres, which were specifically trained *not* to cavort. Eventually, elephants were trained to perform whole routines, to wrestle, to dance, to walk tightropes, and even to put convicted prisoners ceremonially to death.

Let us see how far such behavior and performances had been developed in various countries by the beginning of the historic era. Indian princes in the early Vedic period prior to 1000 B.C. staged regular performances in the courtyards of their palaces to which the populace at large was invited. Some of these courtyards were circular and in them were given displays of all kinds both by men and by animals. Perhaps they were not three-ring circuses, but they were indeed the *first circuses,* and in them performing elephants played a major part from the beginning. Thence the idea spread to the Mesopotamian Valley, where Assyrian and Babylonian kings displayed their royal menageries and especially their trained hunting lions which they used in warfare. These shows gave the public an exciting sense of security; a hundred hunting lions ripping into a bevy of unwanted Bedouin cutthroats went far toward assuring the inhabitants of Babylonia that they had nothing to fear on their southern border. Such was the origin of the circus.

However, of all ancient peoples the Egyptians were the animal tamers and trainers par excellence. Their activities had a highly religious and cultural import, but they contributed a great deal to the circus and to the entertainment business in general. There seems to have been practically no animal that the Egyptians came in contact with that they did not or could not tame. Many of these animals were, moreover, living representatives of their gods, such as Thoth, the baboon-headed, Nekht, the ibis-headed fountain of all learning, Horus the hawk, and Apis the bull. The Egyptians also tamed lions, leopards, cheetahs, servals, wildcats, and dozens of other species, and let them wander freely around their temples, palaces, and homes. They even tamed gazelles of many kinds, including the long-necked Gerenuk; all manner of antelopes; and such oddments as hyenas, maribou storks, geese, and hairy spiders. Nor did this curious talent for animal-training end here. They had armies of Hamadryad Baboons that weeded gardens, stacked cordwood, swept out temples, served at table, and did obeisance to the setting sun. They also had Abu.

The Egyptians appear always to have been less barbaric

than other ancient civilizations. They did not indulge in public or even private displays of horror, nor did they encourage fighting among men, men and beasts, or between beasts. Their pomp and panoply surpassed anything ever devised by other peoples, but it was always strictly formalized and traditional, and was usually mellow and almost gentle. They kept animals to look at, and Abu were primarily for display and not for fighting. Cats were trained to retrieve waterfowl killed by an arrow, and lions were taught to hunt antelope for food, but they were not made to do these things in arenas.

The Cretans too were animal lovers, but their public exhibitions were confined to chasing bulls in mazes. The Greeks were at first too poor to indulge in any such extravagances, and by the time they could afford to keep exotic animals, they were so engrossed in inquiry and the arts that they were given less to training them than to probing into their anatomy and making statues of them.

Elephants, as we have seen, were apparently not known in Europe before the time of Alexander. They may still have been indigenous to Syria and they were certainly owned in some quantity in that country shortly after Alexander's death. Loxodonts had, nevertheless, been known right along to the Egyptians and to the Carthaginian Phoenicians. The spiritless dynasties that ruled Egypt immediately prior to its conquest by Alexander apparently maintained sizable

---

Trampling a Virgin (originally "dedicated to the gods") in a Roman circus. While thousands of humans were "sacrificed" annually in the Roman circuses, the spectators usually "tore up the seats" if an Abu was even harmed.

menageries, and when the Macedonian Ptolemy took over the country, he set about enthusiastically encouraging the collection of animals, particularly Abu.

Ptolemy I had a most inquiring mind and a distinct scientific bent. However, we have only a single record of his zoological activities and that is of his having obtained a Bactrian Camel for his menagerie. His son, Ptolemy II (283-246 B.C.) was even more keen about animal-collecting, and, shortly after his accession, staged a parade that took all day to pass through the stadium in Alexandria, which included twenty-four chariots drawn by four elephants each. These may have been Indian Elephants, for there is evidence that Ptolemy I obtained some of these animals with their mahouts through the Seleucid Antiochus I of Syria. In any case, later in his reign Ptolemy II initiated wild-animal catching in northern Ethiopia and built a special port on the Red Sea called Ptolemais-of-the-Hunt, near modern Suakim, for their export. Loxodonts captured inland in the Sudan were shipped out of this place to Berenice, opposite Asuan, and then walked to the Nile by a road, specially built for the purpose, to Koptos, where they went aboard boats that took them down river to Alexandria.

Ptolemy II also sent a deputation to an Indian king named Vindusara requesting elephants with their mahouts and a number of spare mahouts, because the Egyptians had for hundreds of years known their loxodonts only as pets and did not know how to train them for war. The Seleucids of Syria, on the other hand, had many war elephants.

Ptolemy III founded another port, named Berenice-the-Golden, 300 miles farther down the Red Sea, near Massoua and another inland post at Kolöe. The Egyptians did the catching of the animals because the local people did not know how and refused to try, while the Ethiopians of upland Abyssinia refused to permit any animal catching in their country. Mostly young animals were caught, and they were kept in the south during the training years. Boating elephants up the Red Sea presented great problems, since Egyption ships were very unseaworthy. The animals were heavy and the boats were overladen, while the sea was full of shallows and reefs. Moreover, they could sail only at night to avoid the heat of the day, which killed the animals.

Ptolemy III kept at the elephant-catching business, so that his successor, Ptolemy IV, was able to use seventy-three of them in a battle, at a place called Raphis, against 102 employed by the Seleucid Antiochus III. The loxodonts of Ptolemy IV were, with a few exceptions, either young beasts or Forest Loxodonts, for they were stated to be much smaller than those of the Seleucids. A few big loxodonts did quite well, but the rest ran away. Sixteen were killed and most of the rest captured. However, Ptolemy ultimately won the battle, grabbed all the elephants of the Syrians, and regained his own; but thenceforth he gave up collecting loxodonts.

The Romans were of quite another ilk. From the start they were a rough lot and they were always prone to displays of barbaric splendor. Even during their "democratic" period, individuals were always ready to lay out excessive time and energy and large sums of money on publicity. Quite early they instituted parades and triumphs. The practice was well established before the Punic wars, the Romans already having created many arenas in which dramas, concerts, dancing, contests, parades, and exhibitions were given. In fact, they had *independently* instituted a form of circus and they readily adapted to this, their indigenous invention, all the gimmicks and excesses developed in India and Mesopotamia. One of the great innovations in this was the introduction of elephants.

It was the Romans who really developed the circus as we know it. The oval arenas had a straight fence down the middle around which races were performed. Every kind of entertainment was presented and much of it of a terrifyingly sadistic nature. Girls were torn apart by teams of oxen or lashed between poles as bait for hungry crocodiles; dwarfs and morons gouged each other to death with all sorts of implements; animals were slaughtered by the tens of thousands by both men and other animals, and all sorts of mechanical goads, forms of emasculation, tortures, and drugs, were used to stimulate them to do so. Yet in this nauseating mess there was one animal that even the bloodthirsty Romans apparently did not particularly care to see killed. That was the Abu.

It is recorded that at the *games* put on by Pompey in 55 B.C., in which a number of elephants and hundreds of lions and leopards were entered, the crowd booed and cursed Pompey for having the elephants attacked. The games had to be suspended, and according to Dio, those Abu not already killed were disposed of. There were twenty of them (loxodonts?) brought especially from Africa for this affair, and their keepers had obtained a promise that they were not to be harmed. On the last day of the games they were attacked by a group of Africans named Gaetulians. Cicero wrote to a friend about the incident and stated that the crowd was aroused by pity and "somehow felt that the elephant was allied with man."

But elephants continued to be put into the ring, where even Julius Caesar experimented with them to ascertain what real use they might be in warfare. Some were killed and some killed men; and the Romans seem to have preferred seeing the victory of Abu. On the whole the Abu were spared. The Romans built up a very considerable state-owned stable of elephants in Italy and they seemed even to have bred them, for we read of private trainers purchasing the babies and raising them as performers. Julius Caesar had forty of the official ones march in a night parade in which they carried torches in their trunks—an act that takes a lot of training. Apparently these official elephants were on public display, for there are many casual remarks in contemporary literature such as "it's as easy as giving a penny to an elephant."

In imperial Rome, elephants became a propaganda weapon and were sent along to open triumphs after successful campaigns. There was a *Procurator ad Elephantes* resident at Laurentum in charge of a herd of elephants pastured in the country near Ardea. The Emperor Claudius took a train of them to England when he went to inspect his victorious armies there. The Romans got many elephants from Syria when they annexed that country in 63 B.C. and more when Egypt fell into their hands in 30 B.C. Then they opened a direct trade route to India via the Red Sea and brought still more by that route. Also they continued catching loxodonts in North Africa. Abu continued to be an essential feature of circuses in Rome at least until the time of the General Stilicho, who in A.D. 404 put on magnificent *venationes* (spectacles), which were described by Claudian in jaunty verse. But after the collapse of the western Roman power, they all disappeared. So did the circus, which was not seen again in Europe for almost 1,400 years. However, the latter continued in India and at one time it showed signs of cropping up in China. It finally appeared again in, of all unlikely places, Russia in the late Middle Ages. The Russians, though officially within the fold of the Greek Orthodox Church, were at that time quite barbarous, and the sundry other peoples who then inhabited their country were even more so. To the east of their country lay the vast domains of the Khans, where dwelt Nestorian Christians, Mohammedans, and various pagans. The Khans had elephants and they seem to have marched them either across the Gobi Desert from China or up from the south from India via Persia. At any rate, elephants turned up in Samarkand. There were performing elephants and primitive traveling circuses in Russia before the end of the fifteenth century. The Russians seem always to have delighted in trained-animal acts, one type of which was especially popular—namely, itinerant Asiatics with performing bears. With Polish ascendancy in the Ukraine came regular circuses, which combined jousting, wrestling, bull- and bear-baiting, juggling, and other acts of skill.

The ancient circus as developed by the Mediterranean peoples of "classical" times never really reached western Europe. (Actually, it was revived or, rather, re-created in the United States in the nineteenth century, though in a new guise, and then was introduced "back" to Europe.) However, there grew up in Germany, France, and especially in England a number of curious enterprises in the field of public entertainment which ultimately provided a very fertile ground for the revival of certain ancient ideas and which, once the resultant conglomeration was assembled in a single place, also contributed to the birth of the Modern Circus. These curious enterprises were the primitive "museums" in which were housed all sorts of freaks—living and dead—waxworks, live animals, and other exhibits. There were such even in Elizabethan times in England, and many great mercantile towns in the Germanic States housed similar "curiosities."

There are vague references to an elephant exhibited publicly in London during the reign of Queen Elizabeth I, and Shakespeare certainly knew of the creatures, but it was not until the year 1827 that we have definite evidence of one being on show in that country. This was in one of these "museums." The name of this animal is not recorded, but it was said to have been a "colossal creature" and to have been rented from *Cross' Menagerie* on Exeter Exchange in London. The animal appeared in a scene of *Bluebeard* and was a huge success. Either this animal or another had made the first elephantine appearance in show business in London seventeen years before, also in a performance of *Bluebeard* and on the legitimate stage at Covent Garden. It was very docile but stubborn and took a great fancy to one of the girl ballet dancers, and unless it was led by the ear by this girl, it refused to go on stage. Then, we have an elephant named Mademoiselle Jeck who had built up quite a reputation on the continent of Europe and who gave regular performances at Astley's Circus in London. From then on a steady stream of elephants flowed to England, most of them direct from India. Some were true performing animals, but most were, like that one allegedly exhibited in the time of Queen Elizabeth I, merely tractable.

We lack the name of the first elephant brought to America. Initially it was called simply "The Elephant," but later it was dubbed the "Crowninshield Elephant." Its story is quite a saga and includes a prolonged furor. The excitement began with a brief announcement in the New York *Argus* of April 18, 1796, which stated: "The [ship] *America* has brought home an elephant from Bengal, in perfect health. It is a female, two years old, and of the species that grow to an enormous size. This animal sold for $10,000, being supposed to be the greatest price ever given for an animal in Europe or America." (And that was indeed a colossal sum for those days.)

The story behind this story was, however, much more fantastic. One Captain Jacob Crowninshield of Salem, Massachusetts, had bought the beast in Calcutta for a paltry $450. On the long voyage home he hand-fed it himself with, it is obvious, shrewd Yankee circumspection. The feed bill probably amounted to about $50, so that the $10,000, if true, represented an enormous profit. He did very well out of the deal, whatever the price, and so also did the purchasers—Messrs. Pepin and Breschard, who preferred to remain anonymous at the time.

These gentlemen transported the elephant to New York, where they exhibited it a block from the Battery, in the heart of the business district, and right opposite the Governor's somewhat baronial mansion. The promoters were variously reported to have charged a dollar a head for adults and half a dollar for children (or a quarter for adults, and nine cents for children) to view it, and they whipped up a newspaper promotion that would do credit to Madison

Avenue today. There were advertisements, handbills, and posters, all headlined TO THE CURIOUS and displaying an utterly grotesque sketch of the animal. This shows back legs with hocks like those on a horse, a bulbous body, highly arched back, no neck, small tatty ears, huge humorful eyes, two tusks turning upward like horns, and a long, thin trunk ending in the old conventional trombone-shaped spout. The appended copy was magnificent, reading in part: "He eats about 130 wt. a day, and drinks a barrel of water—he is very fond of ftrong liquors; Porter, Wine, & draws the Corke with his trunk: He is six years old; they grow till they are 40 or 50, to the height of 18 or 19 feet; he is seven feet high, measures in length 17 feet, round the body 13 feet, round his head 8 feet, round his feet 3 foot seven inches, he weighs 3,500 Lbs., he travels 3, 4, and 5 miles an hour; he travels loofe. Admittance a quarter of a Dollar. Children Nine Pence. No admittance twice without paying twice. No admittance after fun fet or Sundays. The Vifitors are cautioned not to come too near the Elephant with papers in their pockets, as he has deftroyed fome valuable ones."

Apart from the fact that the animal was a female and weighed only 2,500 pounds, this promotional copy was not too misleading. The elephant traveled about three miles an hour and took a full month to walk to Philadelphia from New York down Route 1. She would of course have been full-grown at between twenty and twenty-five years, and her maximum height might have then been about 8 feet. The final paragraph of the notice was obviously a very fine attempt at third-party-risk insurance, equivalent to the notices displayed in many zoos and animal exhibits today—"The Management takes no responsibility for any harm done to visitors by the animals."

"The Elephant" had quite a history. She made a killing in New York, partly because America's only zoo at that time consisted of half a dozen animals in pens at the Battery, and because the only circus offered only trick riders, jugglers, and some asinine clowns. On June 22 of the year of her arrival, she headed south with her trainer, a wild-eyed and verbose Welshman named Josh Owen who talked so much he never gave away anything about his employers' business. Exactly one month later "The Elephant" went on exhibit in Philadelphia, then the nation's capital, and was an instant success. Philadelphians swarmed in to see her time and time again, and each time they paid. Here the promotional copy became a little more erudite and informative and considerably more forceful. The animal was said to have "infinite sagacity, the adroitness of the beaver, the intelligence of the ape, and the fidelity of the dog." And who could withstand such goose-pimpling statements as "The earth trembles under his feet; his strength is almost incredible"? After winning triumph upon triumph in Philadelphia, "The Elephant" headed north again to New York and on to an extended tour of New England. She curtsied in Providence the following July, sauntered to Salem, and wintered in Boston. Her success in Boston was such that the proper Bostonians gave her a Christmas present of a monumental pudding. Plaudits were one thing, but the pudding made the poor beast violently ill.

The next spring "The Elephant" sallied forth again, walking all the way to Charleston, South Carolina, where she wintered. This was the year 1798. In March she walked down to Savannah, where she was billed for a month. After that, according to Vail, she appeared in Boston again in 1804 under the new management of a Mr. Savage, an old showman; then she trotted back to Philadelphia in 1806. In New York in 1808 she performed in *Bluebeard*, and made personal appearances in Baltimore in 1811 and in Gettysburg in 1812. In that same year she was purchased for a circus owned by Messrs. Cayetano, Codet, Menial, and Redon. And she thereby became not only the first lady elephant of the land but the first circus elephant in America. Great, patient, faithful trooper that she was, she was still going strong in Brooklyn and in Pennsylvania in 1818; in fact, she may have been the same animal who appeared under the various names of "The Learned Elephant" or "Little Bet," who in 1822 was killed in an accident. Whether this was "The Elephant" we do not know, because curiously her age was not "upped" for some twenty years. The handbills appear to pertain to two animals, but the wording remained similar for years.

The existence of a second elephant may have been discovered (by Miss C. Eleanor Hall) in an old Customs House entry dated August 19, 1805, for the Lake Champlain district of northern New York. The entry lists the cargo of a Federal Packet ex St. John's, Walter Beckwith, master; as one horse valued at $33, one elephant at $110, one bale of dry goods, and 3,456 pounds of salt. On this the total duty charged was $44.15. Which elephant this was and what happened to it is a mystery. It may have been merely a statue of an elephant.

Parenthetically, here are three curious elephant incidents, all supposed to have happened in the United States in the early 1800's. One story names an elephant, one sends an elephant swimming to shore from a sinking ship, and one describes what could have been the first elephant hunt in America—in recent times—and the "legal" sanctioning of the hunt.

Circus promoters of this period were universally raucous

The finale of a modern circus and the "triumph" of the Virgins. Today, the Abu are still the high spot of The Greatest Show on Earth, but while they have fallen under the spell of the so-called weaker sex, they still retain their ancient majesty.

in their tactics for attracting customers. Their typical pitch for business screamed about the ferocity, the wildness, and the danger lurking under the big top or whatever was its equivalent. Consequently, we are startled to learn that The Great Caravan circus took the opposite tack to attract people to see its elephant. It advertised its main attraction in the old *National Intelligencer*, March 8, 1830, as: "The famous Elephant Tippoo Sultan, who saved the life of his keeper from the attack of two Tygers that broke out from their cage. . . ." Then, elsewhere we read: "About the beginning of the last century [1800] an Indian Elephant was shipped from England to Philadelphia on board a sailing vessel. The ship foundered in a storm at the entrance of Delaware Bay, but the elephant managed in some way to break its fastenings and swam ashore. The next morning those who came to view the wreck were astonished on beholding a strange creature wandering about the beach." Aggravatingly, nothing more about this animal was ever published. But another case is amply recorded:

"During the early part of the last century [1800] a traveling circus pitched its tents in a New England town, where, along with the attractions common to the shows of the period, it was exhibiting what none of the villagers had ever seen before—an elephant. Some reckless youths of the village, whose imaginations had probably been wrought up by reading of elephant hunts in India, conceived the notion that it would be a fine thing to shoot the 'critter,' and without more ado loaded their muskets and lay in wait for the pachyderm to pass over a certain route which they knew the circus would take on leaving the village. As the elephant passed all three fired. Their marksmanship was better than their common sense, for by the time the owner arrived the elephant had breathed its last, the bullets from the guns of the youngsters taking effect in the creature's heart. The circus-owner obtained the names of the perpetrators of this deed, swore out warrants, and had them arrested. They were haled before a squire, who handed down a decision not surpassed since Sancho Panza sat on the bench of Barataria. He said:

"'I hev examined the law purty therewly in this case. The laws of this State provides proper penalties fur all them that maliciously, or wilfully, or with malice aforethought kills or cripples up of a hoss, or a keow, or a hog, but there ain't a word abeout killin' a elerphunt. What's more, a elerphunt is a dangersome varmint that hain't got no bizness a-runnin' eround the country a-skeerin' of hosses an' a-frightenin' wimming an' children. Under them circumstances, I reckon I'll hev to turn the defendents loost.'"

The second elephant in America for which there is a clear record was a professional circus performer named Old Bet. She was brought to this country by a sea captain with the familiar name of Bailey, who was a brother of one Hackaliah Bailey, one of the founders of our Big Top. He bought the elephant in London for £20 at an auction and sold her to his brother for $1,000. She was a female loxodont. She was shipped up the Hudson to Sing Sing on a barge and then put on display in barns throughout Westchester and southern Connecticut. She then started in a primitive circus but died in 1818 before her training was complete.

A fair-sized monument was erected to her at the town of Somers, New York, where Hackaliah Bailey lived. Her likeness was made of wood set on a 15-foot granite pedestal and was erroneously dedicated to "Betsy." The monument survived intact until 1931, when an industrious woodpecker went to work on it. The attack brought a reporter from *The New York Times,* who penned the deathless report that "with a persistent tap-tap-tap all summer long a woodpecker has been boring holes in the wooden elephant. Last summer bees nested in the elephant's trunk and this year cement fillings and a coat of paint are needed." But nothing was done until 1935, when the Press was again alerted. Once more *The New York Times* came through with a headline:

"Statue of Elephant Is Found Collapsing." And the accompanying story related that "woodpeckers found the statue a favorite target and riddled it with holes. Recently it received a metal covering to keep away the birds, but today the party [of the Westchester County Historical Society] found that the metal coat was so heavy that it was causing Old Bet's legs to sag. Methods of restoring the lofty statue or of erecting a new one were discussed, but no decision was reached."

The real reincarnation of the circus was a truly American invention. Its roots were the primitive "museums," the waxworks, the exhibits, and the "curiosities" such as were housed in rich European metropolises. However, mobile shows, like jugglers, bareback riders, and pugilists and wrestlers, were ever popular in this country where public entertainment was very scarce. This was a blue-nosed, hidebound, sacrosanctly parsimonious land where all forms of "amusement" were frowned upon and where the hard-working citizenry were left with positively nothing to do on their days off. American cities in the early 1800's were not wealthy enough to support "museums" and other exhibits, apart from a few big centers like Boston, New York, and Philadelphia, and even there the public that could pay to enter such places were few. There was a crying need for, and enormous popular enthusiasm over, any form of entertainment, and the only way this could be provided was by "traveling" shows.

Promoters early conceived the idea of combining their bareback riders with a waxwork and carting it out into the sticks. The enterprise was enormously profitable, and the promoters started vying with each other for novel attractions. There was none greater than an elephant, and quite soon Abu became a "must" for the new traveling shows, or "circuses," as they were called, and once again Abu began to take a grip upon their ancient rivals but in a new guise and in a new land. And with them came a new breed of man—

the "bullhand"—a devoted slave, scallywag though he originally might have been.

While most of the famous circus acts always have been developed in Europe, where generation follows generation in the same skills; and while Russia, Germany, and Britain maintained a large number of circuses—some tremendous, like that of Bertram Mills in England—it was America that really brought the circus back into its own. And during the past century it has once again become perhaps the most outstanding aspect of show business.

It has also become a "cult"; and it has also degenerated. Today nothing is too big for it. Glamorous girls swing from ropes under glaring lights while whole herds of elephants march and countermarch. Everybody still hopes to see one of his own kind fall to his death or get chewed up by a lion, and the circus still remains one of the best outlets for our darker nature, but it is a pallid reflection of the Roman *venationes*.

After the Civil War the importing of elephants increased and the number in this country mounted steadily until World War II. In 1952 there were about 264 elephants in the United States (124 in circuses; 92 in zoos; 28 privately owned; 5 in carnivals; and 15 with dealers), but the most recent census seems to indicate some 400 and there is actually a slight surplus as of the time of writing. Only 6 are males, and only 8 are loxodonts.

[14]

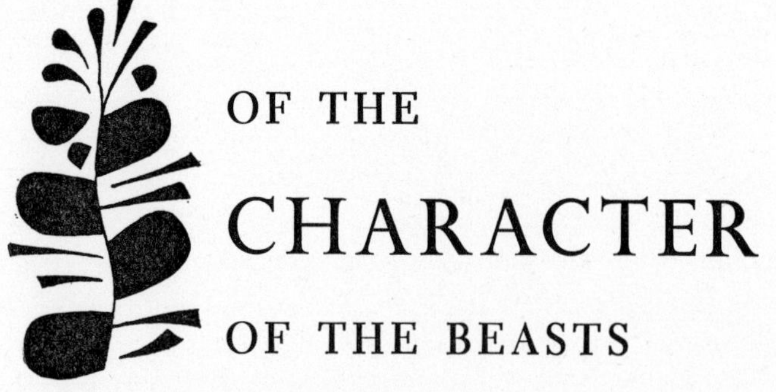

OF THE CHARACTER OF THE BEASTS

The temperament, emotions, and psychology of the Abu. Their intelligence and relationship to Man.

Once upon a time, we are told in the biography of a man who spent most of his life with Abu, there were eight elephants and two men in a large building in a place called Lancaster, Missouri. The youngest of the elephants, a female named Sadie, apparently just could not understand what was required of her during a course of training for forthcoming circus performances. The two men were professionals of long experience in this exacting business. They were good men but hard-boiled; their work was difficult, and they knew, or thought they knew, its every aspect. But, as one of them told his biographer, they still had something to learn about these marvelous creatures. What happened was this.

Sadie finally gave up and tried to run out of the training

ring. The men ordered her back and began to "punish" her —which, I would like to stress once again, does not entail any cruelty in such circumstances—for her supposed stupidity and for trying to run away. At this, Sadie sank to her knees and then lay down on her side, and the two men, as the chronicler records, "stood dumfounded for a few moments," for Sadie was crying like a human being. "She lay there on her side, the tears streaming down her face and sobs racking her huge body."

In almost half a century of close association with the Abu, including and even after reading a substantial part of the vast literature concerning these majestic creatures, I have not encountered anything that has moved me so greatly, and I write this in all seriousness and humility. Its ineffable pathos constantly brings to mind that most famous verse "Jesus wept" (John 11, 35). What on earth are we to make of a so-called "lower animal" crying?

If you shoot an animal, you may expect it to make whimpering noises, even if only as a result of mechanical reaction. Other purely physical stimuli may well cause animals to sweat—if they have the necessary cutaneous glands—or even to emit drops of liquid from their tear glands; but these are purely reflex actions. That any animal, and especially one weighing 3 tons, should lie down and sob her heart out in pure emotional frustration is something else again. It almost looks as if, despite all that we like to believe, we humans are not the only creatures that possess what we call emotions and higher feelings. In fact, if we insist upon making a distinction between ourselves and other animals in this respect, we will then have to provide a special niche for the Abu.

Anybody who becomes interested in the Dynasty of Abu and delves even a little into its history will very soon stumble upon many statements concerning them of an almost unbelievable nature. Some of these crop up in the midst of coldly technical reports. For instance, a very interesting and painstaking investigation of the mental capacity and the memorizing ability of a female elephant was made recently in a scientific institute in Germany. The elephant was presented with two boxes, one marked with a symbol known to her to be "negative" (meaning the box contained no food and was not in any other way desirable) and the other marked with a "neutral" symbol which meant the box might or might not contain something. After a few trials the elephant, it is stated, "became much *annoyed,* but usually chose the neutral, just in case."

These would at first sight appear to be incautious words to use in a scientific report, and the word "annoyed" in particular would seem to be wholly unscientific, for it is not proper to impute human feelings to animals. It is true that one of the commonest reactions of any animal *seems* to be to get "annoyed." However, the experimenters had apparently neither poked a stick at the elephant nor consummated the ultimate insult of laughing at her, nor had they deprived her of something desirable. Moreover, the subject became annoyed *before* making her selection and not after. Her anger was not due to making a wrong choice. She knew perfectly well, by hundreds of past experiments over a period of many months, that one of the boxes definitely did *not* contain the desired object, and she also knew that the other might or might not. Her peeve was apparently with the nature of the experiment, *not* with its result.

In these two cases at least, the elephants concerned displayed emotions that were hardly, if at all, distinguishable from what our own would have been in the same circumstances. This being so, I feel it to be permissible to suggest that other seemingly mysterious actions attributed to elephants should not be discredited out of hand. As an example, I would like to bring up that centuries-old contention of the Brahmans of India—a belief that long ago spread to all the countries of the Orient where elephants live and to the greater part of the Old World as well—that these creatures have a primitive religion and that they worship, in their own way, superior beings, notably the sun and the moon.

What exactly is a prayer? Who can say whether any other person (or other life form) is or is not praying at any particular time, in the absence of a spoken ritual? Why is it that not only elephants but several other kinds of animals have been observed to stand silently every morning and evening, usually just about dawn and sunset, whether the sun itself be visible or not? This has been reported by all manner of people through the ages; and if it is true, who is willing to say that the animals are not then indulging in some emotion that we might justly call "praying," even if they be but moments of wide-awake silence, complete relaxation, or apparent blankness?

There are certain peoples in West Africa who until recently had not come in contact with our culture. I was privileged to be among the first representatives of the latter to visit their country, and after we had lived among them for a while their hunters showed us certain monkeys known as guerezas (from which the "monkey skins" of the fur trade used to come) sitting just so, every dawn and dusk, on the tops of the highest jungle trees, and all invariably facing the coming or going of the sun. Witnessing this gave me an uneasy feeling mingled with awe, so that I went day after day to their feeding grounds to watch. And very soon I found myself "praying" with them during these silences. Yet it took a native companion in that country, as well as a highly esteemed writer of great sensitivity—a man raised as a Brahman for the priesthood in his own country—to break down my misconstructed European intellectual armor, and to make me see how valid was the suggestion that the animals might at those times actually be praying. This is certainly as good an explanation of what they were doing as any of my involved suggestions—such as that they were tired, frightened, digesting, or so forth—for when I came honestly to appraise these suggestions I soon found that each led into a morass of coincidence, improbability, and unwarranted complexity. I was finally forced to admit that the explanation of the locals had much greater simplicity and was, frankly, more logical than any supposedly "logical" explanation I could put forward. The idea of such "praying" may be heartily rejected by anybody who has not witnessed the sight for himself. Nonetheless, whether we occidental pragmatists like it or not, at least a billion of the two and a half billion humans presently on this earth believe that animals do "pray."

These three examples of the more esoteric aspects of the behavior of the Abu may serve to make a point that I very much wish to establish: namely, that these creatures—although not alone in this respect—are just as unlike all other living things as we are. This is not to say that the sons and daughters of Abu should be placed on our side of the fence. On the contrary, if we insist upon placing *ourselves* outside the pale of animal life in a little enclosure of our own, we shall have to do likewise with the Abu. I would like to suggest that no such line can be drawn, and that God created us *all* in His image to some extent; therefore it is readily conceivable that other animals may have emotional response and also what we call intelligence. In this latter consideration, the question of the connection between intelligence and mere brain capacity inevitably comes up.

The brains of elephants and loxodonts are approximately eight times the volume of ours and sixteen times those of the apes, which come next to ours in volume. It is also true that elephants' bodies are forty times bigger than ours; but this does not alter the fact that, according to current scientific thinking, the bigger the brain, the higher the relative intellectual capacity of its owner, and possibly also its comparative quality.

Dr. Rensch and his associates (see Chapter 16 for details) conducted memorizing experiments on an elephant along with corollary researches on the mental ability of other animals, and noted that the ability of big squirrels exceeded that of little squirrels. However, the fact that a beaver is a large member of the squirrel tribe does not mean that it is any more intelligent than a West African Pygmy Squirrel, which is the second-smallest living mammal. On the contrary, the observed facts indicate that a rather complex mathematical formula is needed to assess intelligence —an equation involving over-all weight, size of brain, degree of phylogenetic development, and quite a number of other factors, such as the extent of gregariousness of the animal, its mobility, and so forth. With such a formula it may one day be possible to determine just how "intelligent" each type of animal is—provided, of course, we can define intelligence. In the meantime we cannot promulgate any precise rule. Yet it may be suggested that a small brain cannot have a big "mind," but that a big brain can have.

We have big brains, both in volume and in relation to the size of our bodies. Loxodonts and elephants have brains very big in volume, but comparatively small in relation to their body size. In other words, they have more than enough gray matter to match an IBM machine, but too much overall bulk to permit this to do much more than control their huge bodies. Yet, like us, the Abu have at least *some* excess brain that they can use for activities other than purely mechanical control.

Now, there is another expression of life which is in every way as odd and complex as crying. This is laughing, or what we call a sense of humor. This is often confused with, but is not the same as, a sense of the ridiculous. Many animals do things that appear quite ridiculous to humans. I remember the planned antics of a neurotic and slightly balmy old Japanese "Ape" (*Lyssodes*) which my wife and I saved from extermination and which then lived with us for years. This monkey deliberately tried to be funny and to entertain; she teased us and obviously enjoyed the results; she even laughed outright at our discomposure. However, if we laughed at her, she went into a tantrum; and if we persisted, she fell into the deepest slough of despondency.

Perhaps I may be permitted to suggest that most animals have a sense of humor and that they can on occasion even appreciate a bald joke, but that (like some of us) they do *not* have a sense of the ridiculous. Elephants definitely have a humorous vein, but they seem also to display on occasion a true sense of the ridiculous.

There are many and various schools of thought about the general character of Abu, including two groups of experts who indulge in endless verbal battles: the few really experienced observers of these creatures in the wild and the equally few truly observant trainers of performing Abu. Some observers, of both parties, absolutely deny that Abu display any courage or compassion for either their own kind or anybody else, and who affirm that bulls always run away first in face of danger, that females abandon their young which have fallen into pits, and that no elephant will ever come to the aid of a human being, however well it knows him or however well the man has treated it. Others just as meticulous and experienced assert the exact opposite—namely, that bulls sometimes line up to cover the retreat of the rest of the herd, that mothers will give their lives to protect their young, that young and old will aid stricken comrades, and that many domesticated elephants have subjected themselves to the most appalling risks, including fire, flood, bullets, and even jeopardized the lives of others of their own kind, to protect, aid, and rescue their human friends.

Most hunters assert that the Abu help their wounded and that two or three of them will raise a fallen comrade and then take him away by holding him up on each side and by pushing from behind. Other "experts" deny this and seem quite certain that elephants never aid one that has fallen into a pit. Sanderson, however, states that he knew cases of herd bulls coming miles to unshackle a captured colleague and of one that built a ramp with logs in a pit and hauled out a cow. Several people have related that Abu bogged in mud or quicksand will save themselves, if planks are thrown to them, by first making a catwalk, climbing on to this, and then taking the boards one at a time from behind and placing them in front, and so moving on to safety.

There is the famous case of Jim Brown, the director of the Fort Worth Zoo in Texas, who was saved from certain death under the feet of one elephant by another—the famous old Queen Tut, *doyenne* of that zoo; there is Bill Williams's now almost immortal Bandoola, who led the last refugees out of Burma over the precipitous Naga Hills just ahead of the Japanese invaders in World War II; and there are many other such cases. Some elephants may appear stupid and some may be cowards, but it cannot be said that they are *never* courageous, that they cannot feel compassion, that they fail to know true friendship, or that they invariably lack all "ethical" standards. On the contrary, their actions sometimes seem to demonstrate mental processes of the very highest order.

Recognizing that a creature of another species is in danger from one's own kind; going to the aid of that creature; fighting off its molesters; picking it up and carrying it to safety, and all without any command, are acts of cerebration, and they imply the exercise of true compassion and also some other most sensitive emotions. A dog can be trained to defend his master against other dogs, but in the above instance Queen Tut was *not* trained to do anything. She was a zoo exhibit: Jim Brown was a zoo director. Their relationship was that of a placid clubwoman and a small terrier in a country town. The actions of the elephant were equivalent to the better instincts and actions of any sincere member of the ASPCA in stopping a man from beating a dog to death.

Does this go any way toward answering the age-old question as to whether Abu have any real intelligence? This is a most difficult question, because we have no sound definition of the concept "intelligence." Moreover, many actions that we commonly assert to be intelligent behavior in a man (and thus, in our eyes, in an animal) can readily be shown to be rank stupidity. We do all sorts of things that are manifestly not at all intelligent, such as preserving the unfit and burdening ourselves with great armies of habitual criminals. Yet we presume to deny elephants either compassion or intelligence, and we argue over the "intelligence" of their willingness to help their wounded or to destroy their criminals. Let me be bold, therefore, and forthrightly say that I believe elephants are exceedingly intelligent; that they have a form of intelligence which manifests itself in many ways that are very like our own; and that, in these respects, they stand as far apart as we do from all other living things—the great apes not excluded.

This, however, is a generalization and must be handled carefully. Half of the battle of words about elephants, indeed, seems to be due to the fact that almost everybody feels qualified to generalize freely on this subject. Almost without exception, people seem to assume that every species of animal has a single set of unvarying characteristics and that each follows hard-and-fast rules of behavior at all times. Thus all lions are "terrible" and eat only meat; all deer are "gentle" and eat only grass; all anteaters are "silly" and eat only

---

It has often been alleged that both Elephants and Loxodonts will go to the aid of wounded companions and endeavor to support them and move them out of danger. This sketch is based on the description of such an incident in Kenya, given to the author by his father, who was one of Africa's first "White Hunters."

ants. In point of fact, most lions are rather timid and, under natural conditions, they eat a fair amount of vegetable and mineral matter, while the "meat" they take ranges from scorpions to baby-elephant steaks. Deer can be irascible, dangerous, and aggressive, and they customarily eat a lot of insects, snails, and other live flesh, and regularly clean up rotten meat and carrion. Also, it now seems possible that the bucks grow horns primarily for the does to eat, so that they may be assured of a sufficiency of calcium salts, during pregnancy and foetal development, for proper lactation. Anteaters may be and usually are extraordinarily ingenious and efficient creatures and very few of them even attempt to eat ants—they prefer termites.

But, actually, every individual animal of every species is itself a distinct personality and, in some small way at least, different. Take, for example, the matter of dietary preferences. There is no such thing as a purely and exclusively carnivorous, vegetarian, piscivorous, or insectivorous animal. Even the blood-lapping bat (*Desmodus*), which has such a short, straight alimentary canal that it is alleged to be able to digest only fresh blood, may in some cases eat vegetable matter in the form of certain kinds of leaves. It follows that one cannot make rules about elephants, and least of all about their behavior.

There are saintly elephants and damned-fool elephants; there are among them heroes and cowards, thieves and imbeciles, geniuses and morons, funny elephants and elephants that think we are funny. Further, they may change their opinions periodically or unexpectedly and for all manner of reasons or for none at all. Also, you can change *their* opinions, by cruelty or by kindness; perhaps by diet or by music; by temperature variations or by injections; and, it seems, by many other methods. Then again, there are many things about elephants—as about most other animals—that we do not as yet know. Let me take an extreme case.

The existence of mental telepathy between human beings has not been demonstrated to the satisfaction of science, though it has been thought of and talked about for centuries. One of man's commonest intellectual "toys," it is only now being investigated under controlled conditions. Men and elephants have, however, been using this "whatever-it-is" for centuries, and the very lives of both parties have in innumerable cases depended solely upon just such a procedure. If you choose to deny this, simple logic will demand that you accept the only alternative: namely, that men can "talk" to animals, because thousands of elephants all over the world have for centuries been doing complex and, to them, unnatural tasks at the spoken commands of men. If they did not fully understand what was required of them, the work simply would not get done and no "show" would ever be performed by them. Indeed, how else could a 150-pound man consistently get a 12,000-pound animal to do what he wants it to do if the animal did not fully understand?

The standard reply is, of course, that the animal is "trained" to respond to certain commands by word of mouth, by gesture, or by pressure exerted on its body with an elephant hook or with the hand, heel, or another part of its trainer's body. This is quite true up to a point, but it is not the whole story. Almost everybody who regularly handles elephants or who has observed them extensively in their natural state concurs in the opinion that they communicate among themselves, even if they are separated by a solid—but not too solid—wall. Elephants are gregarious animals and are very companionable. Among themselves, they often pair off and form great friendships. When this pairing is for sexual purposes, they go through all the phases of puppy love, flirtation, and "necking" on a monstrous scale, ending in a regular courtship and a ceremonial "mating." Their relationships with men—and they seldom select more than one man at a time to be their companion and confidant—are exactly the same as those which they maintain with others of their own kind. An elephant will usually take orders from its trainer but not from anybody else, and there is a rapport between the two which extends far beyond spoken commands or the mere performance of remembered tricks. The man can literally *tell* the elephant what to do.

Many of the elephants I have handled personally have been with me on "shows," and most were previously quite unknown to me. In fact, I had seldom set eyes on them until about an hour before I had to perform with them, and then often *without* their trainer. At first I used to be in a near-panic and go through the most extreme tortures of anxiety —for the show, for myself, for other people, and for the elephant, lest it cut loose and mangle somebody or fall into the orchestra pit or through the stage floor itself. But from the succession of wonderful bullhands I met during this work I learned valuable pointers that changed this whole picture.

First, I learned that I must be "introduced" to the elephant and let it feel me gently all over with its trunk, while I stood as nonchalantly as possible, looking away from but partially facing it. Second, it transpired that a supply of small, tasty objects relished by the particular elephant on hand—little cubes of milk chocolate seem to be the most popular—should be available about one's person at all times, both for making introductory gestures and for gentle persuasion later. Third—and this is what changed everything—I learned that, if the elephant approved of me, his trainer could literally *tell* him, and in only a few minutes, to do what *I* said.

This may sound ridiculous, but it has happened to me many times. What was more, as I did not then know any recognized elephant language (and there is such), all I could do was to follow the trainer's advice and just speak loudly and firmly to the vast beast in my own tongue. Although all of these elephants were used to receiving commands in other languages, or at least in accents pronouncedly different from mine, they invariably responded exactly as I desired. There were always several quite complicated actions to be performed in a very limited space and sometimes in a most particular manner, pointing in a specified direction and following split-second timing. But—and this was even more surprising to me—on several occasions elephants who had known me less than an hour did some of these things *before* I gave any verbal command and when I was at a distance from them. Moreover, none of these feats was done in any set pattern that the animal might have previously learned.

I have been handling both wild and trained animals for many years on television, and there the animal is as much on its mettle as is the human performer. Television "time" is quite different from ordinary time or even from business time, and in this medium there are many different "routines" to be followed simultaneously. These include your own actions, those of the show's master of ceremonies, and those of the animal. Lighting, timing, the cameras, and the safety of yourself, of the studio crew, of the audience, and of the animal have also to be borne in mind. The animal's appetite must be considered, your supply of food for it, the condition of its bowels, and various potential embarrassments. Finally, there is the routine of getting the animal on and off stage on cue.

Strangely, many, if not most, animals—particularly entirely wild ones—seem, in some uncanny and inexplicable way, to grasp the significance of the occasion and either go profoundly asleep as soon as they are "on camera" or really put on a show. Nevertheless, they still have to be moved around physically. Trained animals are much less reliable in such circumstances because, I believe, they are more temperamental. If they don't like the set-up, they often will not perform at all. But, among all non-human performers, elephants are in this respect the only consistent exceptions—at least in my experience.

I have never known one to "muff" in any circumstances, and I am prepared to swear that they work at the business on hand as solemnly as, and much more patiently than, any of us humans. When we were able to rehearse them—which it may perhaps be rather surprising to learn is rather rare in television—a brief "walk-through" was invariably enough for them to figure out a complex routine devised to show as much as possible of what they could do in the time allotted. Even more inexplicable were occasions when we humans forgot our routines but the elephant remembered its part in every detail. When we were not able to rehearse, all I could do was to stay backstage and "talk" to the creature just as I would to any intelligent human. Then we went on together and, without outside prompting, went through our paces and, on the part of the elephant, perfectly every time.

This brings us to another everlasting question about elephants: do they or do they not ever forget? This is a question as complex as any other so far raised, and it cannot be answered by a flat "yes" or "no."

It seems to be the considered opinion of those most qualified to make statements on this point that: (1) elephants have very good memories for a lot of things because they have good brains and actually "think" all the time; (2) they tend to remember little things but to forget big ones, just as we do; (3) they have memories just as good as, but not better than, humans, within their more limited field of experience; and (4) their memorizing ability varies among individuals as much as it does among us and in the same way, so that morons may have phenomenal memories for some things and near-geniuses almost no memory at all.

One aspect of "memory" among elephants which does seem to be more nearly universal than any other is their inability to carry a grudge. This is quite contrary to the popular belief that an elephant never forgets an insult or an injury. Elephants seem to be, on the whole, far more forgiving than we are, but there are cases recorded in which one has apparently carried a deep resentment for years and ultimately vented it upon a particular person. Sudden attacks upon people by allegedly tame elephants may, however, take place at any time and for quite other reasons. One of these is called *musth.* Another is, apparently, the simple fact that no elephant wants to be bothered by anybody except its own chosen friend or trainer, and if it is molested or even carelessly approached by anybody else, it may take a swipe at him. As many, if not most, people seem prone to tease elephants at every opportunity, there is a fair chance that the teaser will, if he persists, sooner or later be clobbered.

Despite their majestic and for some strange reason docile and kindly appearance, elephants are really very dangerous creatures. Also, they are all howling individualists and often very sensitive and sometimes very moody creatures. They know their strength, but they don't use it aggressively and they abhor fighting or physical violence of any kind. Most of them show noticeable signs of revulsion to bloodshed or death in any form and display distress in face of these things.

There are, of course, a few really "bad" elephants and some stupid elephants, and both may give every appearance of having been "tamed" (a misleading word when applied to these creatures) when actually they have merely been constrained by fear. The worst, in these respects, are middle-aged females, and notably elephants as opposed to loxodonts; and most particularly those silent ones that never squeal or mumble even when they are young and that persistently display a form of half-obedience, always pretending to misunderstand commands, always working a little more slowly than necessary, always involved in whatever errors occur.

I knew one such, named Cracow, who was owned by a Chinese circus family in Europe. She was a deadly killer, but, being the only money-maker in her "family," she kept bobbing up in circuses in different countries all over the world, billed under different names so that she would not be ordered destroyed by official orders. How many people she actually killed will never be known, as all of them were, luckily for the owners, backstage nonentities or prowlers. The latter were Cracow's speciality, and only pieces of them were found, for she invariably tore them apart. She was said deliberately to shorten her chain shackles and then stand innocently back as the unwary prowler approached. When he came close enough, she would reach out, with that almost electrical speed with which all elephants can move, grabbing the fellow in such a way that he could seldom make any sound, and would then commit quiet mayhem.

Cracow was undoubtedly a "sick" elephant. However, elephants are also, from time to time, really "mad." In the wild state there are what are called "rogues," the true status and occurrence of which will be described later. Among captive elephants the mentally unbalanced are more common in zoos than elsewhere, as they naturally cannot be tolerated in work camps or in show business. Moreover, in zoos, boredom, lack of proper exercise, lack of normal sexual activity, and, above all, loneliness are factors that promote insanity. Keepers are often to blame, though, it must be stressed, usually through mere lack of time rather than any deliberate intent. Lack of *human* companionship can be almost as disastrous to an elephant's soul as the absence of other elephants, and even a little daily talk by a man can make all the difference to its well-being and mental stability.

Few people seem to realize that, with all their higher qualities, their possible real intelligence, the apparent ease with which they can be tamed, their normal reliability, and even their historical record, both elephants and loxodonts are at all times *potentially* very dangerous animals. Their size alone makes them enormously powerful; they can outdistance any Olympic champion on open ground; and they can move their trunks and legs with lightning speed. They cannot see well, but they can smell a popsicle in a package half a block away. They have a "hand"—their trunk—as sensitive as our own, and with it they can pick up from a smooth, shiny surface anything that we can grasp with our fingernails. Their tusks can batter through a reinforced concrete wall, and they have other weapons, even more deadly, in their teeth and jaws. Work elephants pick up small logs with their teeth, and they hold the ropes that move vast tree trunks in the same way.

Despite anything that may be said to the contrary, it is advisable for all except those who have to work with them to keep strictly out of range of all elephants—even little ones—unless a recognized zoo directorate specifically allows contact in one form or another. Even then, everybody should adhere strictly to whatever rules are laid down by the zoo or the animal's attendant for such contact, and all should refrain from approaching an elephant and petting it, slapping it, or feeding it, except under the eyes of and with the express permission of its keeper. Further, it is best to stay out of an elephant pen, even when the animal's trainer or keeper is present. The majority of zoo keepers are first-class animal men and most cautious, but even they are not infallible, and all sorts of things can happen: new surroundings, physical malaise, or even a strong odor—particularly of your perspiration—may offend an elephant, which has a much more acute sense of smell than you have.

Circus elephants should be most strictly avoided. Because they are valuable animals, there is a great temptation not to destroy bad ones, but to change their names and keep them "in the line." Many bullhands also are notorious "drifters" in both the good and the bad senses, and the one on hand may have taken over the elephant only the day before. Further, show elephants are subjected to constant teasing, aggravations, noises, and other irritations; and, although they work at it, *they don't like performing* in any case, so that they tend to build up tensions until a trivial gesture may cause them to "crack." Even the most experienced and conscientious bullhand may fail to notice the symptoms, so well can the elephant conceal them. Then, suddenly, anything can happen.

Above all, keep small children away from elephants. Young elephants and loxodonts spend much of their time between their mothers' legs, and they travel there, even in an all-out stampede, and never seem to come to any harm. Mother elephants are very solicitous of their young and usually more than ready to defend them from real or imagined dangers, and childless females very often take a great interest in small humans. The result may be more dangerous than any attack on a human adult. The danger is twofold. The child may panic and behave like a human instead of an elephant child, and get hurt. Or the elephant may decide to *adopt* the human child, whereupon all her maternal cunning comes to the fore. Then there is practically nothing that any number of adult humans, including her trainer, can do. My first experience with an elephant was at a very tender age when I got myself into just this predicament in a zoo. Of course I panicked, but luckily I could do nothing, as I was firmly held by the happy pachyderm between her forelegs and by her trunk, while a host of excited adults milled around. It was my nurse, stout Briton that she was, who finally ended the crisis by marching up

---

The mother Elephant keeps her infant between her forelegs as much as possible. Childless female Elephants often adopt or endeavor to adopt children, and, in India, they often become greatly attached to toddlers of either sex, who can then take great liberties with their vast foster mothers.

to the behemoth, saying sharply: "Give me *that!*" (or words to that effect), clouting the animal's pillar-like trunk with the umbrella she always carried, and bearing me off triumphantly. I was very lucky.

While the extant representatives of the Dynasty of Abu thus display many of our own traits, they manage to maintain an air of regality seldom achieved by man. Just why this should be, nobody has as yet been able to say. The Asiatic Elephant is ineffably regal, and even its skittish little babies behave as if their worst prank had been divinely approved. The African Loxodont is absolutely imperious in mien and at all times—even in confinement. The famous Jumbo was a bull loxodont, and he maintained his lordly bearing through almost thirty years of indignities, such as carrying armies of caterwauling brats on his back in the London Zoo and then being sold to P. T. Barnum. The cowed inmates of the "official" elephant farm in the Congo, often bowed down with overgrown tusks as much as 10 feet long and harnessed to a plow, still manage to plod along with the utmost dignity and to stand proudly erect when lined up for inspection. Moreover, an elephant quivering with fright, all its limbs shaking and its whole skin twitching so much that it can hardly walk, will enter a plane with four engines roaring and stand perfectly still through a rough passage across an ocean (often continuously vomiting and moaning pitiably)—provided it has a live chicken perched on its head. Why? I do not know, and the airlines do not know; but it is a fact. Almost equally incongruous is that elephants have been shown how to do such unexpected things as play soccer, and in this they have shown the keenest interest, kicking goals with the precision of professionals and trumpeting with glee.

A learned Indian once said: "If *We* are made in the image of God, then the Hathis [Elephants] were made only in the *image* of animals." I know no truer statement.

[15]

OF THEIR BIRTH AND BEHAVIOR

Love and procreation among the Abu.

Birth, youth, and tribal training.

The everyday life of the Abu.

Despite the age-old and intimate association of Man and Abu, the latter have always been the ones who have had to cope with unnatural conditions. To tame, use, and live with Abu, men have to alter their normal ways of life only to a certain extent, but the Abu have to alter theirs almost completely. Even in the Burmese lumber camps their lives are almost entirely unnatural. What about their lives in their own natural environment?

Our information on this comes from an extraordinarily limited number of people and most of these have not left any written records, while those who have done so mostly wrote in languages with which we are not familiar. This is more the pity, as there is a brilliant literature on the subject in several languages of the Southeast Asian area and notably of India. There are translations of a few of these texts and there are one or two Orientals who have written of the subject in our occidental languages—and I am thinking especially of that past master of animal tales Dan Gopal Mukerjee, who died an American citizen. For the most part, however, we have to rely on the publications of a handful of westerners who have lived in the Orient or Africa and who either made a study of Abu their especial concern, or who just observed all wildlife objectively in the countries in which they lived, and who tell us of the activities of elephants or loxodonts when man was not interfering with the even tenor of their lives. What they tell us is often most unexpected. It must be understood, however, that we will herein be speaking primarily of *elephants,* for very little is recorded about the private lives of the loxodonts and especially of the Forest species. What is said hereafter, in fact, refers to elephants unless otherwise stated.

The Abu, it appears, often strike up friendships of the closest kind in the wild, two of them becoming inseparable. They approach the more serious matter of "marriage" in the same manner, pairing off and enjoying a long courtship. Not infrequently, and just as with us, two boys will fall for the same girl and she may tease both, choose one, or try to take on both. Sometimes the old bachelor chum of the boy gets annoyed and tries to muscle in, whereupon, females being what they are, he may succeed, he may be ignored, or he may be driven off by both the lovers. The females are not aggressive but they are very sure of their rights and many of them are great flirts, especially if they are getting a bit passé.

The males are ready and keen to mate at any time and they may make passes at the females, "date" them regularly, shower them with little gifts, neck with them outrageously, and "go steady" with them for months. However, the males have to observe a strict moral code; otherwise they will get not only a walloping from their chosen one, but will probably get it in the neck and on the backside from some of the other girls as well. They may even lose their prospective mates.

A much higher proportion of male Abu have roving eyes than do even human males, and, being less inhibited, they will try anything once, even the head tusker's bride of the moment. Then they can get into real trouble, and if they have the audacity to persist in this and are not prepared to challenge his leadership and see the matter through, they may lose their lives. Abu, in fact, appear to go through all the phases of real love, and there can be nothing more charming than the idyl a young Abu couple enjoy while courting; constantly together and alone; caressing each other with their trunks, and handing each other little tidbits of the choicest food. But then comes the time when the female's body tells her to end the courtship and get down to the business of procreation. Female Abu do not reach this urge with any regularity or at any particular time of the year in any one place, so that they may breed in any month and give birth in any month.

However, when the female does reach mating time, rivals for her affection have to settle their contentions. At this stage of the game the female has lost her say, for if she has encouraged the attentions of more than one male she has to wait for the winner of the contest, which is fought to the finish. This may, but very seldom does, result in the death of either of them, or one may be permanently crippled. It may also result in one's leaving or having to leave the herd. He can then join another herd after a long period of apprenticeship, or he may remain forever a lone fellow.

These fights are spectacular and are performed in sight of the whole herd, which usually stands around indifferently, feeding or pretending to feed. Only in exceptional cases does a third elephant join in, usually a homosexual who had previously paired up with one of the protagonists. The contenders charge each other head on, coming together with a dull wallop that sounds like a dynamite blast underground. They may together weigh as much as 20 tons and may meet at a combined speed of as much as 30 miles per hour! Two 10-ton trucks meeting at that speed would be concertinaed, but the high-balling Abu just bounce back several yards. They also belt each other with half-ton thwacks with their trunks, and tuskers may really go at it with their "professional" weapons, their tusks, which they can use at almost every angle. They kick forward like punting fullbacks and go into prolonged clinches. They keep at it for hours. When one either falls to his knees or flees, he is immediately and henceforth ignored. Then the "girl-friend" of the victor appears and just passes him by, and he, of course, goes trotting off after her, and the herd goes back to the more serious business of feeding. If, however, there is more than sex involved in the fight, Abu may fight to the death or until one *drives* the other away. In leadership contests one or the other *has* to be the conclusion.

Elephants start breeding around their sixteenth year; but a female as young as nine is recorded as becoming pregnant. Bush Loxodonts apparently start only at about their eighteenth year. No similar information is available about the Forest Loxodonts. Elephants are not monogamous except when in captivity. Males and females usually change mates after each pregnancy. Bush Loxodonts seem to stay with their mates for many years, and through more than one pregnancy. Several forest tribes believe that Forest Loxodonts are truly monogamous, for they go about in family parties or associations of family parties. These parties become known and do not seem to change over the years except by the departure of the mature young.

In order to copulate, the Abu do *not* have to dig pits for

the females or find logs to stand on; nor do the females have to lie on their backs, reverse themselves, or perform any of the other remarkable gyrations accredited to them. Nor does the copulation last for days or even hours: it takes about four minutes and may be repeated a number of times during the day or night. The male mounts the female with ease and grace, his fore limbs straddling her neck and holding her firmly. The male is almost upright at this time and for all his great weight his body is as lithe as a man's. The Abu become pregnant about every two and a half years, averaging seven pregnancies during their lives under *unnatural* conditions, i.e., in captivity. It is believed that in the wild state they continue to reproduce for a much longer period and, according to "native" belief, continue until about 70, during which time they may bear 17 to 20 young.

Elephants usually have their first calf between the ages of 16 and 20. The period of gestation in elephants varies a little according to the four races or subspecies, but averages about 20 months. G. P. Sanderson says Indians give 18 to 20 months if the female is carrying a cow calf and up to 22 months if a bull calf. Among Bush Loxodonts it seems to be about 24 months for both; Forest Loxodonts have given birth at the end of 16 months. Both elephants and Bush Loxodonts may have twins. Mother elephants do not seem to appreciate that they are pregnant for about ten months; then they set about making certain preparations, change their diet, and start taking special care of themselves by, among other things, pushing off their lover. Abu seldom breed in captivity or full domestication due to several factors—segregation of the sexes, too much hard work, cage neurosis, or insufficient or improper food. However, they do breed fairly regularly in the seminatural conditions of a lumber camp, where they are turned out every night to find their own food and where they feed on natural foods when resting in the off season. About fifty per cent of the present Burmese work elephants were thus bred.

Births of Abu in Europe, Australia, South and North America, and Russia have been rare, and most were stillborn. There were two that survived in England, and one in the United States which was not raised. One elephant was born in Germany and raised. I was told, but have been unable to confirm, that one was raised in Argentina. However, and strangely enough, the zoos in Rome and Warsaw are recorded as having had more outstanding successes. Old records tell of births in Cairo, Egypt; Baghdad, Iraq; and, of course, many in India and Ceylon. But in India and Ceylon the business was not encouraged, because it cost so much and took so long for the baby to grow up to a point where it could earn its keep. Healthy Abu females start mating again eight to ten months after delivery, so that there may often be two or three different-aged offspring suckling at the same time.

Lewis remarks that the Abu are "true to the Kinsey report in that the males begin to lose interest in sex [in captivity] at 35 and become staid after 45, while the females sustain the urge right along at a middle level." For loxodonts in the wild such is far from being the case, as even herd tuskers mate regularly and may do so with half the females in the herd before they retire, and they keep it up right into advanced age. As young are born in the herds at regular intervals and in proper proportions to the whole, the old males must therefore be fully potent.

Birth is a tremendous event among the Abu and a very important one to the herd. We speak primarily of the Elephant, since, as far as I know, the birth of a loxodont in the wild has never been properly observed and recorded. Birth is anticipated weeks in advance by the mother. She selects an experienced "nurse" to assist her from among the older and more reliable unwed or currently unattended matrons who have no growing children. These nurses are called "Aunties" in Burmese lumber camps. The mother then selects a place, usually beneath a large and spreading tree surrounded as far as possible by thick cover. There she makes a very large, circular open space, with the assistance of the Auntie, clearing it of all vegetation and debris and sometimes piling the stuff in a rough rampart all around. The expectant mother and the nurse then take up quarters there, sometime before the blessed event is due, the exact time of which both have an uncanny way of knowing. They are always near good and plentiful food; they go out to eat daily, stay away from the herd, and retire to the area to sleep by night and to rest by day. Meantime, the herd does not interfere nor does it go on trek; instead, it waits around until two or three days after the birth.

When all is in readiness, the mother usually lies down for a long rest while the Auntie rumbles around her. When the time comes, the mother rises to her feet and the Auntie stands behind her and facing away from her. Then—as described by those few lucky Burmese oozies who have been allowed by their elephants to be present or who have crept up on them undiscovered by the Auntie—amid tremendous heaves and gargantuan sighs and groans, delivery takes place. The baby is just about 3 feet tall when it first stands up, and weighs between 150 to 200 pounds. It emerges neck first with its head tucked between its forelegs and is gently lowered to the ground by the mother squatting. Actual birth may take as little as two minutes once the fluid begins to run. The afterbirth may be passed anywhere from immediately after delivery to hours later, and the mother usually consumes it. In any case, as soon as she has separated her child she sets about cleaning up while the faithful Auntie stands guard, attending to the infant. Every scrap of evidence of the birth is eliminated in one way or another by the mother, and any scrap of litter that might smell of the event is destroyed or removed. Only then does the mother take charge and start cleaning and currying her child. All this care is apparently devised with one primary end in view—protection against the great cats. (Tigers alone are estimated to kill twenty per cent of all elephant youngsters in Burma.)

The baby's trunk at birth is a ridiculous little affair and its owner has no idea what it is for or how to use it. It suckles with its mouth like any other animal and at first finds great difficulty in keeping its trunk out of the way. In fact, it takes the baby about six months to learn how to employ it deftly, and many months to learn how to use it to put food into the mouth without missing the appropriate cavity. Nothing, apart from a baby seal learning to swim, is more comical to watch than a baby elephant trying to feed itself in imitation of its mother. This lack of knowledge is one of the major causes of collapse among young orphaned elephants.

The mother's attitude toward her young one may often seem odd to us. In the wild she is probably just as violently and protectively maternal as any other animal. With man around, however, she often appears to become extremely offhand. Thus, Sanderson writes that "the female elephant evinces no particular attachment to her offspring," and Tennent says that if a mother is separated from her calf for as little as two days, even if suckling, she never again recognizes it and her milk seems to dry up. What is more, the orphans are buffeted about by everybody in the elephant tribe and are usually doomed. Sanderson said that only once in thirty-five years did he hear of a female adopting an orphan.

All this may be so, but it conflicts with everything "na-

A newborn Elephant with its "Auntie." Immediately after birth, a motherless female takes over the baby while the mother clears up all evidence of the birth—probably, for the most part, to prevent detection by tigers.

tives" say about both wild elephants and loxodonts. Moreover, their statements are backed up by those of many hunters, poachers, and naturalists. Wild mothers, they insist, are enormously solicitous of their babies and protect them with their bodies at all times. Also, after birth the youngster is kept perpetually between the mother and the Auntie for some weeks. Moreover, even in a stampede, which is a state of unreasoning hysteria, the pace conforms to that possible for the smallest of the herd. When in flight the mothers and babies may turn on their pursuers and come roaring back in a mass while the "gallant" bulls carry on, headlong.

In swamps the mother and the Auntie will support the young one with intertwined trunks. In an emergency the mothers and young females and even some bulls band together and charge shoulder to shoulder while the Aunties flee with the young, which are sorted out afterward. Mothers in captivity will let humans handle their babies immediately after birth, and not even loxodonts seem to get worried at this; while the babies themselves will, if separated from their mothers, follow a human around like a puppy. In the wild, tigers are known to attack full-grown elephants but usually prowl around until they can make a rush for a baby. Lions do not attack loxodonts, even lone babies,[1] and leopards, which will sneak up on anything, think several times before attacking any Abu.

Unless a tiger is very clever and lucky, he will lose his life even to a female elephant, who can literally demolish him against a tree with one throw or smash him almost in half with a single swat of her trunk, or simply stomp the life out of him with her feet. A tusker may ram a tiger through a few times with his tusks. Sometimes an elephant will just lie down on a tiger and flatten him; or simply put a foot on him, pull his legs off one at a time and throw them about,

[1] This is probably for the most part because lions hunt in pairs, the male driving the game to the female, who makes the actual kill and usually at night. Loxodonts refuse to be so herded.

and then bash the marauder's head in with a foot. After that the elephant goes off and washes himself thoroughly. A mother elephant will give a tiger a very rough time, thumping at him with her forehead and often pinning him to the ground by this method.

To get back to the infancy of the calf: after two days the mother has recovered and the baby can march with the best of them, climb nimbly, and even swim rivers. At first he is held up in the water by his mother's trunk; later he climbs on her back, and later still he swims alongside on the downstream side of her vast body.

Calves subsist exclusively on their mother's milk for the first six months; then they begin to nibble at little bits and pieces of vegetation. The milk of the Abu is exceedingly rich. It contains exactly one hundred times more albumen per volume than cow's milk. Orphaned baby elephants cared for by man seldom lived until Major Pretorius, of Johannesburg, analyzed the milk of Bush Loxodonts and developed a baby-elephant feeding formula consisting of one gallon of raw cow's milk, half a pint of heavy cream, the white of twenty-four hen eggs, and four pounds of overboiled rice. The formula has proved a complete success with *all* Abu. (The King of Ava [i.e., Burma] once received an orphaned semi-albino elephant, which was, of course, extremely holy. As it showed signs of wilting, the King issued a ukase, which resulted in relays of twenty-four young girls presenting themselves at the palace daily and suckling the little monster for *five years!* The baby and presumably the honor of the Court of Ava were thus saved.) Incidentally, all healthy baby Abu scream; if one does not it is either sick, neurotic, or mad, and will either die or be extremely troublesome. I have known only one that never made a sound but that did not go bad. She was named *Pas çe soir, Josephine,* had a lot of curly black hair, the wrong number of nails, and came to the United States from Siam by mistake. She never did anything wrong except pin a lady into a phone booth in a New

York hotel lobby, obstruct another's exit from an elevator, and imprison an inexperienced animal man in his truck. She rode around to TV and other shows in an extended-chassis limousine, the gasoline consumption of which she reduced markedly by her everlasting fore-and-aft rocking motion, which imparted unexpected momentum to the vehicle. She was a little show-business "doll" and never gave any other trouble except once after a TV show when she was bumped by a taxicab and in her excitement charged a line of ladies waiting to enter a cooking show.

Young Abu are fully weaned at six years; then they enter tribal life and have to learn how to behave. As with our youngsters, this is rather difficult for them, because herd life is complex and circumscribed by many rules. It seems that Elephant herds under completely natural conditions used to consist of about 100 animals. Today 30 to 50 make up a herd. Herds of the Forest Loxodonts are loose associations of families usually totaling about 100 animals. Bush Loxodont herds number from 500 to 1,000. If food is scarce, the herd breaks up into parties which stay about two miles apart. These parties are extended families all the members of which are related. They keep in touch through their sense of smell.

Elephants are *always* led by an old female; loxodonts sometimes, if not always, are led by a bull. In both, the females and young form the advance guard, the tuskers bringing up the rear and ranging widely on either flank. In flight the situation is immediately reversed, the tuskers taking off first and the cows bringing up the rear. There is no specific record of tuskers having covered a retreat. Herds never mix. They will take in females that have escaped from human captivity, but never wild ones, whereas they will readily accept lone young males.

Scattered herds drift as a whole in the same direction. They close up to rest and when alarmed, at which times the females and young bunch together while the bulls move off.

When first disturbed, they all fall silent and then move off swiftly without making a sound. Their normal speed is about three miles an hour, but they can make four or even five miles per hour and keep it up for ten miles. During a stampede, Elephants can increase their speed to fifteen miles per hour for short distances. In a charge, loxodonts can make twenty-five miles an hour and overtake the best human runners on open level ground.[2] A stampede is uncontrollable and overwhelming, and if pressed, the females and young may waltz about and come charging straight back into danger. They cannot surmount a 5-foot bank or jump at all but can climb precipitous mountains, though Williams says he once saw one clear a wide and deep gulley when stampeding downhill. When a herd moves from danger they go full tilt for some way, then slow to a walk, which they usually keep up for from ten to twenty miles.

Herd tuskers feed alone in the morning and rejoin the herd about eight to nine A.M.; lone males go on feeding till later. The daily routine of the Abu is to rest during the heat of the day, standing up, then to feed all afternoon, bathe in the evening, move and feed until after midnight, sleep for two to three hours, and then feed again right up to the midday rest period. They get along with very little sleep. They sleep usually lying on their sides, snoring gently through their trunks, their free ear involuntarily flapping from time to time and making a very special noise. If they are standing still, you had better not shout at them, because they almost invariably then charge. So-called "rogues"—if such things really exist—are no more dangerous or determined than other lone males. Females with young are much more dangerous.

Both Elephants and loxodonts move about a lot in dull weather but take shelter in bad weather. Elephants and Bush Loxodonts love the sunshine provided the air is not too

[2] The best human sprinters make twenty-two miles per hour over 100 to 220 yards; fifteen miles per hour over one mile.

hot and dry, and they like to stand about doing nothing on open rocky places by rivers. When on the march, elephants proceed single file and stay constantly on the move, seldom spending more than one or two days in the same place. The stride of a large Elephant is about 6 feet, but that of a large Bush Loxodont may be as much as 10 feet, for they are much longer-legged. They have no other pace but a walk, though this may be speeded up into a sort of shuffle when both legs on the same side follow each other so closely as to approximate almost a camel gait. Normally they slow up going downhill, and that is the best direction for you to take if one is after you. Zigzagging is useless, as I once found out;[3] the animal simply goes straight ahead and turns on you when you are at one of your zigs or zags. It is a most disconcerting maneuver.

All the Abu are very fond of water and all of them are good swimmers. In fact, it looks very much as if their ancestors may have been partially aquatic, at least to the extent that hippos are. The Bush Loxodont has little cause to swim, for there are very few rivers in his country which are too deep for him to wade. Elephants can fill their stomachs with water to weight them down, and then walk across the bottom of rivers with their trunks held aloft like schnorkels. Forest Loxodonts are very competent swimmers and spend a great deal of time in deep water, even in very swift rivers. The little ones actually dive, and all of them can regulate the depth at which they float by swallowing air or water. Normally, they lower themselves till just the top of the head is above water, whereby they are still able to see. Then they curve the trunk into an "S" so that it forms a breathing tube ahead. Forest Loxodonts make the same motions with their legs when swimming as when walking on dry land, and for some quite inexplicable reason this propels them ahead at a

[3] Luckily, it just so happened that there was a concrete platform handy on which a frame house had stood and which had a gaping cellar door into which I darted with rodential aplomb.

really astonishing rate. One would imagine that the drag against the water caused by the movement of their stubby legs forward would just about counteract any backward push, but you have to paddle hard in a native canoe to keep up with them.

Elephants are almost as good swimmers as Forest Loxodonts and can keep up a steady one mile an hour for several hours. Sanderson records that in the year 1875 he took seventy-five from Dacca across the delta of the Ganges to Barrackpur, near Calcutta. They swam continuously for six hours, then rested on a sandbank for an hour, and finally swam another three hours. None was lost. He believes, and I agree with him, that the Abu swim better than any other mammal regarded as being primarily terrestrial. Lewis says he doesn't believe any of this, including Sanderson's story, but he admits that they are great swimmers buoyed up, he says, by their "large body cavities." This is, of course, a misconception, as is also his remark that they are the only animals that float when dead. About a third of all mammals float when dead.

Dietary deficiencies and especially a lack of certain enzymes or vitamins may be the cause of "rogues," as may be a glandular imbalance with which a few individuals are born. We know several reasons why some Elephants and loxodonts, and particularly males, may live alone. The Abu suffer much from neuroses and they sometimes appear to be born, or to become insane, just about as often as human beings do. Then, there are those that lose in mating fights and have to do a time of penance; those that lose leadership battles and are driven off; those that are lost; and also those that are really old and decrepit. Any lone-bull Abu may be dubbed a "rogue" just because he is alone. Most of those that are alone are sick either physically or mentally and they may then behave irrationally and, to us, dangerously. Deliberate killer elephants are as rare as true man-eating (or eating-man-by-preference) large cats. Yet they do exist. But whereas the big cat kills humans apparently merely because he finds them easy game and likes their taste, the Abu are neither carnivorous nor hunters. The real killers seem indeed to be individuals that are utterly soured on life and that will attack other Abu as readily as they will men. They also lash out at little inoffensive animals and rip up palm trees. These "rogues" certainly seem to be batty.

On the other hand, there are authenticated cases of wild Abu apparently attacking humans without provocation and then, having really only stunned them, picking them up gently, carrying them into the shade, and covering them with leaves. The idea that "rogues" are animals thrown out of the herd is quite untrue. They are either the lords of a herd who prefer to go off alone, or they are sick animals waiting to recover before rejoining the herd. Most tabbed "rogues," moreover, are not old, decrepit animals—which are harmless and are allowed to tag along with the herd as long as they can keep up with it—but vigorous, younger, middle-aged bulls who have no official status in the herd or who have not claimed leadership of it. Sanderson mentions some genuine cases of dangerous Abu, one of which was "The Mandala Elephant," which killed a large number of people and was alleged to have eaten several of them, though it may have merely been seen carrying them around in its mouth before tearing them apart.

Mother Elephant and baby. It appears that the length of the trunks of newborn Elephants and Loxodonts varies remarkably. Some have trunks only a few inches long; others are born with trunks reaching the ground. Also some are almost fully haired, while others are almost "naked."

Every person today who really knows something about Abu in Africa and Asia asserts that their numbers are increasing, in spite of a contrary general impression. Before World War II only 6,000 wild Abu were supposed to be left in Burma but the lumber men protested that this was a gross underestimation; they themselves had at least 6,000 in captivity. Then, in this area we must add the Abu population of the whole of Indochina, Malaya, the southern edge of China, Assam, a substantial part of India, Ceylon, Sumatra, and the northern fifth of Borneo. How many Abu live in all these areas combined nobody knows, but there are certainly many thousands and probably still some tens of thousands. Of loxodonts we appear to have some accurate counts made in the upland territories of East Africa, from Ethiopia and Somaliland in the north to the Cape in the south, but it is utterly impossible even to attempt to estimate the number there might still be in the vast savannas that stretch from the Nilotic Sudan in the east to Senegambia in the west. As to what Abu live in the two great tall forest blocks of the Guinea Coast and the Cameroons-Gabun-Congo, nobody knows; there could be therein tens or even hundreds of thousands of Forest Loxodonts.

Loxodonts are now well protected[2] throughout their range, and while a number are killed every year under license for "sport" or by farmers in self-defense, are poached for ivory and meat, or are "officially" destroyed as predators, they are definitely increasing. The important fact is that the Abu, despite their size, are *not* a "dying race." They are fertile, vigorous, and adaptable, and their kind has not yet run its course on this planet, but we cannot make any predictions about their future. They were contemporary for millions of years with tens of thousands of other kinds of vast beasts, most of which have passed. They are the only wild creatures *larger than* us that, despite all we have done to them, have not succumbed to our onslaughts.

[2] See footnote on page 257.

[16]

OF THEIR LIFE AND DEATH

The senses and physiology of the Abu.

Their age and longevity;

and their death.

There still remains an almost endless list of questions about the Abu which we would like answered, and among these are some of those most commonly asked. But, not only can we as yet by no means answer all the questions asked; we also find ourselves in the distressing position of not really being able to offer final solutions to any of the most vital and obvious ones. A tremendous amount of information about these lordly creatures has now been recorded by all manner of people: hunters, naturalists, poachers, traders, farmers, and even tourists, as well as by professional bullhands, forest officers, managers and workers in the teakwood camps, show people, Indian mahouts, Brahmans, and savants. But, apart from a few men like G. P. Sanderson, who actually spent a lifetime studying these creatures, very little purely scientific study has been made of them, and only very recently have scientists prosecuted a few researches under fully controlled conditions on their anatomy, physiology, behavior, and habits. Of the body-functioning of Abu something is now known in the case of the Elephant, but all too little of that of the loxodonts. Let us consider first their senses.

The Abu do not see very well. The Elephants and the Forest Loxodonts are as much nocturnal as diurnal and are more active at night than in the day, when they rest. If they are up-wind of some object or other animal that does not make a noise, they seldom see it until they are almost on top of it and then usually not until it moves—which is true of most animals other than the Primates, which have stereoscopic vision like ours. The eyes of the Abu are peculiar, too, in that, as the animals are unable to turn their heads appreciably, they have a kind of double-scanning vision of a rather low angle to right and left. To see forward, they must raise their heads and look down their "noses," so that their aim is unreliable when heading at something straight-on. They can, however, see unexpectedly far *backward* on either side.

Their sense of hearing is better, but even with their vast, radarlike ears, it is still rather limited. Reinert set up experiments using two pure tones (750 cycles per second as the positive and 500 cycles as the negative) and found that an Elephant could learn to differentiate six pairs of sounds, including two sounds as close as a single note apart. After eighteen months this animal got nine out of twelve right the first time. She also learned a pair of melodies—up-down-up, and down-up-down. These were then changed in every possible way, toward higher or lower frequencies, in intensity, in rhythm, in timing, and on various instruments. She got them all right every time. Thus, in acoustical discrimination, the Abu can rate high, but they make a poor showing in *direction* and *distance* discrimination. They will pick up a sound at a considerable distance but then be unable to locate it exactly and may walk right over its place of origin, even if the sound is given out rhythmically.

Abu can make a great variety of sounds, and obviously use sound in communication among themselves. These sounds emanate from their trunks and throats. They trumpet with rage when charging, but grumble deep in their throats if wounded or hurt. They seem to express fear either by a shrill trumpet or by a deep-throated roar. A small, low squeaking seems to indicate pleasure, and a low purring in the throat, contentment. Loxodonts also gurgle and whine, and all Abu can make a terrifying pumping noise not unlike that sometimes heard during earthquakes. Female Forest Loxodonts make a very strange hollow "chipping" sound, and all of them can produce an astonishing noise by rapping on hard ground with the tips of their trunks. This has best been likened to the noise made by waggling a large piece of thin sheet-metal or by a saw improperly played with a bow. It is the most extraordinary noise made by any animal.

The Abu's sense of smell, their most acute sense, is quite astounding. They can smell a man miles away, though they can walk into him downwind. They can detect water at great distances. No specific experiments on their sense of smell have been undertaken, but every hunter has a lot to say on the matter. They use their trunks like antennae. Their sense of taste is apparently equally acute, or they have some *other* sense as yet unexplained, which tells them unerringly what is poisonous and what is not, and what is good to eat and when. Still, they sometimes poison themselves with unfamiliar substances when they are in strange country and desperately hungry. Doping Abu is quite easy, but killing them with poison is virtually impossible. They love alcohol and most narcotics and, like any human, they can get mildly plastered, semiconsciously somnambulant, or uproariously drunk; and, also like humans, their reactions vary according to their basic individualities—the naturally cheery becoming more happy, and the morose becoming downright dangerous.

We acknowledge that we have five basic senses. Actually, many more than these have now been detected in humans, such as our senses of hunger, thirst, balance, electrical flux, and so forth. The Abu have all these, but they react in—to us—unexpected ways, and there are some odd things about their fifth basic sense—i.e., that of touch. Their skins and particularly their trunks are extremely sensitive, and they are frightfully ticklish! Mosquitoes bother them greatly. They are also much distressed by heat, although the Bush Loxodonts can graze placidly for hours under a streaming equatorial sun and in dry air. Elephants cannot stand heat; yet both they and Bush Loxodonts can endure a lot of cold, and they regularly pound up into the snow on mountains both in Asia (the Himalayas) and in Africa (Kilimanjaro and the Ruwenzori Range), sometimes even to heights of over 10,000 feet, though for what reason we do not know, as there is nothing there for them to eat and they have to eat practically all the time. In Europe and North America they may be walked and worked in deep snow and they seem to enjoy it, suffering not at all. With lesser senses they are well endowed. They have an uncanny sense of balance, and they, above all other animals, seem to be immune to electrical shock. They also have still other senses that we do not understand at all.

Another most peculiar thing is common to Abu and, as far as is known, unique to them. This is a business called *musth*. Nobody knows exactly what it is, what it is for, exactly how it works, or what it will do. There are as many theories about it as there are variations of its incidence. Most experts seem to agree that it is not *primarily* a sexual manifestation, although it may bring on actions on the part of the males which appear to have sexual implications or import. It cannot be correlated with any cyclical sexual urge on the part of either the male or the female. *Musth* starts during the adolescence of male Abu and first really bursts out about the year of their maturity. It increases in intensity annually until their prime and then slowly subsides until in old age they do not seem to suffer it at all. It is common to almost all males, but there are some that never undergo it, as far as we know. Moreover, these are *not* the asexuals and homosexuals. It has been recorded in females (though rarely in captivity) and especially in certain aggressive types which seem to spurn normal sexual activities but which are not necessarily "old maids" or "wallflowers." The whole thing is very odd.

From a physical standpoint, *musth* is connected with glands between the eyes and the mouth which form small pockets lined with special cells and which have external openings. At certain times, usually annually and at about the same time of year, these glands become active and, during the "ripe" years of the individual, exude a tarlike substance that in extreme cases flows down the animal's cheeks into its mouth. The substance appears to add to the animal's then unbalanced state or even to drive it crazy, so that it is constantly sucking at the angle of its lips with its trunk. This substance is extremely bitter in taste to us. Old mahouts and oozies say that mother Abu place small twigs of certain vines in these glandular pockets of their male offspring and sometimes, by mistake, in those of females, and that the twigs have something to do with musth. Certainly small twigs have sometimes been found in these glands.

Musth comes on suddenly, usually at the beginning of the drier season—if there is one. It may last from a week to five months, and during that time the animal may be completely batty. In extreme cases it may attack almost anything living; it usually forgets temporarily any training it may have had; and it acts generally in a dazed or a furious manner. Tamed, domesticated, and trained animals coming on musth have to be shackled immediately and chained fore and aft to something substantial. It is said that the Burmese have a way of shortening the duration of the process by starving the animal and giving it certain herbs, but the details of this treatment are not recorded, and the Indians say that it does more harm than good by simply storing up "musthiness" that results in a greater outburst the next time. At these times bulls may literally rape any females they can come by, but they may, on the other hand, gore them—a performance that seems to be mad rather than sexual.

I have heard only one explanation of musth which seems to make some sense. This is that the oily exudation is, *in the wild,* rubbed off on trees to signal to the females that mating is desired, being thus, in a wider sense, a manifestation of sex comparable to the songs of male birds. Sometimes, instead of being violent, musth animals become drowsy and lethargic. Curiously, musth does not seem to occur in animals that are physically below par, and it does not drive them crazy in the wild. Abu in North America usually come on musth in winter.

Loxodonts come on musth just as Elephants do, but their reactions are different. If they are confined, it seems to make them so miserable that they shiver like sick dogs. If not confined, they may go absolutely berserk, but for a much shorter period than Elephants. What they do in the wild is simply not known, though young mature bulls have been seen suddenly to run amuck in their own herds and to take

---

Elephant bathing. Elephants bathe every day; Forest Loxodonts are almost semi-aquatic, but Bush Loxodonts can go for months without water. Elephants in captivity should be bathed or hosed down every day.

on stately patriarchs in combat, seemingly without sense, and to have the stuffing knocked out of them as a result. They may be in musth, and it has been suggested that this strange physiological speciality is Nature's device for stimulating the otherwise most placid of her creatures to get up and fight for their position in the tribe. If the young mature bulls did not do this, the ancient patriarchs might, by their immense size and strength, continue to dominate all the eligible cows for decades, even after they were long impotent, and thus cause the downfall of the Dynasty.

The strength of Abu is another hotly debated matter. Astonishing feats are on record, such as Lewis's Tusko, who battered through a steel-enforced concrete wall while in musth and then with one leg pulled two loaded trucks with their wheels locked. This animal also once acted as a brake for a runaway trailer truck on a steep hill. They can do the work of 200 laborers, or two bulldozers, or four tractors of medium size, in a day; they have picked up fallen cranes being used to pick them up, and they have hauled trucks, transporting them, out of ditches and snow banks and then towed these to the nearest repair stations. They are used to shunt railroad cars, and a bull Elephant jerked to a start twenty-one such cars on a level track and then rolled them five miles. They can push down deep-rooted trees 3 feet in diameter by making them sway, and loxodonts can tear up roots over a foot in diameter. Unfortunately, there appear to be no precise figures on record of actual measurements of their power to push, pull, strain, jerk, or haul. We cannot say exactly what they can do, but their over-all strength is quite terrifying.

At work they never use their trunks for heavy duty but tuck them away in a curl. They pull log ropes by holding them between their teeth and they also hold light logs in this way. Tuskers lift logs on their tusks, balancing them with their trunks curled over the top. They pull well in a heavy harness, but no *really* efficient harness has ever yet been devised that does not interfere with one or other of their muscles. Mostly they push with the bump above their trunks, and they use their front feet to push or roll things. Their trunks are their most priceless possessions and they use them carefully to transfer food and water to their mouths and to spot danger by taste and smell. They of course do not drink through their trunks but use them to suck up the water to a height of about 15 inches and then squirt it into their mouths. If their trunks get damaged, they go into deep water to drink, sucking the water up by mouth as an anteater does.

The Abu ought to be bathed regularly in captivity and preferably twice a day. Every housed Abu should have a swimming pool in its stall, just as every hippopotamus has. Bush Loxodonts can get along with only a daily hosing. If bathing is impossible, they should be thoroughly well-oiled with horse grease or neat's foot oil about three times a year.[1] This kills lice and keeps the skin supple. However, two days after each application they should be thoroughly scrubbed with soap, warm water, and a hard brush and then hosed down. This scours off the dead surface skin and "scale" that will accumulate dust, harden, and form a crust sometimes half an inch thick. Such a crust prevents the animal from breathing. Treated thus and then given a massage with two or three gallons of vanishing cream, as manufactured for our own gentler sex, the animals will keep in splendid condition.

Keeping Abu healthy is an exacting procedure. Only real experts should write upon the health and hygiene of living things and all such writings should be both *inclusive* and professional. What I will note of these subjects are therefore only interesting highlights of vast and complex matters into which I cannot delve here in any detail. The care of healthy Abu and the treatment of sick Abu are highly complicated subjects, and what has been discovered about

[1] Some mahouts use coconut oil.

them is most specialized. I can only urge anybody and everybody having something to do with the care of these animals to obtain copies of the following books and to keep them on hand at all times: *The Care and Management of Elephants in Burma* by A. J. Ferrier; *A Short Treatise on the Management of Elephants* by A. J. W. Milroy; *Elephant Bill* by J. H. Williams; *Elephant Tramp* by George Lewis; and *An Atlas of the Elephant* by Professor W. C. Osman Hill.

It is my most earnest desire, and the reason why I list these works specifically and in the main body of this text rather than just in the bibliography, that every person who deals with Abu should have, or at least know about, these works, for it is extremely hard to find any reliable published information in this field. These are not of course the only sound works on the subject, but there are none better and, used together, they not only suffice but should cover almost all known eventualities. Owners of Abu can also always use the services of a good vet. One specializing in cows, moreover, seems to be better than one concentrating on horses, although a cow is a ruminant and an Abu is not. However, the best thing an Abu handler can do is to make himself into an Abu vet, by learning all he can about the animals. He must then be prepared to do some pretty big things!

For instance, giving an enema to a large Abu is often necessary and is fairly easy provided you know how to do it and have a big enough pump. In certain circumstances, without such equipment, you must be prepared to take off your shirt, reach into your charge's anus as far as you can, and remove as much of the "obstruction" as you can reach. As for abscesses, you must attack them with a 12-inch blade, square at the top and sharpened to a razor edge, and a mallet to drive this home. And when you make the first cut you must not lose your nerve or fail to get to the bottom of matters with one stroke; otherwise your patient may panic. Abu will take a lot of pain if they know you are trying to help them. In any case, you will probably be drenched in pus, often filled with live maggots. Giving an Abu a pedicure is also not a pleasant job. This must, however, be done at regular intervals, for they have a lot of trouble with their feet.

Abu are very susceptible to snake bites, especially on their feet and on the tips of their trunks. In fact, they succumb to snake bite almost as fast as we do. You therefore must cut and very quickly in such an eventuality, even while the victim is raving. The other pest to look out for is ants, but only in the tropics. Driver, Rover, and Army Ants can kill a tethered or stalled Abu in a surprisingly short time, and their death from that cause is so ghastly that it will haunt you for the rest of your life.

Under natural conditions the Abu customarily suffer certain sicknesses at yearly intervals. They then starve themselves, fill their stomachs with certain alkaline earths (like kaolin), go on a strict diet of special astringent leaves and barks, and so purge themselves. They also know how to treat wounds—washing them and then plastering them with clay to keep flies away. To obviate heatstroke they pile branches on their heads. If they get an abscessed tusk they will wedge it between appropriately shaped branches of a tree and then tug and haul away till it comes out, giving vent the while to excruciating screams and howling with pain. They may thus work away for hours while the rest of the herd stands around rocking slowly back and forth or from side to side and not even eating. They sometimes, though not frequently, succumb to a form of murrain, like that of cattle. This is about ninety per cent fatal in domestication but seems to be curable by them in the wild. In captivity they are prone to just about all the diseases and physical disabilities that we are, and they have some dreadful ones of their own like *Lurza, Zahirbad,* and sundry parasitic worms with most unpleasant life-histories. But for details of these I refer you to the technical works listed above.

In the wild they seem to be one of the healthiest of animals and are more or less immune to disease and virtually indestructible. The clue to their good health seems to be their immense and selective knowledge of their diet. They eat all types of grasses and sedges, some leaves, much fallen fruit, and green nuts. They drink from twenty to forty gallons of water a day but can go entirely without it for several days. Lewis and others familiar with captive Abu state that they can regurgitate any water they swallow. Almost everybody else says that they cannot. Having received about ten gallons of rather dirty water with bits of lettuce floating in it right in my face on two consecutive occasions, I can assert that some Abu, at least, can do so.

There is an equal amount of argument as to their habitual practices in urination and defecation. They do not urinate while walking, as they do not like to wet their legs. They will hold their urine for a very long time like well-house-trained dogs, but, if frightened, will let go with a seemingly endless torrent. They defecate while walking unless they are suffering from diarrhea. The average Abu not only like to drink alcohol in any form but, contrary to a popular belief, do not object to their human friends doing so. They also like to eat tobacco, and a few cigarette butts (without filter tips) each day seems to be good for them; cigar butts are even better. Their diet in captivity should be varied, like that of any other animal. Abu are not, any more than ourselves, exclusively herbivorous. They have to take in also a certain amount of mineral matter that can be obtained only from other animals, and if they don't get it they may do very strange and sometimes unpleasant things. Lewis, again, notes an Abu named Romeo with the Ringling Circus which customarily ate fish; and there was one that apparently ate a young woman, complete, overnight. This incident occurred in 1944 in Zurich, Switzerland, and I quote from a letter written by a Mr. W. K. Teppler of Des

Moines, Iowa, to *True* magazine, and published by them in their October 1958 issue. This reads:

"*Chang*, a pampered 8-year old bull, was punished for unruliness by being deprived of his daily walk through the zoo and confined to the elephant pit. To console her favorite zoo animal, a young office girl left her home after dinner one night with bread for Chang and did not return. In the morning, keepers found blood on the pit floor and, among the straw, a human hand and a toe. That Chang had eaten the missing girl was established by evacuation of her undigested clothes, hat and handbag. Chang was saved from immediate execution by the pleading of his keeper and kept in chains, but three years later he seized the keeper, battered him to death against the bars, and was dispatched with four bullets in his brain—the first and only elephant ever known to have turned carnivorous."

No two people, even those who have lived with Abu, seem to agree exactly as to how much food these animals need per day to keep healthy. The estimates for adults range from as little as 80 pounds to 1,100 pounds. G. P. Sanderson, after carrying out protracted feeding experiments in India, came to the conclusion that 600 to 700 pounds of suitable green fodder in eighteen hours was needed to keep the average adult elephant healthy, but that a larger tusker would need 800 pounds. These figures very closely approximate the results found best for the Congo work loxodonts, namely 800 pounds for females and 1,000 pounds for bulls. Everybody agrees that most of the food ingested is roughage and that the more the animal gets, the better, but there is endless argument as to what *else* the animal needs. The Indian work elephants get in addition to their bulk feed a daily ration of grain, usually paddy or unhusked rice; some salt; and various other items. Lewis advocates at least 100 pounds of the best timothy or alfalfa hay per day plus grain, fruits, vegetables, and bread in "reasonable" amounts. Oats give Abu too much pep and are not fully digested; bulls should not be given too high an energy diet.

I worked out the cost of keeping a full-grown Abu in New Jersey in basic food alone. At current wholesale prices and based on the conservative estimate of bulk at 500 pounds per day—the best bulk food being alfalfa hay, which costs $50 a ton—the annual outlay would be $4,550.

There comes, now, an aspect of the Abu's over-all biology which should be given attention. It is perhaps the one question about them which interests people most of all, and is linked to several matters already discussed: namely, how long do they live?

This question has irked the cautious and encouraged the rash among both the orthodox and the iconoclasts for centuries. More simple hearsay, misquotes, and outright lies have probably been published on it than, possibly, on any other subject in zoology. Nobody really knows the true facts, and they may not be discovered before the Abu become extinct, for there is probably only one way to get at the truth. This is to brand with a date a number of each of the three kinds of Abu within a short time of their birth in the wild; then have a check kept on them, whether for fifty years or for 200 years, until they die; and then get them and cut out and preserve the brand before it is eaten by something. This would give us some idea of the age to which the Abu live: nothing else could really settle the matter.

Large bull Bush Loxodont feeding. Very large bulls of this species (such as the record that stood 13 feet at the shoulder) can reach succulent branch tips 20 feet from the ground. Seen from the front, when so feeding, they present a most surprising sight.

In the meantime, the best we can do is to record some salient beliefs held by people who *do* know something about live Abu, and the opinions of those who know them when dead. First we must note that the average person believes or has been told that all Abu "live to over a hundred," and most people think they live so much longer than that, that they seem virtually immortal. It is rather alarming, therefore, to hear a highly educated and scientifically trained person who lived with Abu both in the wild and in captivity—none other than G. P. Sanderson—state that Abu possibly *never die* except in epidemics or by accident.

Where the popular notion started that Abu live forever, or at least much longer than other animals, is itself a mystery. It was current long before Pliny gave it credence. Perhaps it is a hangover from man's early days when he lived with the animals in the fields and forests and was a consummate naturalist. In those early times he may have observed that, as a general rule, the smaller the creature, the shorter period it seemed to survive. Man lived longer than his dog if both were lucky, and the horse may have appeared to outlive men in those rugged days. (A horse 38 years old is recorded in Liverpool, and a donkey branded when it was young was said to be still alive after 78 years in Brockenhurst, Hampshire, England.) Similarly, a lot of animals were in ancient times huge. Thus, size and longevity may have *seemed* to go together. The modern discovery of dinosaurs has further, by a sort of miscorrelation between geological and individual age, tended to enhance this myth.

In point of fact, no law that we have yet identified governs either the normal or the occasional ages reached by any animal. A man kept an eel in a jar for 46 years in Scotland, and a tame crow is alleged to have lived with a gatekeeper's family in a French château for 107 years. Marmosets are tiny, monkeylike creatures and are "supposed" to live for about 5 years: I owned one for 11 years and another, of an even tinier species, for 7. A large tortoise was taken from its island home of Aldabra in the Indian Ocean to the island of St. Helena in the Atlantic about the year 1809. Napoleon saw it in St. Helena and marked its shell in 1815; it is still alive 145 years later. Moreover, it was mature when taken there, and these animals seem to take 30 years at least to reach that estate. We have not yet found any law of nature which explains how one kind of animal can live for an immense period of time while its comparatively close relations do not. Furthermore, we have very few reliable statistics on the longevity of any animal in the wild and little more of those in captivity. Of the Abu in the wild we have none.

Let us therefore start with the considered beliefs and opinions of the natives of those countries where these animals live. They have dwelt with the Abu for millennia, and so-called "natives" have an uncanny habit of turning out to be right about practical and physical, as opposed to psychical and immaterial, matters. If a native tells you that that there are two kinds of any animal in his country, he is probably right. The Burmese say that their Abu live in the wild up to 120 years, though, because of disease, accident, and other causes, 80 years is about average. The Indians concur exactly, adding that Abu can live to 80 in captivity, but only when used as parade and not as work elephants—and this is also from G. P. Sanderson, who prefaces these statements with the expression "experienced Indians say." The Indians even affirm that elephants can breed till 80. Mahouts can, on occasion, estimate with almost uncanny accuracy the age of an Abu despite the animals' wide range of build, facial expression, and demeanor. The young up to 25 years, though full-sized, and the very old can be spotted by anybody with only a little experience, but to judge the middle-aged is very difficult, and experts can be as much as 15 years off. The signs of old age in elephants are: shiny and shriveled skin; lean and rugged heads; sunken eyes and temples; forelegs the same size all the way up; the top of the ears lopping over; and the animal putting its heels down first rather than walking on the flat of its feet.

Africans tend to estimate time by generations, but not so many years ago a man in their lands was ancient at 45; therefore, when a native of that continent says that loxodonts live "for five fathers in my house before me" he means about 150 of our years. Nevertheless, by whatever way you estimate their time scale, the maximum they give is usually greater than 150 years and often up to 250 years. I have been told by tribal Africans, however, that "they live as long as everything else"; when pressed for an explanation, they added in substance: "Well, just like you and me or our fathers. Some of us live a long time and others die young." And if you persist by asking: "How long *can* they live?" you almost invariably get the reply: "At least for five generations, but after that *we* forget."

The people next most likely to know, though admittedly they are often rather unreliable on other matters, are the professional "non-native" hunters and poachers. John Taylor, an American professional ivory hunter,[2] believes that loxodonts live from 200 to 300 years if lucky, and he has spent his life observing them. Major P. J. Pretorius, perhaps the greatest loxodont hunter of all time, tried to estimate their age by the weight of their tusks and the rate of the tusks' growth. This he found to be, on an average, three quarters of a pound a year, but could be up to one pound yearly. A tusk weighing 168 pounds could thus mean that the animal was almost 200 years old. By this reckoning, I am constrained to point out, a 440-pound tusk, such as described above, would represent an age of approximately 525 years!

Stuart Cloete, summing up this subject, has written that 150 years in the wild is quite likely, but that a maximum of

[2] Although killing loxodonts for their ivory is permitted, under stringent regulations, to a few licensed hunters, the term "professional ivory hunter" normally denotes a poacher. Mr. Taylor is, of course, one of the best-known legally approved hunters.

70 years in captivity would be unusual because of unnatural work and improper diet. He points out also that there are 2,000 human centenarians in the United States, so that animals of comparative age may be equally numerous in the wild. G. P. Sanderson expresses his opinions flatly, saying: "My own opinion is that the Elephant attains at least to 150 years," and he then reports that a female named Bheemruttee, belonging to the Maharaja of Mysore, was captured in Coorg in 1805 when 3 years old and was still alive with that worthy's family in 1906, or 101 years later. This sounds like an authentic record. But he goes on to say that he knew of work elephants in India still in good trim at 76 years and not a bit sunken or otherwise aged, though beyond their prime. He adds that he had seen older females in the wild with calves, though the question of how he could estimate their age casts doubt upon his other statements.

Next we come to the estimates and beliefs of Europeans who have lived with work elephants or who have had experience in the international circus and entertainment fields. They are in opposed camps, but in this matter they seem to concur. Referring to loxodonts, the famous game warden Colonel Charles Pitman told Stuart Cloete that he considered 200 years a ridiculous figure and 120 too much except *possibly* for Forest Loxodonts. But then we have none other than the famous Dr. F. C. Simpson, for long Veterinary Surgeon of the Pretoria Zoo, in the Union of South Africa, stating for publication that he believed Abu lived in the wild for from 100 to 150 years but only to about 50 in captivity. Cloete also refers to an Abu that was owned by the Dutch government (in the Orient) from 1656 to 1788—i.e., 132 years. The famous Bombay-Burma Trading Company has records kept for more than 150 years, of 1,700 elephants, but none of these animals reached 70. There were 24 over 65, and 167 over 55; but 99 per cent died under that age. Finally, we come to the records kept in zoos and museums, and to the opinions of zoologists. T. C. S. Morrison-Scott, of the British Museum, once stated categorically that "they lose their last teeth long before they could reach 200. . . . The oldest ever authenticated Loxodont or Elephant was 67." Other museum men state that they may live to 70, but that the animals probably have just the same life-expectancy as we do, so that there may be centenarians.

Tying in with these opinions are the actual recorded facts about four historically famous Abu—namely, "Napoleon's Elephant," which was actually three different animals: "Waddy," "Babe," and "Jumbo." Waddy, owned by the Franklin Park Zoo in Boston, was arthritic and had greatly sunken temples; she was about 50 years old when she died. Babe, who was presented to the National Zoo in Washington by a circus that had owned her for 51 years, died 3 years later, in 1937. Jumbo the Great, the "elephant" par excellence of all time, who gave us our common household name for all the Abu, was a bull loxodont who, when 4 years old, was shipped from Paris to the London Zoo in 1865. After becoming a great favorite there, he was sold (for very peculiar reasons that have never been satisfactorily explained) to Barnum and arrived in New York, in spite of vocal protests from almost the whole of Britain, in 1882. In Ontario, Canada, in 1885, he lost his nerve and charged a train, derailed the engine, and killed himself doing it. He was just 24 years old, although in my files I have *nine* published statements that he was over 100.

A "mystery elephant," a cow, said to have lived or to still be living in Germany, allegedly gave birth to her first child in 1871 on the day the Franco-Prussian War ended, her second calf in 1918 on the day World War I ended, and her third in 1945 on the day Germany signed an unconditional surrender at the close of World War II. This is an engaging story, but the "elephant," said to have been 12 years old in 1871, must therefore have been 71 when she gave birth to her last child! Further, I cannot trace any such "elephant."

Those who have known most about the Abu for the longest time—the allegedly superstitious and unreliable natives —seem thus to have been proven wrong once again, but, we would point out, only because they have not yet produced a single centenarian Abu. The non-native hunters, who have spent their lives with wild Abu, have, however, gone way out on a limb, and at least one scientist seems to have, perhaps incautiously, followed them. The circus people and lumbermen stick pragmatically to their work elephants and give the Abu the same life span as that of man. Zoo directors, saddled with the remnants of the proboscidean market which cannot be sold as parade, work, or performing Abu, simply enter them in their books and wisely keep quiet. But the museum men, who collect only verified evidence, say that they cannot find a single authenticated record of any Abu *ever* having lived longer than 67 years. What are we to make of all this?

All I can do is submit my own humble opinions, basing them on three factors—note-taking over many years from several hundred books and other publications on the Abu; a lifetime of consorting with all sorts of animals and animal people; and what I hope may be considered mere common sense.

First, it has been proven that certain animals have lived for 150 years or more and probably can live up to 200 years —some giant land tortoises, for instance. There is also considerable documentation on quite a number of cases of other kinds of animals living for unexpectedly long periods—geese, donkeys, ravens, swans, eagles, *some* parrots, and, in relative terms, such creatures as eels and certain shellfish and even worms. Everyone who claims first-hand knowledge of Abu in the wild says he "feels" or "believes" that these animals can live to be 150 years old and that they may last a lot longer. At the same time, those writing only about work, cage, or show animals seem to me to be perfectly right in their estimates of the longevity of Abu in such circumstances. The argument that the teeth would not last long enough to permit great age is, in my opinion, unjustified—at least till we determine how many sets of teeth the Abu really have to draw upon, and just what the physical qualities of the teeth are. Knowing, moreover, to what remarkable ages some little animals can live, I do not see why big ones should not also exceed "expected" limits. Finally, by what logic can anyone assert that Abu must age at the same rate as we do? How do animals age, anyway? At present we simply do not know. Abu seem to be generally much healthier in their natural environment than we are in ours, and I have to concur with the opinion of my namesake—G. P. Sanderson—that there may be no reason for their dying at all except from accidents or epidemics. I wonder how old the giant squids of the ocean depths are, and those monstrous *Tridacna* bivalve shellfish with up to 170,000 layers of shell. After all, in California there are trees said to be 4,000 years old, and a professional botanist has stated that some individual trees of the Cycad group in Australia are 16,000 years old.

To sum up this subject conservatively, I would therefore offer the opinion that, taking all hazards into account, the average life of an Elephant in the wild is about 100 years, and that of a Bush Loxodont in the same circumstances 120 years. The Forest Loxodont, I believe, ought to be able to reach 150 years. I feel that the zoologists are quite right in saying that under unnatural conditions both Elephants and Bush Loxodonts have just about the same life-span as we do: an average of about threescore and ten if they are lucky. That there could be ancient ones in small numbers among all Abu, I am sure. Further, I know of no reason why some Abu should not have passed the 200-year mark before mod-

---

"Perhaps they just lie down one night and shed a tear."

ern man arose as their only real rival and started messing up the surface of the earth. There is no doubt that the strange physiology of the Abu has much to do with their life-span. Of this we know only too little as yet.

The last of the great myths about the Abu is that they have a few graveyards to which they all go to die. This is complete rubbish. The idea probably grew out of the fact that vast accumulations of elephantine bones and tusks have been found, since time immemorial, all over the world from the frozen tundras of the north to the tops of the Andean mountains, and in Greece, Florida, Malta, and in the Appalachian swamps. But these fossilized or semifossilized masses were, as we have explained, probably the victims of sudden cataclysms. They were *not* the result of a lot of old Abu plodding off to die among the pickled bones of their ancestors. Yet the question remains: where *do* the Abu die?

Nobody really knows; but nobody, for that matter, really knows where anything else dies of natural causes in the wild. I have spent twenty years in the tropics and yet I have never met anyone who has ever seen the veriest scrap of any dead animal in any jungle anywhere. On the other hand, I have seen a fresh jungle leaf totally demolished in an afternoon by bugs and bacteria, and I have lost innumerable corpses of small animals by just putting them down for a moment while I went to look at other traps. Curiously enough, just about the only animal remains that are ever reported by hunters and game wardens and forest officers as being seen in the jungle are those of Abu.

Williams has the notion that old Abu may customarily die near or in water and thus be washed away, and it is true that a sick Abu will seek water before all else. Others have suggested that they go away by themselves when they are too old or weak to keep up with the herd, seeking places where there is plenty of the soft foods their old worn teeth can masticate, and then just wilt away there when the season changes and the supply of food gives out. This is a nice gentle picture filled with infinite pathos, but nobody has ever actually witnessed such an end to any Abu. For the Forest Loxodont, and to a considerable extent for the Elephant, there is little, if any, seasonal change in the availability of soft food, so that a lone Abu would have a much greater abundance of food than would a herd. What the Bush Loxodonts would do we cannot say. They may just wander off; but ancient-looking ones may almost always be seen in herds of all kinds of Abu. They lag behind on the march and they wander off alone to feed, being no longer interested in sex or leadership; but they still seem to stay within the fold. Then, suddenly they are simply not there any more.

The most plausible theory I have heard as to the manner of their dying is that they simply go to sleep one morning as they have always done before but do not wake up when time to march arrives. What the other Abu do then we do not know. Perhaps they wait around for a time and make profound silence, as the Brahmans say they do, or they may just leave the place and go on their way. We do not know and we possibly never will.

I have a feeling that Abu, when their time eventually comes, just lie down wearily on their sides in some cool place of their most beloved forest. I believe they love life as much as we do, however hopeless it may sometimes seem to be to them, just as to us, and however useless it may in the end be proved to have been. I believe that they may cry a little at the end.

GENEALOGY OF THE ABU

GEOLOGICAL TIME SCALE	
HOLOCENE	LOXODONTA, ELEPHAS
PLEISTOCENE ca. 1 million years 1,000,000 B.P.	MASTODON, STEGOLOPHODON, STEGODON, MAMMUTHUS, LOXODONTA, ELEPHAS, ANANCUS, STEGOMASTODON, NOTIOMASTODON and CUVERIONIUS, DINOTHERIUM
PLIOCENE 11 million years 12,000,000 B.P.	CUVERIONIUS, STEGOMASTODON, STEGODON, GNATHOBELODON and EUBELODON, SYNCOLOPHUS, GOMPHOTHERIUM, PLATYBELODON and AMEBELODON, PLIOMASTODON, ANANCUS, TETRALOPHODON
MIOCENE 14 million years 26,000,000 B.P.	STEGOLOPHODON, SYNCOLOPHUS, PLATYBELODON, MIOMASTODON and MASTODON, GOMPHOTHERIUM and SERRIDENTIUS, RHYNCHOTHERIUM
OLIGOCENE 8 million years 34,000,000 B.P.	DINOTHERIUM, ARSINÖITHERIUM, PHIOMIA and PALAEOMASTODON, MÖERITHERIUM
EOCENE 21 million years 55,000,000 B.P.	MÖERITHERIUM, [COMMON ANCESTOR]
PALAEOCENE 23 million years 78,000,000 B.P.	[?]

UNIVERSAL UNCONFORMITY OR *"TIME BREAK"*

BIBLIOGRAPHICAL NOTE

There is a vast literature on elephantines in all the major languages. Books on "Elephants" have been appearing annually for almost a century, and sometimes more frequently in the English language alone. This creates somewhat of a problem, one of many, for the non-specialist with a particular interest in the subject. While there are a number of most entertaining and excellent general works, no standard-sized book is large enough to encompass more than generalities and a few examples of the numerous aspects of the subject.

The Abu belong to an arbitrary assemblage of some hundred assorted animals that have been domesticated by man. The remainder of the million species of living animals offers, for the most part, but a single aspect to the layman—their biology; though the deeper we delve into the life of any animal species the more we discover. There is a two-volume work on the housefly with more words than the Bible; its author remarked at the end that although he had devoted his life to the subject, he felt that he had only scratched its surface. In dealing with domestic animals, however, we start out with more than simple biological interest. With the sheep, we have such other matters of interest, as their origin and history, their flesh as food, their genetics, and the almost separate subject of wool.

Abu surpass all other domesticated animals in these multifarious claims on our attention and interest. First, they are in many respects both psychologically and anatomically one of the strangest of all mammals; second, they have been associated with man in a dual capacity for countless millennia, both as objects of the chase and as work animals. Also, they have played a leading role in the entertainment business, have been used in war, and have taken a prominent part in economic history. More than almost any other animal they have appeared in man's art, and in all manner of forms—on coins, in architecture, in sculpture and painting, and in literature. Finally, they are the originators of something that has played a very great part in the plastic arts—ivory.

There is literature on all of these special aspects of the Abu, but it is often rather hard to find, for most of it is scattered through periodicals, some obscure, many old and rare, and most of them technical. Even more regrettable, there are no books on various, more important aspects of the Abu themselves: on their overall past history (palaeontology), present behavior in the wild, anatomy and physiology, or psychology. An immense amount of work has been done on these subjects but, again, this is scattered through a mass of technical literature. Thus, the non-specialist wanting more information on the subject, either as a whole or in any of its special parts, has nowhere to turn.

In a perhaps vain attempt to at least make a start in solving both these problems, I herewith append a list of the books (and a few articles in journals) that I have found to be the most informative on various aspects of the Abu. This list is divided by subject-heads.

The technical bibliography that follows is prepared in accordance with the International Rules for the listing of scientific literature, and employs the approved abbreviations for technical journals. These references may not appear in this form in the older public library catalogues, but will in those of technical libraries or departments. A fair percentage are rare, and expert advice will probably be needed in tracing them in other than the few largest museum libraries. Some of the listings may not appear to the casual peruser to have anything to do with Abu. These are works that were used either as source-material or as references for related matters mentioned in the text.

A comprehensive and definitive work on the Abu would necessitate some fourteen very large volumes, each with its own extensive bibliography. The astonishing thing to contemplate is that such volumes could be as readable to non-specialists as detective stories and just as thrilling; yet each would call for several more volumes to cope with the technicalities.

SUGGESTED FURTHER READING

GENERAL

Carrington, R.: *Elephants.* New York: Basic Books, Inc.; 1959.

Fenner, P. R.: *Elephants, Elephants, Elephants; stories of rogues and workers, tuskers and trekkers, jungle trails and circus tanbark.* New York: F. Watts; 1952.

Herbert, A.: *The Elephant.* London: Hutchinson & Co., Ltd.; 1916.

Holder, C. F.: *The Ivory King; a popular history of the elephant and its allies.* New York: Charles Scribner's Sons; 1888.

Jordan, J. A.: *Elephants and Ivory.* New York: Rinehart; 1956.

Robinson, W. W.: *Elephants.* New York: Harper and Brothers; 1935.

Sanderson, G. P.: *Thirteen Years Among The Wild Beasts of India . . . with an account of the modes of capturing and taming elephants.* Third edition. London: W. H. Allen & Co.; 1882.

Sunamoto, E.: *The Elephant.* Osaka; 1931-2.

Williams, J. H.: *Elephant Bill.* London: R. Hart-Davis; 1950.

IN ART

Abbott, G. H.: *The Elephant on coins.* Sydney: The Sydney and Melbourne Co., Ltd.; 1919.

Druce, G. C.: "The Elephant in Medieval Legend and Art." *Archaeological Journal,* Ser. 2, Vol. XXVI (1919), pp. 1-73.

Kunz, G. F.: *Ivory, and the Elephant in art, in archaeology, and in science.* Garden City, New York: Doubleday, Page & Co.; 1916.

BEHAVIOR

Eardley-Wilmot, S.: *The Life of an Elephant.* London: E. Arnold & Co.; 1912

CAPTURE

Brown, G. C.: *Elephant catching in Mysore.* London; 1890.

Mayer, C.: *Trapping wild animals in Malay Jungles.* New York: Duffield and Company; 1921.

Tennent, Sir J. E.: *The wild elephant, and the method of capturing and taming it in Ceylon.* London: Longmans, Green, Reader and Dyer; 1867.

CARE

Evans, G. H.: *Elephants and their Diseases, a treatise on elephants. . . .* Rangoon: Superintendent, Government Printing; 1910.

Ferrier, A. J.: *The care and management of elephants in Burma.* London; 1947.

Gilchrist, W.: *A practical treatise on the treatment of the diseases of the elephant, camel, and horned cattle, with instructions for preserving their efficiency.* Calcutta; 1851.

Milroy, A. J. W.: *A short treatise on the management of elephants. And the management of elephant catching operations in Assam.* Shillong: Printed at the Assam Govt. Press; 1949.

Pfaff, G.: *Reports on the investigation of diseases of elephants.* Rangoon; 1940.

Slym, M. J.: *Treatise on the treatment of elephants in health and disease.* Maulmain, Burma; 1873.

Steel, J. H.: *A manual of the diseases of the elephant, and his management and uses.* Madras; 1885.

CONSERVATION

Pitman, C. R. S.: . . . *A report on a Faunal Survey of Northern Rhodesia, with especial reference to game, elephant control and national parks.* Livingstone: Government Printer; 1934.

Pitman, C. R. S.: *The Elephant in Uganda.* London; 1953.

HISTORY

Armandi, P. D.: *Histoire Militaire des Eléphants, depuis les temps les plus reculés jusqu'à l'introduction des armes à feu; avec des observations critiques sur quelques-uns des plus célèbres faits d'armes de l'antiquité.* Paris: Librairie d'Amyot; 1843.

Breuil, H.: *Four Hundred Centuries of Cave Art.* Montignac, Dordogne, France: Centre d'études et documentation préhistoriques; 1952.

DeBeer, Sir G. R.: *Alps and Elephants: Hannibal's march.* London: G. Bles; 1955.

Smith, G. E.: *Elephants and ethnologists.* New York: E. P. Dutton & Co., Inc.; 1924.

HUNTING

Bell, W. D. M.: *The Wanderings of an Elephant Hunter.* London: N. Spearman; 1958.

Daniell, W.: *Elephant Hunting. A panoramic view of the capture and taming of wild elephants on the island of Ceylon.* London: Schulze and Co.; 1835.

Finaughty, W.: *The Recollections of William Finaughty, Elephant Hunter, 1864-1875.* Philadelphia: Press of J. B. Lippincott Company; 1916.

Hardwick, A. A.: *An Ivory Hunter in North Kenia: The record of an expedition through Kikuyu to Galla-land in East equatorial Africa; with an account of the Rendili and Burkeneji tribes.* London: Longmans, Green, and Co.; 1903.

Hubback, T. R.: *Elephant hunting in the Federated Malay States.* London; 1905.

Hunter, J. A.: *African Hunter.* New York: Harper and Brothers; 1954.

Lake, J. A.: *Killers in Africa.* New York; 1953.

Muirhead, J. T.: *Ivory Poaching and cannibals in Africa.* London: Macmillan & Co., Ltd.; 1933.

Neumann, A. H.: *Elephant-hunting in east equatorial Africa, being an account of three years' ivory-hunting under Mount Kenia and among the Ndorobo savages of the Lorogi Mountains, including a trip to the north end of Lake Rudolph.* London: R. Ward, Ltd.; 1898.

Selous, F. C.: *A Hunter's Wanderings in Africa; a narrative of nine years spent amongst the game of the far interior of South Africa, containing accounts of explorations beyond the Zambesi.* London: R. Bentley & Son; 1890.

Stanley, W. B., and Hodgson, C.: *Elephant Hunting.* London: G. Bles; 1929.

Stigand, C. H.: *Hunting the elephant in Africa, and other recollections of thirteen years' wanderings.* New York: The Macmillan Company; 1913.

Taylor, J.: *Pondoro; last of the ivory hunters.* New York: Simon and Schuster, Inc.; 1955.

Tennent, Sir J. E.: *Sketches of the Natural History of Ceylon; with narratives and anecdotes, illustrations of the habits and instincts of the mammalia, birds, reptiles, fishes, insects, &c. including a monograph of the elephant.* London: Longmans, Green, Reader and Dyer; 1868.

IVORY

Cust, A. M.: *The ivory workers of the Middle Ages.* London: George Bell & Sons, Ltd.; 1902.

Dutt, G. C.: *A monograph on ivory carving in Bengal.* Calcutta: Bengal Secretariat Press; 1901.

Griffis, W. E.: "Japanese ivory carvings." *Harper's Magazine,* Vol. LXXVI (April 1888), pp. 709-14.

"Ivories, Ancient and Medieval." *Every Saturday* (February 1873), pp. 126-8.

"Ivory." *Chambers' Journal* (November 16, 1895), pp. 726-8.

"Ivory and its Applications." *Chambers' Journal,* Vol. XVII (1852), pp. 57-60.

"The Ivory Trade." *Chambers' Journal,* Vol. LXIII (1886), pp. 287-8.

Maskell, A. O.: *Ivories.* New York: G. P. Putnam's Sons; 1905.

Moore, E. D.: *Ivory, Scourge of Africa.* London: Harper and Brothers; 1931.

Natanson, J.: *Early Christian Ivories.* London: A. Tirant; 1953.

PALAEONTOLOGY

Digby, G. B.: *The mammoth and mammoth-hunting in northeast Siberia.* London: H. F. & G. Witherby; 1926.

Osborn, H. F.: *The Age of Mammals in Europe, Asia, and North America.* New York: The Macmillan Company; 1910.

Osborn, H. F.: "Mastodons and Mammoths of North America." *American Museum of Natural History, Guide Leaflet Series,* No. 62 (1926).

PERFORMING

Jennison, G.: *Animals for Show and Pleasure in Ancient Rome.* Manchester: University Press; 1937.

Lewis, G.: *Elephant Tramp.* Boston: Little, Brown & Company; 1955.

Rankin, J.: *Historical Researches on the Wars and Sports of the Mongols and Romans in which elephants and wild beasts were employed or slain.* London; 1826.

Richards, R.: *Life with Alice; 40 years of elephant adventures.* New York: Coward-McCann, Inc.; 1944.

Tyrwhitt-Drake, G.: *Beasts and Circuses.* Bristol, England: Arrowsmith; 1936.

ZOOLOGY

Miall, L. C.: *Anatomy of the Indian Elephant.* London: Macmillan & Co., Ltd.; 1878.

Osborn, H. F.: *Proboscidea. A monograph of the discovery, evolution, migration and extinction of the mastodonts and elephants of the world.* New York: American Museum Press; 1936-42.

Ward, R.: *The Elephant in East Central Africa.* London; 1953.

TECHNICAL BIBLIOGRAPHY

Adams, A. L. (1870). *Notes of a naturalist in the Nile and Malta.* Edinburgh.

Adams, A. L. (1877-81). *Monograph on the British fossil elephants.* London.

Adams, A. L. (1877). On the dentition and osteology of the Maltese fossil elephants. *Trans. zool. Soc. Lond.*, Vol. 9, pp. 1-124.

Ad-Damiri (1906). *The Hayat Al-Hayawan.* A Zoological Lexicon. Translated by Lt. Col. A. S. G. Jayakar. 2 Vols. London.

Aelian (1858). *Aeliani de Natura Animalium.* Recognovit adnotatione critica et indicibus instruxit R. Hercher. Book 2, Ch. 2, pp. 23-5: Elephantorum docilitas. Paris.

Akeley, C. E. (1912). Elephant hunting in Equatorial Africa with rifle and camera. *Nat. geogr. Mag.*, Vol. 23, pp. 779-810. Washington.

Akeley, C. (1921). Elephants. *World's Work.*, Vol. 28, pp. 40-58. London.

Albion, R. G. (1926). *Forests and sea power. The timber problem of the Royal Navy, 1652-1862.* Cambridge.

Aldrovandi, U. (1639). *De Quadrupedibus Solidipedibus.* Ch. 9, pp. 418-79: De Elephanto. Bologna.

Allen, G. M. (1937). Zoological results of the George Vanderbilt African expedition of 1934. Pt. 2, The forest elephant of Africa. *Proc. Acad. nat. Sci. Phila.*, Vol. 88, pp. 15-44.

Allen, W. E. (1941). *Fun By The Ton.* New York.

Anderson, K. J. (1873). *The Lion and the Elephant.* London.

Andrews, C. W. (1904). On the evolution of the *Proboscidea. Phil. Trans. Roy. Soc. Lond.*, Ser. B, Vol. 196, pp. 99-118.

Andrews, C. W. (1906). *A descriptive catalogue of the Tertiary vertebrata of the Fayum, Egypt.* British Museum, London.

Andrews, C. W. (1928). *On a specimen of* Elephas antiquus *from Upnor.* British Museum, London.

Andrews, F. H. (1904). The elephant in industry and art. *Journal of Indian Art and Industry.*, Vol. 10, pp. 51-4. London.

Aristotle (1862). *Aristotle's history of animals.* Translated by Richard Crewswell. London.

Arrian (1729). *Arrian's History of Alexander's expedition.* Translated from the Greek by Mr. Rooke. 2 Vols. London.

Ashe, T. (1806). *Memoirs of mammoth, and various other extraordinary and stupendous bones, of incognita, or non-descript animals, found in the vicinity of the Ohio, Wabash, Illinois, Mississippi, Missouri, Osage and Red rivers.* Liverpool.

Baber, Z. M. (1826). *Memoirs of Zehir-ed-din Muhammed Baber, Emperor of Hindustan,* written by himself. Translated by John Leyden and William Erskine. London.

Bailey, T. (1942). Trained tuskers of the Teak forests. *Nat. Hist. Mag.*, Vol. 5 (Dec. 1950), p. 229. London.

Baker, Sir S. W. (1874). *Eight years in Ceylon.* London.

Baker, Sir S. W. (1890). *Wild beasts and their ways.* 2 Vols. London.

Bannerman, J. (1955). The tragic death of the great Jumbo. *Maclean's Mag.* (12 Nov.). Montreal.

Barakatullah, M. (1904). The elephant as a machine. *Cassier's Mag.*, Vol. 26, pp. 276-80. New York.

Barber, E. A. (1882). Mound Pipes. *Amer. Nat.*, Vol. 16, No. 4 (April), pp. 265-81. Philadelphia.

Barras, J. (1885). *India and tiger-hunting.* London.

Barrett, O. W. (1935). Notes concerning manatees and dugongs. *J. Mammal.*, Vol. 16, pp. 216-20. Baltimore.

Barth, H. (1857). *Travels and discoveries in North and Central Africa, being a journal of an expedition undertaken under the auspices of H. B. M.'s government, in the years 1849-1855.* 3 Vols. New York.

Bartlett, A. D. (1899). *Wild animals in captivity.* London.

Barton, P. (1907). Capturing wild elephants in Mysore. *Badminton Mag.*, N. S. Vol. 24, pp. 30-8. London.

Battis, W. (1948). *The artists of the rocks.* Pretoria.

Bazé, W. (1950). *Un quart de siècle parmi les éléphants.* Saigon.

Bazé, W. (1950). *Just elephants.* London.

Beddard, R. E. (1893). On the brain of the African elephant. *Proc. zool. Soc. Lond.* (1893), pp. 311-15.

Bell, J. (1763). *Travels from St. Petersburg in Russia to diverse parts of Asia.* 2 Vols. Glasgow.

Bell, W. D. M. (1949). *Karamojo safari.* London.

Benedict, F. G., and Lee, R. C. (1936). Studies of the Body Temperature of Elephants. *Proc. Nat. Acad. Sci., Wash.*, Vol. 22, No. 6, pp. 405-8.

Benedict, F. G. (1936). The physiology of the elephant. *Carnegie Institution of Washington.* Publication No. 474.

Benedict, F. G., and Lee, R. C. (1938). Further observations on the physiology of the elephant. *J. Mammal.*, Vol. 19, pp. 175-93. Baltimore.

Bentley, E. C. (1950). *Elephant's work, an enigma.* New York.

Bernier, F. (1826). *Travels in the Mogul Empire.* 2 Vols. London.

Bibby, G. (1956). *The Testimony of the Spade.* New York.

Bible, The. Psalm 45, 5, 8. I King 22, 5, 39.

Bigalke, R. (1957). The ages to which elephants live. *Afr. wild Life.*, Vol. 2, pp. 140-3. Johannesburg.

Blair, P. (1710). Osteographia Elephantina. *Phil. Trans. Roy. Soc. Lond.*, Vol. 27, pp. 53-153.

Blair, P. (1718). A description of the organ of hearing in the Elephant, with the figures and situation of the ossicles, labyrinth and cochlea in the ear of that large animal. *Phil. Trans. Roy. Soc. Lond.*, Vol. 30, pp. 885-98.

Blanford, W. T. (1870). *Observations on the Geology and Zoology of Abyssinia, made during the progress of the British expedition to that country in 1867-68.* London.

Blumenbach, J. F. (1825). *A manual of elements of natural history.* London.

Blunt, D. E. (1933). *Elephant.* East Africa.

Boas, J. E. V., and Paulli, S. (1908-25). *Elephants head.* 2 Vols. Copenhagen.

Bolau, H. (1887). *Elephants and all about them.* London.

Bolau, H. (1887). Der Elephant in Krieg und Frieden und seine Verwendung in unsern afrikanischen Kolonien. *Samml. gemeinverst. wiss. Vortr.*, N. F. Ser. 2, Heft 6. Hamburg.

Bolk, L. (1917). Anatomische Bemerkungen über einen Fetus von *Elephas Africanus. Verh. Akad. Wet. Amst.*, Sectie 2, deel 19, No. 6. Amsterdam.

Brandis, D. (1862). *Selections from the records of the government of India (Public Works Department); No. 35; Reports on the Teak forests in Pegu and the Tenasserim and Martaban provinces,* 1860-61.

British Museum, London (1908). Guide to the Elephants (Recent and Fossil).

British Museum, London (1909). Department of British and Mediaeval antiquities. *Catalogue of the Christian era, with examples of Mohammedan art and carvings in bone.*

Brocklehurst, H. C. (1931). *Game animals of the Sudan, their habits and distribution.* London.

Brodrick, A. H. (1948). *Prehistoric painting.* London.

Brown, C. E. (1934). Captive pigmy elephants in America. *J. Mammal.*, Vol. 15, pp. 248-50. Baltimore.

Brown, G. B. (1928). *The art of the cave dweller.* London.

Bruce, J. (1790). *Travels to discover the source of the Nile, in the years 1768-1773.* 5 Vols. Edinburgh.

Bryden, H. A. (1903). The decline and fall of the South African elephant. *Fortnightly Review*, Vol. 79, N. S. Vol. 73, pp. 100-8. London.

Buckland, W. (1835). *Über den Bau und die mechanische Kraft des Unterkiefers des Dinotherium.* Heidelberg and Stuttgart.

Burne, E. C. (1943). A record of gestation periods and growth of trained Indian elephant calves in the Southern Shan States, Burma. *Proc. zool. Soc. Lond.*, Ser. A, Vol. 113, p. 27.

Burton, M. (1955). *Animal legends.* London.

Burton, Sir R. F. (1856). *First footsteps in East Africa.* London.

Burton, Sir R. F. (1860). *The lake regions of Central Africa.* 2 Vols. London.

Burton, Sir R. F. (1863). An account of an exploration of the Elephant mountain, in Western Equatorial Africa. *Geogr. J. Roy. Soc. Lond.*, Vol. 33, pp. 241-50.

Caldwell, K. (1927). Elephant domestication in the Belgian Congo. Reprinted from Report of Game Warden, Kenya, to the Uganda Government, 1925. *J. Soc. Pres. Fauna Emp.*, N. S. Part 7, pp. 71-82. London.

Cameron, V. L. (1877). *Across Africa.* 2 Vols. London.

Campbell, J. (1843). *Excursions, adventures and field-sports in Ceylon.* London.

Campbell, R. (1930). *Elephant King.* New York.

Canestrini, A. (1928). *I cacciatori di elefanti.* Rovereto.

Carrington, R. (1956). *A guide to Earth history.* London.

Carrington, R. (1957). *Mermaids and mastodons.* London.

Carter, D. (1927). Circus Day—2,500 years ago. *The World Review* (April), pp. 158-9. Illinois.

Chadwick, W. S. (1945). *Sultan on safari.* Cape Town.

Champion, F. W. (1927). *With a camera in tiger-land.* London.

Champion, F. W. (1928). On natural deaths in wild elephants. *J. Bombay Nat. Hist. Soc.*, Vol. 33, pp. 433-4. Madras.

Chang, H. T. (1926). On the question of the existence of elephants and rhinoceros in North China in historical times. *Bull. Geol. Soc. China,* Vol. 5, pp. 99-105. Peking.

Chaturvedi, M. D. (1957). The elephant and I. *Nat. geogr. Mag.*, Vol. CXII, No. 4 (Oct.), pp. 489-506. Washington.

Cherville, G. G. marquis de (1895). *Les Eléphants.* Paris.

Christy, C. (1922). The African elephant. *J. Afr. Soc., Lond.*, Vol. 21, pp. 92-104, 187-98, 291-301; Vol. 22, pp. 30-42.

Christy, C. (1924). *Big game and pygmies.* London.

Cloete, S. (1952). *The curve and the tusk.* Boston.

Cobbold, T. S. (1875). On the destruction of elephants by parasites; with remarks on two new species of entozoa and on the so-called earth-eating habits of elephants and horses in India. *Veterinarian, Lond.*, Vol. 48, pp. 733-43.

Cobbold, T. S. (1875). Further remarks on parasites from the horse and elephant, with a notice of new amphistomes from the ox. *Veterinarian, Lond.,* Vol. 48, pp. 817-21.

Cocchi, I. (1899). I denti (zanne) dell'elefante africano e il commercio dell'avorio. *Nuova Antol.*, Ser. 4, Vol. 82, pp. 478-89. Rome.

Colbert, E. H. (1955). *Evolution of the vertebrates.* New York and London.

Colyer, F., and Miles, A. E. W. (1957). Injury to and rate of growth of an elephant tusk. *J. Mammal.*, Vol. 38, pp. 243-7. Lawrence, Kansas.

Cooke, H. B. S. (1939). New fossil elephant remains from the Victoria falls, Northern Rhodesia, and a preliminary note on the geological archaeology of the deposit. *Trans. Roy. Soc. Afr.*, Vol. 27, pp. 287-319. Cape Town.

Coomaraswamy, A. K. (1927). *History of Indian and Indonesian art.* New York.

Cooper, C. R. (1934). *Boss elephant.* Boston.

Cooper, R. D. (1914). *Hunting and Hunted in the Belgian Congo.* London.

Cooper, W. (1824). Account of the discovery of a skeleton of the Mastodon Giganteum. *Annals of the Lyceum of Natural History of New York.*, Vol. 1, pp. 143-7. New York.

Corbett, J. E. (1953). *Jungle Lore.* New York.

Cornhill Mag. (1867). Objects of ivory. Vol. 16 (Nov.). London.

Corse, J. (1799). Observations on the manners, habits, and natural history of the elephant. *Phil. Trans. Roy. Soc. Lond.*, Vol. 89, Pt. 1, pp. 31-328.

Cort, M. L. (1886). *Siam*. New York.

Crawford, J. (1829). *Journal of an Embassy from the Governor-General of India to the court of Ava, in the year 1827*. London.

Cumming, R. G. (1850). *Five years of a hunter's life in the interior of South Africa*. 2 Vols. London.

Cuper, G. (1735). Gisberti Cuperi. *De elephantis in mummis obviis exercitationes duae*. In Sallengre, A. H. de: *Novus Thesaurus Antiquitatum Romanarum. Venetiis.*

Curtius, Q. (1747). *The history of the wars of Alexander the Great*. 2 Vols. London.

Cuthbertson, R. M. (1920). Hunting the Addo elephants. *Wide World Mag.*, Vol. 44, pp. 461-6. London.

Cuvier, Baron G. L. C. F. D. (1806). Sur les éléphants vivans et fossiles. *Annales du Muséum d'Histoire Naturelle,* Vol. 8, pp. 1-58; 93-155; 249-69. Paris.

Cuvier, Baron G. L. C. F. D. (1806). Sur le Grand Mastodonte. *Annales du Muséum d'Histoire Naturelle,* Vol. 8, pp. 270-310. Paris.

Cuvier, Baron G. L. C. F. D. (1817). *Le Regne Animal*. 4 Vols. Paris.

Cuvier, Baron G.L.C.F.D. (1834). *Recherches sur les Ossemens Fossiles*. Paris.

Da Costa, C. (1578). *Tratado de las drogas y medicinas de las Indias orientales*. Burgos.

Dampier, W. (1906). *Dampier's voyages*. Edited by John Masefield. 2 Vols. London.

Daubenton, L. J. M. (1782-1825). *Histoire Naturelle*. Tome 1–2. Paris.

Dawkins, W. B. (1904). On the discovery of *Elephas antiquus* at Blackpool. *Manchester lit. and philos. soc.*, Mem. and Proc., Vol. 48, No. 18. Manchester.

Dawson, W. R. (1925). The earliest records of the elephant. *Ann. Mag. nat. Hist.*, Ser. 9, Vol. 16, pp. 656-60. London.

De Blainville, H. M. D. (1874). *Ostéographie des éléphants*. Paris.

Delafosse, M. (1922). *L'Âme Negre*. Paris.

Deraniyagala, P. E. P. (1951). Elephas maximus, *the elephant of Ceylon*. Vol. 1. Colombo.

Deraniyagala, P. E. P. (1953). The extinct *Loxodonta* elephant of North Africa. *Spolia zeylan.*, Vol. 27, No. 1, pp. 15-16. Colombo.

Deraniyagala, P. E. P. (1955). *Some extinct elephants, their relatives, and the two living species*. Colombo.

De Watteville, V. (1935). *Speak to the Earth; wanderings and reflections among elephants and mountains*. New York.

Dietrich, W. O. (1916). *Elephas antiquus* Recki n. f. aus dem Diluvium Deutsch-Ostafrikas. *Arch. Biontol., Berl.*, Bd. 4, pp. 1-80.

Diggelan, T. van (1954). We made the elephant a killer. *Animal Life* (Dec. 1954), pp. 9-10, 49-50. London.

Dollman, G. (1934). Pigmy elephants. *Nat. Hist. Mag.*, Vol. 4, pp. 266-71. London.

D'oyly, Sir J. Bart. (1939). The elephant kraal of 1809. *Royal Asiatic Society of Great Britain and Ireland*, Vol. 34, pp. 240-60. Ceylon Branch, Colombo.

Dowsett, J. M. (1939). Elephant, past and present. *J. Afr. Soc., Lond.*, Vol. 38, No. 52, Suppl.

Drummond, W. H. (1875). *The large game and natural history of South and South-east Africa.* Edinburgh.

Dugmore, A. R. (1925). *The wonderland of big game.* London.

Dunbar, C. O. (1952). *Historical Geology.* New York.

Eannes de Azurara, Gomes, 15th Cent. (1936). *Conquests and discoveries of Henry the navigator; being the Chronicles of Azurara.* Translated by Bernard Miall. London.

Eardley-Wilmot, Sir S. (1933). *The life of a tiger and the life of an elephant.* London.

Elephant, The (1844-48). Originally published in the Library of Entertaining Knowledge. The Menageries. London.

Ellerman, J. R., and Morrison-Scott, T. C. S. (1951). *Checklist of Palaearctic and Indian mammals, 1758-1946.* London.

Ellerman, J. R., Morrison-Scott, T. C. S., and Hayman, R. W. (1953). *South African mammals, 1758-1951.* London.

Elwes, H. J. (1915). Altitude to which elephants ascend. *J. Bombay nat. Hist. Soc.*, Vol. 24, p. 355. Bombay.

Engell, M. C. (1911). Verbreitung und Häufigkeit des Elefanten und Löwen in Afrika. *Dr. A. Petermanns, Mitteil ungen aus Justus Perthes' geographischer Anstalt.* Ergänzugsheft. Nr. 171. Gotha.

Evans, G. H. (1894). *Notes on elephants in Burma.* Simla.

Evans, G. H. (1904). *Traite sur les éléphants, leur soins habituels et leur traitement dans les maladies.* Traduit par J. Claine. Paris.

Everest, Rev. R. (1834). On the climate of the fossil elephant. *J. Asiatic Soc. Bengal.*, Vol. 3, pp. 18-24. Calcutta.

Falconer, H., and Cantley, P. T. (1845-49). *Fauna antiqua Sivalensis, being the fossil zoology of the Sewalik hills, in the North of India.* London.

Falconer, H. (1868). *Palaeontological memoirs.* 2 Vols. London.

Ferishta, M. C. (1768). *The History of Hindostan.* 2 Vols. London.

Ferrand, D. (1903). *Discours en faveur de l'éléphant.* Société rouennaise de Bibliophiles. Rouen.

Fitz-Gerald, W. G. (1907). The working elephants of India. *St. Nickolas Mag.* (Dec.), pp. 148-53. New York.

Fleming, G. (1873). The diseases of elephants. *Veterinarian, Lond.,* Vol. 46, pp. 172-83.

Flower, S. S. (1931). Contributions to our knowledge of the duration of life in vertebrate animals. *Proc. zool. Soc. Lond.,* pp. 145-234. Order 12, *Proboscidea,* pp. 190-7.

Flower, S. S. (1943). Notes on age at sexual maturity, gestation period and growth of the Indian elephant, *Elephas maximus. Proc. zool. Soc. Lond.,* Ser. A, Vol. 113, pp. 21-6.

Flower, S. S. (1947). Further notes on the duration of life in mammals. *Proc. zool. Soc. Lond.,* Vol. 117, pp. 680-8.

Foot, A. E. (1936). Age of puberty in the Indian elephant. *J. Bombay nat. Hist. Soc.,* Vol. 38, p. 392. Madras.

Forbes, J. (1813). *Oriental memoirs.* 4 Vols. London.

Forbes, W. A. (1879). On the anatomy of the African elephant (*Elephas africanus Blum.*). *Proc. zool. Soc. Lond.,* pp. 420-35.

Foran, W. A. (1933). *Kill: or be killed.* The rambling reminiscences of an amateur hunter. London.

Foster, W. (1921). *Early Travels in India, 1583-1619.* Edited by William Foster. London.

Fox, H. (1933). Some notes upon the nature, health and maintenance of the Hyrax. *Proc. Amer. phil. Soc.,* Vol. 72, pp. 1-24. Philadelphia.

Fraser, A. G., Jr. (1928). The cult of the Kwahu hunter on the question of sasa animals, especially the elephant. *Gold Coast Review,* Vol. 4, pp. 155-71. Accra.

Funk & Wagnalls Standard Dictionary of Folklore, Mythology and Legend (1949). New York.

Gaidoz, H. (1874). Les Eléphants à la Guerre. *Revue des deux Mondes,* pp. 481-513. Paris.

Gallot, J. (1931). *The Elephant of Siam.* Philadelphia.

Gary, R. (1956). *Les Racines du Ciel.* Paris.

Gaudry, A. (1891). Quelques remarques sur les Mastodontes à propos de l'animal du Cherichira. *Société Géologique.* Mémoires, Paléontologie. Tom. 2, Fasc. 1. Paris.

Gee, E. P. (1949). Wild elephants in Assam. *Ceylon Game and Fauna Protection Society*, Vol. 5, pp. 98-104. Colombo.

Gee, E. P. (1950). How clever is an elephant? *Ceylon Game and Fauna Protection Society, 1948-51*, Vol. 5, pp. 150-4. Colombo.

Gee, E. P. (1950). Wild elephants dying in Assam. *Ceylon Game and Fauna Protection Society, 1948-51*, Vol. 5, p. 170. Colombo.

Gerahty, D. G. (1948). *Elephant Walk*. London.

Gesner, C. (1551-87). *Conradi Gesneri Medici Tigurini Historiae Animalium*. 4 Vols. Zurich.

Gibbon, E. (1788). *The History of the Decline and Fall of the Roman Empire*. 6 Vols. London.

Gibson-Hill, C. A. (1950). The dugong. *Malay. Nat. J.*, Vol. 5, pp. 25-9. Kuala Lumpur.

Golish, V. de (1954). *Mamba-kan*. Toronto.

Goodwin, G. G. (1925). The first living elephant in America. *J. Mammal.*, Vol. 6, pp. 256-63. Baltimore.

Goodwin, G. G. (1938). Freshman year in Africa. *Nat. Hist. N. Y.* (Nov.), pp. 272-5.

Goodwin, G. G. (1951). The Crowninshield elephant. *Nat. Hist. N. Y.*, Vol. 60, pp. 357-9, 385.

Gowers, Sir W. R. (1895). *Lectures on diseases of the Nervous System*. London.

Gowers, Sir W. R. (1899). *Manual of diseases of the Nervous System*. London.

Gowers, W. F. (1931). On the gestation period of the African elephant (*Loxodonta africana*). *Proc. zool. Soc. Lond.*, Pt. III (Sept.), pp. 1207-8.

Gowers, W. F. (1948). African elephants and ancient authors. *Afr. Affairs*, Vol. 47, pp. 188, 173-80. London.

Great Britain and the East (1939). Burma Teak Development (16 March), p. 303. London.

Great Britain and the East (1939). Burma Teak: The ideal timber (16 April), pp. 396-7. London.

Gregory, W. K. (1910). The orders of mammals. *Bull. Amer. Mus. nat. Hist.*, Vol. 27. New York.

Gromier, E. (1907). Protection et utilisation de l'éléphant d'Afrique. *Bull. Soc. Géogr. Lyon.*, Vol. 22, pp. 89-108, 165-186.

Gromier, E. (1951). *Mammouths et hommes des cavernes*. Paris.

Grzimek, B. (1956). *No room for wild animals*. London.

Gubernatis, A. de (1872). *Zoological mythology, or the legends of animals*. 2 Vols. London.

Guillot, R. (1954). *397th White Elephant*. Toronto.

Guillot, R. (1955). *Sama*. London.

Hagenbeck, J. (1954). *Im Reich des weisen Elefanten; macht und Reichtum Siams verstricken in gefahrliche Abentener.* Frankfurt am Main.

Hakluyt Society, No. LVII (1878). The Hawkins voyages during the reigns of Henry VIII, Queen Elizabeth, and James I. London.

Hakluyt Society (1905). The Journal of John Jourdain, 1608-1617. Cambridge.

Hakluyt Society (1938). The voyage of Pedro Alvares Cabral to Brazil and India. Translated by William Brooks Greenlee. London.

Hakluyt Society (1954). Some records of Ethiopia, 1593-1646. Ser. 107, Vol. 13. London.

Hall, D. G. E. (1945). *Europe and Burma.* London.

Hallock, E. S. (1905). The American Circus. *Century Mag.,* Vol. 70, N. S. Vol. 48, pp. 568-85. New York.

Hapgood, C. (1958). *Earth's shifting crust.* New York.

Harper's Book of Facts (1906). New York.

Harris, T. M. (1824). *The Natural History of the Bible.* London.

Hatto, A. (1939). The elephants in the Strasburg Alexander. *London Mediaeval Studies,* Vol. 1, Pt. 3, pp. 399-429. London.

Hay, O. P. (1925). A further and detailed description of the type of *Elephas roosevelti Hay* and descriptions of three referred specimens. *Proc. U. S. nat. Mus.,* Vol. 66, Art. 34. Washington.

Hediger, H. (1955). *Animals asleep.* No. 4. Basle.

Heller, E. (1934). Nature's most amazing mammal. *Nat. geogr. Mag.,* Vol. 55 (June), pp. 729-59. Washington.

Heurn, F. C. van (1929). *De olifanten van Sumatra.* Den Haag.

Hibben, F. G. (1951). Man in America. *Sci. Mon. N. Y.* (Nov.). New York.

Hicks, H. (1892). *On the discovery of mammoth remains in Endsleigh Street.* London.

Hinton, A. (1956). *Wild animals of Africa.* Edited and translated from the French by Anthony Hinton. London.

Hirth, G. (1879-1911). *Ivories.* Munich.

Hkyan, Ye (1913). *Manual of Elephant Medicines.* Rangoon.

Hoier, R. (1950). A Travers Plaines et Volcans au Parc National Albert. Institut des Parc Nationaux du Congo Belge. Ch. 2, pp. 12-21: Elephants. Brussels.

Home, Sir E. (1814-28). *Lectures on comparative Anatomy.* 6 Vols. London.

Horne, R. H. (1873). The great fairs and markets of Europe. *St. Paul's Mag.,* pp. 171-85. London.

Houel, J. P. L. L. (1803). *Histoire Naturelle des deux Eléphants, mâle et femelle, du Muséum de Paris.* Paris.

Howorth, H. H. (1887). *The mammoth and the flood.* London.
Hulme, F. E. (1895). *Natural History, Lore and Legend.* London.
Humboldt, A. (1810-34). *Voyage de Humboldt et Banpland. Vues des cordillères et monuments des peuples indigènes de l'Amérique.* Pt. 1, Sect. 2, Vol. 3. Paris.
Hundley, G. (1922). The breeding of elephants in captivity. *J. Bombay Nat. Hist. Soc.*, Vol. 28, pp. 537-9.
Hundley, G. (1934). Statistics of height increments of Indian calf elephants. *Proc. zool. Soc. Lond.*, pp. 697-8.
Hunter, J., and Owen, R. (1861). *Essays and observations on natural history, anatomy, physiology, psychology, and geology.* London.
Hutchinson, R. C. (1949). *Elephant and Castle.* New York.

ibn-Battuta (1929). *Travels in Asia and Africa, 1325-1354.* Translated by H. A. R. Gibbs. The Broadway Travellers Series. London.

Jardine, W. (1836). The Natural History of the Pachyderms. *The Naturalist's Library:* Mammalia. Vol. 5, pp. 104-52. Edinburgh.
Jardine, W. (1834). *The Naturalist's Library:* Pachyderms. Vol. 9. Edinburgh.
Jeannin, A. (1947). *L'Eléphant d'Afrique:* zoologie, histoire, folklore, chasse, protection. Paris.
Jillson, W. R. (1936). *Big Bone Lick.* Louisville, Kentucky.
Jillson, W. R. (1947). *The Elkhorn mammoth;* an account of the discovery of *Elephas columbi* in Franklin County, Ky. Frankfort, Kentucky.

Kaempfer, E. (1727). *The history of Japan together with a description of the Kingdom of Siam.* Translated by J. G. Scheuchzer from High Dutch. London.
Kearton, C. (1929). *In the Land of the Lion.* London.
Kempe, J. E. (1950). The training of elephants. *Ctry. Life, Lond.*, Vol. 107 (27 Jan.), pp. 2238-9.
Kerr, R. (1811-16). *A general history and collection of voyages and travels.* Vol. 1. 17 Vols. Edinburgh.
Keynes, Q. (1951). Africa's uncaged elephants. *Nat. geogr. Mag.* (March). Washington.
King, L. W. (1923). *A history of Sumer and Akkad.* London.

Kircher, A. (1667). *Athanasii Kircheri China monumentis qua sacris qua profanis, nec non variis naturae & artis spectaculis, aliarumque rerum memorabilium argumentis illustrata, etc.* Amsterdam.

Koch, A. C. (1841). *Description of the Missourium, or Missouri Leviathan;* together with its supposed habits, etc. St. Louis.

Kolb, P. (1731). *The present state of the Cape of Good Hope:* or a particular account of the several nations of the Hottentots. With a short account of the Dutch settlement at the Cape. 2 Vols. London.

Korvenkontio, V. A. (1914). Ein Mammutzahn-Fund in *Fennia.* Vol. 35, No. 9. Helsingfors, Finland.

La Décade Philosphique, Littéraire et Politique (1798). Du pouvoir de la Musique sur les Animaux, et du Concert donne aux Elephans. Tome 18, No. 32, pp. 257-64; No. 33, pp. 321-9. Paris.

La Loubere, S. de (1693). *A New Historical Relation of the Kingdom of Siam.* London.

Lander, E. T. (1877). Ivory and its imitations. *Galaxy Mag.*, Vol. 24 (Dec.), pp. 792-805. New York.

Langsdorff, Baron de (1909). Une chasse à l'éléphant en Ouganda. *Tour d. Monde,* N. S. Année 15, pp. 517-28. Paris.

Lartel (1859). Sur la dentition des proboscidiens. *Bull. Soc. géol. Fr.*, Ser. ii, p. 16. Paris.

Layard, A. H. (1849). *Nineveh and its remains.* New York.

Leach, F. B. (1940). The Teak industry. *Great Britain and the East* (6 June), p. 398. London.

Leidy, J. (1873). Contributions to extinct vertebrate fauna of the western territories. *U. S. Geol. Survey of the Territories.* Vol. 1. Washington.

Lemaitre, S. (1936). Evolution du motif de l'éléphant dans les agrafes de la collection Coiffard. *Revue des arts asiatiques,* Tome 10, pp. 132-42. Paris.

Leonowens, A. H. C. (1870). *The English governess at the Siamese court.* London.

Liddell, D. M. (1937). *Chessmen.* New York.

Lindner, K. (1950). *Le chasse préhistorique.* Paris.

Linquist, W. (1953). *Burma boy.* Toronto.

Lipkind, W., and Mordvinoff, N. (1955). *Chaga.* London.

Literary Digest (1912). King Rogers, elephant poacher. Vol. 45 (7 Sept.). New York.

Lockhart, G., and Bosworth, W. G. (1938). *Grey Titan.* The book of elephants. Burns, Oates & Washburn, Ltd. London.

Loisel, G. (1912). *Histoire des ménageries de l'antiquité.* 3 Vols. Paris.

Longstreth, T. M. (1953). *Camping like crazy.* New York.

Lorenzo, G. de (1933). L'uomo paleolitico e *l'Elephas antiquus* nell'Italia meridionale. *Reale accademia delle scienze fisiche e matematiche, Naples,* Atti. Vol. XIX, Ser. 2a, No. 5.

Lorenzo, G. de (1938). Avanzi di elefante e di ippopotamo nelle valle del Sele. *Rassegna storica salernitana,* Anno 2, No. 2, pp. 203-20. Salerno.

Loud, G. (1939). *The Meggido ivories.* Chicago Oriental institute. Publications V. LII. Chicago.

Ludwig, E. (1936). *The Nile.* Translated by Mary H. Lindsay. London.

Lull, R. S. (1908). The evolution of the elephant. *Amer. J. Sci.,* Ser. 4, Vol. 25 (Vol. 175) (March), pp. 169-212. New Haven.

Lull, R. S. (1908). The evolution of the elephant. *Annual report Smithsonian inst.,* pp. 641, 653-5, 662, 672-4. Washington.

Lydekker, R. (1907). The ears as a race character in the African elephant. *Proc. zool. Soc. Lond.,* pp. 380-403.

Lydekker, R. (1926). *The game animals of Africa.* London.

Lyell, D. D. (1924). *The African elephant and its hunters.* London.

Macinnes, D. G. (1940). Miocene and Post-Pliocene *Proboscidea* from East Africa. *Proc. zool. Soc. Lond.,* Vol. 25 (1941-6), pp. 33-106.

MacLean, J. P. (1880). *Mastodon, mammoth, and man.* 2 ed. Cincinnati.

Macphail, J. G. S. (1930). The Bandala method of hunting elephant on foot. *Sudan Notes,* Vol. 13, pp. 279-83. London.

Maddux, R. (1945). L'éléphant rose. *Les oeuvres libres,* Vol. 229, pp. 59-110. Paris.

Mahanama, 5th cent. (1908). *The Mahavamsa.* Translated and edited by William Geiger. London.

Manning-Sanders, R. (1938). *Elephant, the romance of Laura.* New York.

Manning-Sanders, R. (1952). *The English Circus.* London.

Maputo (Mozambique) (1917). Administrator 1908-09 (P. Viana Rodriques). Relatorio duma caçada aos elefantes na circumcriaçâo do Maputo.

Matthew, W. D. (1915). Mammoths and mastodons. *Amer. Mus. J., No. 43. Guide Leaflet Series.* New York.

Maxwell, M. (1924). *Stalking big game with a camera in equatorial Africa.* London.

Maxwell, M. G. (1906). Mantra gajah. *Royal Asiatic Society of Great Britain and Ireland,* Malayan Branch. Journal, No. 45 (June), pp. 1-53. Singapore.

Mayer, C. (1924). *Jungle beasts I have captured.* New York.

McClung, R. M., and G. S. (1957). America's first elephant. *Nature Mag.* (Oct.), pp. 400-4, 442. Washington.

Melland, F. H. (1938). *Elephants in Africa.* London & New York.

Menageries, The (1831). *Quadrupeds described and drawn from living subjects.* The Library of Entertaining Knowledge. Vol. 2. London.

Miller, S. (1815). *A letter to DeWitt Clinton on the fossil bones of the mammoth discovered in the state of New York.* New York.

Mitchell, P. C. (1905). On the intestinal tract of Mammals. *Order Proboscidea. Trans. zool. Soc. Lond.* (Dec.), pp. 466-7.

Mitchell, P. C. (1929). *Centenary history of the zoological Society of London.* London.

Mitchell, Brig. Gen. W. (1924). Tiger-hunting in India. *Nat. geogr. Mag.* (Nov.). Washington.

Moffett, C. (1898). Hunting on elephant. *McClure's Mag.,* Vol. 12, pp. 136-46. New York.

Morewood-Dowsett, J. (1939). Elephant past and present. *Supplement to the J. Afr. Soc., Lond.,* Vol. 38. No. 152 (July), pp. 1-40.

Morris, R. C. (1927). On natural deaths in wild elephants. *J. Bombay nat. Hist. Soc.,* Vol. 32, pp. 794-5. Madras.

Morrison-Scott, T. C. S. (1947). A revision of our knowledge of African elephants' teeth, with notes on forest and pygmy elephants. *Proc. zool. Soc. Lond.,* Vol. 117, pp. 505-27. London.

Mullen, A. (1682). *An anatomical account of the elephant accidentally burnt in Dublin, on fryday, June 17, in the year 1681.* London.

Muller, J. B. (1720). *Leben und Gewohnheiten der Ostiaken unter dem Polo Artico wohnende.* Berlin.

Mury, F. (1900). Les éléphants au Siam et au Cambodge. *Nature, Paris,* Année 28, Sem. 1, pp. 159-62.

Natura Viva (1959). Gli elefanti. (January 31) Milano.

Naumann, E. (1887). *Fossile Elephantenreste von Mindanao, Sumatra und Malakka.* Berlin.

Neuville, H. (1919). De l'extinction du mammouth. *Anthropologie,* Tome 29, pp. 193-212. Paris.
Nila-kantha, of Raja-mangalam (1931). *The elephant lore of the Hindus; the elephant sport (Matanga-lila) of Nilakantha.* Translated from Sanskrit by Franklin Edgerton. London.
Noack, T. (1906). A dwarf form of the African elephant. *Ann. Mag. nat. Hist.,* Ser. 7, Vol. 17, pp. 501-3. London.

Oberheimer, H. (1939). Hunting the mammoth as a source of food supply. *Res. & Progr., Berl.,* Vol. 5, pp. 275-82.
Oberjohann, H. (1950). *Meine Tschadsee Elefanten.* Spaten-Verlag. Grenchen.
Oberjohann, H. (1952). *Komoon! Capturing the Chad elephant.* Translated by Rhoda de Terra. New York.
Oberjohann, H. (1953). *Wild elephant chase.* London.
Oldfield, E. (1855). *Catalogue of select examples of ivory carvings from the 2nd to the 16th century.* London.
Once A Week (1860). Art in ivory. Vol. 4 (Aug.), pp. 161-4. London.
Once A Week (1862). Ivory carving in Dieppe. Vol. 4 (Oct.). London.
Oriental Sporting Mag. (1868). Elephant hunting extraordinary. Extract from a letter from Sergona, Feb. 25, 1802. Vol. 1, pp. 752-3. Calcutta.
Orr, G. (1943). *Here come the elephants.* Caldwell, Idaho.
Osborn, H. F. (1900). *The angulation of the limbs of Proboscidia, Dinocerata, and other quadrupeds in adaption of weight.* Boston.
Osborn, H. F. (1907). *A mounted skeleton of the Columbian mammoth (Elephas columbi).* New York.
Osborn, H. F. (1907). Hunting the ancestral elephant in the Fayum Desert. *Century Mag.,* Vol. 74, pp. 815-35. New York.
Osborn, H. F. (1925). The elephants and mastodonts arrive in America. *Nat. Hist. N. Y.,* Vol. 25, pp. 3-23.
Osborn, H. F. (1930). The romance of the woolly mammoth. *Nat. Hist. N. Y.,* Vol. 30, pp. 227-41.
Osborn, H. F. (1934). Evolution and geographic distribution of the proboscidea. *J. Mammal.,* Vol. 15, pp. 177-84. Baltimore.
Ouchterlony, J. W. (1873). An essay on the management of the elephant, and its treatment in ordinary diseases. *Veterinarian, Lond.,* Vol. 46, pp. 65-75.
Owen, R. (1840-45). *Odontography.* 2 Vols. London.
Owen, R. (1842). Report on the Missourium now exhibiting at the

Egyptian Hall. *Proc. geol. Soc. Lond.*, Vol. 3, No. 2, pp. 689-95. London.

Owen, R. (1866-68). *On the anatomy of vertebrates.* 3 Vols. London.

Packard, A. S., Jr., M.D. (1868). The hairy mammoth. *Amer. Nat.*, Vol. 2, pp. 23-35. Philadelphia.

Palakapya (1894). *The Hastyayurveda; a treatise on the diseases of elephants.* Edited by Sivadotta. Poona.

Pavlova, M. (1894). Les Mastodontes de la Russie. *Academia Scientiarum.* Mémoires, VIII series, Vol. 1. St. Petersburg.

Peale, R. (1802). *Account of the skeleton of the mammoth.* London.

Pelsert, F. (1925). *Jahangir's India.* London.

Penny Mag. (1839). The origin, nature and uses of ivory. Vol. 8, pp. 231-2. London.

Perry, J. S. (1952). Some observations on the growth and tusk weight in male and female African elephants. *Proc. zool. Soc. Lond.*, Vol. 124, pp. 97-104.

Perry, J. S. (1953). The reproduction of the African elephant, *Loxodonta africana. Phil. Trans.*, Ser. B, Vol. 237, pp. 93-148. London.

Perry, W. J. (1918). *Megalithic culture of Indonesia.* Manchester University Publications. Ethnological Series, Vol. 3. London.

Perry, W. J. (1923). *The Children of the Sun.* E. P. Dutton & Co., Inc. New York.

Petri von Hartenfelss, G. C. (1715). *Elephantographia curiosa.* Erfurt.

Phil. Trans. Roy. Soc. Lond. (1737). Elephant's bones found in Siberia. Vol. 40, pp. 124-38. London.

Pinkerton, J. (1814). *A general collection of the best and most interesting voyages and travels in all of the world.* London.

Plimmer, C. and D. (1951). White treasure from the dark continent. *Sat. Eve. Post,* Vol. 24 (Nov.), pp. 32-3, 73-4. Philadelphia.

Pliny, the elder (1855). *Natural History.* Translated by J. Bostock and H. T. Riley. 6 Vols. London.

Pocock, R. I. (1943). Notes on the Asiatic elephant (*Elephas maximus*). *Ann. Mag. nat. Hist.*, Ser. 2, Vol. 10, pp. 273-80. London.

Pohlig, H. (1895). Eine Elephantenhöhle Siziliens und der erste Nachweis des Cranialdomes, von Elephas antiquus. *Kon. Bayer. Akad. d. Wiss. Abh. Math. Phys.*, Kl. XVIII., Bd. 1., pp. 73-109. Munich.

Polo, M. (1903). *The book of Ser Marco Polo, the Venetian.* Translated and edited by Colonel Sir Henry Yule. London.

Polybius (1823). *The general history of Polybius.* 2 Vols. Oxford.

Poppleton, F. (1957). An elephant birth. *Afr. wild Life,* Vol. 2, pp. 106-8. Johannesburg.

Poskin, A. (1903). Une capture d'éléphants au kraal d'Ayouthia. *Tour d. Monde,* N. S. Année 9, pp. 457-68. Paris.

Priezac, S. de (1650). *L'Histoire des Eléphants.* Paris.

Qutayba, I. (1949). *The Uyun Al-Akhbar.* Translated by L. Kopf (Jerusalem). Academia Internationale d'Histoire des Sciences. Paris.

Ravenscroft, G. (1914). James Sutherland, ivory hunter. *Fry's Magazine of Sports,* Vol. 20, pp. 719-23. London.

Rawlinson, H. G. (1937). *India.* London.

Rees, Sir J. D. (1891). *H. R. H. the Duke of Clarence and Avondale in Southern India, with a narrative of elephant-catching in Mysore, by G. P. Sanderson.* London.

Rice, F. P. (1885). *An account of the discovery of a mastodon's remains in Northborough, Worcester County, Mass.* Worcester.

Río, A. del, and Cabrera, P. F. (1822). *Description of the ruins of an ancient city discovered near Palenque in the kingdom of Guatemala, translated from the original manuscript report of Captain Don Antonio del Río.* London.

Robinson, J., and Crowell, T. J. (1952). *The Universe We Live In.* New York.

Rogers, C. G. (1920). Logging Teak in Burma. *The Literary Digest,* Vol. 11 (Sept.), pp. 138-9. New York.

Romer, A. S. (1945). *Vertebrate paleontology.* Chicago.

Roosevelt, T., and Heller, E. (1915). *Life histories of African game animals.* 2 Vols. London.

J. Asiat. Soc. Beng. (1844). The osteology of the elephant. N. S. Vol. 13, Pt. 2, pp. 915-19. Calcutta.

Rushby, G. G. (1953). *The elephant in Tanganyika.* London.

Russell, J. R. (1947). Jumbo. *University of Rochester Library Bulletin,* Vol. 3, No. 1 (Autumn), pp. 12-20. Rochester.

Schaub, S. (1948). Das Gebiss der Elephanten. *Verh. naturf. Ges. Basel,* Bd. 59, pp. 89-112.

Schlegel, A. W. von (1823-27). *Indische Bibliothek.* Vols. 1-2. Bonn.

Schneider, K. M. (1930). Einige Beobachtungen über das Geschlechtsleben des indischen Elefanten. *Zool. Gart. Lpz.*, Vol. 3, pp. 305-14. Leipzig.

Schutze, W. (1906). Der Elefant in British Ostafrika und Uganda. *Globus*, Vol. 89, pp. 141-144. Braunschweig.

Scidmore, E. R. (1906). The greatest hunt in the world. *Nat. geogr. Mag.*, Vol. 17, pp. 673-92. Washington.

Scott, W. B. (1937). *A history of land mammals in the western hemisphere.* New York.

Sharpe, A. (1899). The preservation of the African elephant. *Blackwood's Edinburgh Mag.*, Vol. 165 (January), pp. 89-92. London.

Sharpe, H. B. (1946). Goodbye, Diksie. *Ctry. Life, Lond.*, Vol. 99, pp. 526-9, 582-3.

Sherborn, C. D. (1935). The elephant before A.D. *Ann. Mag. nat. Hist.*, Ser. 10, Vol. 15, pp. 492-5. London.

Shikary, Y. (1868). On the Malayan elephant. *Oriental Sporting Mag.*, Vol. 1, pp. 644-50. Calcutta, Bombay.

Simpson, G. G. (1945). The principles of classification and a classification of mammals. *Bull. Amer. Mus. nat. Hist.*, Vol. 85. New York.

Singh, St. Nihal (1946). India's elephant lore. *Times of India.* Annual. Pp. 25-29. Bombay.

Slade, H. (1903). On the mode of copulation of the Indian elephant. *Proc. zool. Soc. Lond.*, Vol. 1, pp. 111-13.

Smith, A. W. (1930). Working Teak in the Burma forests. *Nat. geogr. Mag.* (Aug.). Washington.

Smith, E. C. (1939). *Kongo the elephant.* New York.

Smith, G. E. (1915). Pre-Columbian representations of the elephant in America. *Nature, Lond.*, Vol. 15 (Nov.), pp. 340-1.

Smith, G. E. (1915). Pre-Columbian representations of the elephant in America. *Nature, Lond.*, Vol. 16 (Dec.), p. 425.

Smith, V. (1938). *The elephant shepherd.* New York.

Snodgrass, J. J. (1827). *Narrative of the Burmese War.* London.

Soergel, W. (1912). *Elephas trogontherii Pohl. und Elephas antiquus Falc. ihre Stammesgeschichte und ihre Bedeutung für Gliederung des deutschen Diluviums.* Vol. 60. Stuttgart.

Sommanader, S. V. O. (1957). Gentlemen of the jungle. *Nature Mag.* (June/July), p. 292. New York.

Southall, J. C. (1878). *The epoch of the mammoth, and the apparition of man upon the earth.* London.

Stevens, J. L. (1841). *Incidents of travel in Central America, Chiapas, and Yucatán.* 2 Vols. New York.

Stockley, C. H. (1953). *The elephant in Kenya.* London.

Stolberg, B. (1665). *Disputationem physicam de elephanto, sub praesidio*. Wittenberg.

Strong, W. D. (1934). North American Indian traditions suggesting a knowledge of the mammoth. *Amer. Anthrop.*, Vol. 36, pp. 81-8.

Sutherland, J. (1912). *Adventures of an elephant hunter*. London.

Swaffham, J. (1902). With a camera in a keddah; or, How elephants are caught alive. *Strand Mag.*, Vol. 24, pp. 284-93. London.

Symes, M. (1800). *An account of an Embassy to the Kingdom of Ava, sent by the Governor-General of India, in the year 1795*. London.

Szechenyi, Z. (1935). *Land of Elephants*. G. P. Putnam's Sons. New York.

Tavernier, J. B., Baron D'Aubonne (1679). *Les Six Voyages de Jean-Baptiste Tavernier*. Paris.

Thibout, M. (1947). L'éléphant dans la sculpture romane française. *Bulletin Monumental*, Vol. 105, pp. 183-95. Paris.

Thomas, C. (1894). *Report on the Mound explorations of the Bureau of Ethnology*. Washington, D.C.

Thomas, O. (1892). On the species of *Hyracoidea*. *Proc. zool. Soc. Lond.*, pp. 50-76.

Tilesius, T. V. (1812). *De Skeleto Mammonteo Sibirico*. Mém. de l'Acad. de St. Petersburg.

Toldt, K. (1914). Über die auszerek orpergestalt eines Fetus von *Elephas maximus* (Indics). *Kaiserliche Akad. der Wissenschaften. Denkschriften. Mathematisch-natur-wissenschaftliche Klasse*. Bd. 90, pp. 259-300. Vienna.

Topsell, E. (1607). *The historie of foure-footed beastes*. London.

Tournier, G. (1909). *Les éléphants*. Paris.

Trapier, B. (1937). *Les Voyageurs Arabes au Moyen Age*. Tome 2. In the collected works *La Découverte du Monde*, by Raymond Burgard. Paris.

Traversa, G. (1902). Nei guraghi. Una caccia agli elefanti. *Rivista d'Italia*. Anno 5, pp. 302-15. Roma.

Tressler, D. K. (1943). *The freezing preservation of foods*. New York.

Tristram, H. B. (1873). *The natural history of the Bible*. London.

Turner, W. (1876). *Lectures on comparative anatomy of the placenta*. Edinburgh.

Tylor, E. B. (1865). *Researches into the early history of mankind and the development of civilization*. London.

Unterwelz, R. W. (1925). *Ligohoya*. Stuttgart.

Vail, R. W. G. (1933). Random notes on the history of the early American circus. *American Antiquarian Society Proc.*, Vol. 43, N. S. Pt. 1, pp. 116-85. Boston.

Vaufrey, R. (1929). Les éléphants nains des îles méditerranéennes et la question des isthmes pléistocènes. *Arch. Inst. Paléont. hum.* Mém. 6. Paris.

Vogel, J. P. (1920). *Tile mosaics of the Lahore fort.* Calcutta.

Waldeck, J. F. M., comte de (1838). *Voyage pittoresque et archéologique dans la province d'Yucatán pendant 1834 et 1836.* Paris.

Wales, H. G. Q. (1931). *Siamese state ceremonies.* London.

Walker, E. L. (1947). *Elephants never forget.* London.

Ward's Natural Science Establishment, Inc., Rochester, N. Y. (1878). *Notices on the mammoth* Elephas primigenius, *Blum.* Compiled to accompany the exhibit of the specimen at the Inter-State Industrial Exposition, Chicago.

Ward, R. (1935). *Rowland Ward's records of big game.* London.

Warren, J. C. (1852). *The Mastodon giganteus of North America.* Boston.

Watkins, L. A. (1937). *Rhumbo.* Philadelphia.

Watson, M. (1871). Anatomy of the Indian elephant. *J. Anat., Lond.*, Second Ser. V, Vol. 6, pp. 82-94.

Watson, M. (1873). Contributions to the anatomy of the Indian elephant. Part III: The Head. *J. Anat., Lond.*, Second Ser. 7, Vol. 8, pp. 85-94.

Watson, D. M. S. (1946). The evolution of the Proboscidea. *Biol. Rev. Cambridge Philosophical Society,* Vol. 21, pp. 15-29. Cambridge.

Welch, G. (1949). *North African prelude.* New York.

Westwood, J. O. (1874-77). Ivory carvings. In Parker, J. H.: *The archaeology of Rome.* Part 10, pp. 56-75. Oxford.

Wetherell, C. C. V. D. (1843). *A North American Indian record, to prove the indubitable existence of the Behemoth.* Dublin.

Wheeler, P. (1943). *Hathoo of the elephants.* New York.

Whitaker, J. (1794). *The course of Hannibal over the Alps ascertained.* 2 Vols. London.

White, E. L. (1937). *The elephant never forgets.* London.

Whitman, S. F. (1903). Elephant catchers. *Everybody's Mag.*, Vol. 8, pp. 195-209. New York.

Whitney, C. (1904). The King's Mahout. *Outing,* Vol. 45, pp. 51-71. New York.

Williams, C. A. S. (1931). *Outlines of Chinese symbolism.* Peiping.

Wilson, J. C. C. (1922). The breeding of elephants in captivity. *J. Bombay nat. Hist. Soc.*, Vol. 28, pp. 1128-9.

Winter, O. (1926). *Der Herr des Urwaldes*. Berlin.

Witsen, N. C. (1705). *Noord en oost Tartarye*. Amsterdam.

Wright, F. B. (1903). The mastodons and mammoth contemporary with man. *Record of the Past*, Vol. 2, Pt. 8, pp. 243-53. Washington.

Yule, Sir H. (1855). *Narrative of the mission sent by the governor-general of India to the court of Ava in 1855, with notices of the country, government, and people*. London.

Zeuner, F. E. (1942-43). The Pleistocene Period. *Ray Soc.* Publications 1942-43. Pub. 130. London.

Zeuner, F. E. (1950). *Dating the past*. London.

Zittel, K. von (1925). *Textbook of Palaeontology*. London.

INDEX

A NOTE ABOUT THE AUTHOR

IVAN T. SANDERSON was born in Edinburgh, Scotland, in 1911, and was educated at Eton College and at Cambridge University, where he took honors in botany, geology, and zoology. He has visited most areas of the world since he was five years old and began to travel with his family. In 1927-9 he went around the world, stopping in Indonesia to collect zoological specimens for the British Museum of Natural History. On leaving Cambridge he organized and led a scientific expedition to West Africa, collecting over 20,000 specimens. In 1935-6 he made an expedition through the West Indies, particularly studying the vampire bats that carry human rabies. In 1936-7 he went to Surinam, again collecting more than 20,000 specimens. Returning to the Caribbean in 1937-8, Mr. Sanderson made a complete forest and faunal survey of British Honduras and purchased a sixty-foot schooner that he refitted as a home and laboratory. The west-coast mountain ranges of Mexico were explored in 1938-9 for rare species of rats, and the Caribbean expeditions were continued in the schooner in 1939-40. From 1940 to 1945 Mr. Sanderson was in war service. In 1945 he became attached to the British Ministry of Information in New York. He resigned from British Government service in 1947, becoming a permanent resident of the United States. In 1952 he founded in New Jersey a small private zoo to house rare animals for research, exhibition, and television. He has been widely heard on radio and television. Some of his published books are: *Caribbean Treasure, Animal Treasure, Animal Tales, Living Mammals of the World, Follow the Whale,* and *The Continent We Live On.*

A NOTE ON THE TYPE

The text of this book is set in Caledonia, a Linotype face designed by W. A. Dwiggins, the man responsible for so much that is good in contemporary book design and typography. Caledonia belongs to the family of printing types called "modern face" by printers—a term used to mark the change in style of type-letters that occurred about 1800. It has all the hard-working feet-on-the-ground qualities of the Scotch Modern face plus the liveliness and grace that is integral in every Dwiggins "product," whether it be a simple catalogue cover or an almost human puppet.

This book was composed, printed, and bound
by H. Wolff, New York.
Typography, ornaments, and binding design by
VINCENT TORRE